BEYOND LANGUAGE

Beyond Language

Adventures in Word and Thought

DMITRI A. BORGMANN

Charles Scribner's Sons NEW YORK

A-4.67 [UJ]

PRINTED IN THE UNITED STATES OF AMERICA

Library of Congress Catalog Card Number 67-15487

Diagrams by Mary Frances Gazze

ILLUSTRATION ACKNOWLEDGMENTS

   Page 52: Reprinted by permission of Grosset & Dunlap, Inc. publishers of *Minute Glimpses of American Cities* by Herbert S. Kates.
   Page 143: New York Public Library, Prints Division

To
Word Lovers Everywhere

CONTENTS

PREFACE

The generally favorable reception accorded to *Language on Vacation*, the author's first literary venture, has emboldened him to offer the public a second work.

Like its predecessor, *Beyond Language* is a book entirely original in the field of word puzzles. While inspiration for the particular format displayed here was drawn from a kindred realm, that of mathematical puzzles, words are creatures of a sort different from numbers, and an identical style of treatment is not within the bounds of the possible. As the text came into being, it developed an incisive personality of its own, uniquely appropriate to the subject matter under consideration and not really within the author's power to control. A Frankenstein, one might almost say!

Language mirrors many subjects. In keeping with this communicative function, *Beyond Language* proceeds through and beyond language, to the provinces of logic, literature, history, geography, science, mathematics, and general information. It serves as a recreational bridge between language and the areas of thought and knowledge forming the basis for language. The book will, therefore, it is hoped, strike a responsive chord among individuals not ordinarily interested in word games.

In deference to the reader whom this comparatively sweeping survey is not enough to satisfy, an "Afterword" has been included. There, a historic first endeavor is made to give recreational linguistics its proper status on the most fundamental philosophical grounds.

The temptation to have that fabulous Professor, the Honorable Ravenscroft J. Cloudesley, make a return appearance, proved irresistible. So—Cloudesley rides again!

In creating material for *Beyond Language*, the author was fortunate to receive valuable ideas and information from various readers. Special thanks are due to: Mr. Howard W. Bergerson, of Sweet Home, Oregon; Mr. Rudolph W. Castown, of Manhattan, New York; Mr. David Kahn, of Great Neck, New York; Mr. Temple G. Porter, of Washington, D.C.; and Mr. Dwight D. Ripley, of Greenport, Long Island, New York.

Permission from their authors to reproduce two pertinent poems is gratefully acknowledged: *Doppelgänger*, by Mr. J. A. Lindon, and *Collective Farm*, by Miss Felicia Lamport.

A number of the problems included in *Beyond Language* have previously appeared, in somewhat modified form, in the author's WORD Row column in *Books/Magazine*, and are reprinted with the kind permission of the publisher, The Agel Publishing Company in New York.

Every effort has been made to avoid errors, factual, logical, or otherwise, but infallibility is a goal for tomorrow rather than a reality of today. The author will welcome all corrections and suggestions from readers.

DMITRI A. BORGMANN

11 Ontario Street
Oak Park, Illinois 60302
January, 1967

BEYOND LANGUAGE

INTRODUCTION

$\mathbb{D}$ANGER lies ahead!

You will have to exercise the greatest caution in making your way through this book. Unless you do so, you are liable to learn how to *think*.

We are living in a time unprecedented for the rapidity and extent of the changes occurring in man's environment. Most of us are not equipped, mentally or emotionally, to cope with so much change. On the intellectual level, a thoroughgoing reorientation is required if we are to survive. We must retrain our thinking processes, making them more flexible and multifaceted. Problems must be seen and analyzed from totally new, previously unsuspected viewpoints, and entirely original answers must be found, solutions without historical antecedent. This and only this will enable men's minds to move into an unknown future along as yet uncharted pathways.

Beyond Language is an attempt to lay the groundwork for the more versatile, untrammeled thinking patterns we must adopt in order to remain masters of our fate. To succeed in our undertaking, we are employing language

1

as an instrument for exploring the thought that lies beyond language. So as to make our adventure not merely instructive but also entertaining, our sallies are dressed up in the form of word games, with curious information about literature, geography, history, science, mathematics, contesting, and other subjects injected for heightened effect.

The word games, considered from the standpoint of wordplay, are of a largely novel character, bearing only a superficial kinship to conventional word puzzles. Many of them have not been treated in any previous literature on the subject. Accordingly, this book should make an interesting addition to any word lover's library, even if its role in the field of recreational linguistics is an accidental one.

You, the reader, have the option of regarding our word games as nothing more than games, dismissing the serious purpose behind them; a purpose, by the way, which comes fully into the open in our "Afterword," following the diversions. Yet, if you apply yourself earnestly and intelligently to solving the numerous and diverse problems in *Beyond Language,* you will unconsciously assimilate the unshackled, advanced thinking processes that it is the aim of this book to generate in its readers. How can we be so positive of success? Because we know that routine mentation, developing along worn-out channels, is incapable of dealing with the problems in *Beyond Language,* any more than it is capable of dealing with those in the strange new world that now surrounds us all.

On the surface, the structure of *Beyond Language* is similar to some books of mathematical puzzles. There is a series of complex problems, requiring considerable alertness to be solved correctly; for those baffled by the problems as first presented, there are hints or leads designed to shift the reader's cerebrations to the frequency on which the problems are pitched; there are solutions, analyzing and explaining both problems and leads in detail; and there is a group of special problems the full solutions to which are not yet known, though some of them are partly solved. In addition, there is a comprehensive bibliography, listing books, pamphlets, and magazines of related interest.

Each section or unit of the book is preceded by introductory remarks. These should be read before examining further material in the section, if the full potential of the section is to be realized.

While the structure of *Beyond Language* is itself a most unusual one—its application to the field of word puzzles is without known parallel—this fact alone would not invest the work with the mantle of uniqueness. Rather, it is the underlying current of adventures in the realm of pure thought that may confer the distinction of peerlessness on this book.

Admittedly, the ideas expressed in *Beyond Language* are being sent out across the window, so to speak, without illusions about their probable reception by most readers. If at least a few readers are inspired to reach toward new levels of creative thinking as a consequence of their browsing here, whether that result be conscious or unconscious in its development, it shall surely be enough.

PROBLEMS

This is it.

You are face to face with our problems (the easy ones—the hard ones are in a later section, entitled "Bafflers").

Read them, study them, try working them out. If you want or need help with a specific problem, turn to the page on which "Hints" for that problem are offered. In some instances, you will find the hints quite direct; in others, rather enigmatic. Occasionally, the hints introduce additional facets of the problem for you to solve. All aspects, both those in the problem itself and any woven into the hints, are explained in the "Resolutions" section. Because some of the hints bring up new angles, we recommend that you examine all of them, whether or not you require assistance.

The first few problems are likely to throw you for a loss. Analyze and absorb the hints and resolutions given, and you'll catch on to what we're doing here. As you learn from experience, solving our problems will become progressively easier.

If you are not inclined to exert yourself mentally, there is a different way of enjoying *Beyond Language*. Simply read each problem, then the hints applicable to it, then its resolution. You will discover a great deal to delight you, amaze you, confound you, provoke you. All of it is intended to prod you into thinking creatively and independently.

For each problem, the page numbers of the corresponding hints and resolutions are shown at the end of the problem text.

1 A JUG OF WINE, A LOAF OF BREAD— AND THOU

Lovers of poetry with definitely mystical overtones will immediately recognize this stanza:

> "Wake! For the Sun behind yon Eastern height
> Has chased the Session of the Stars from Night;
> And, to the field of Heav'n ascending, strikes
> The Sultán's Turret with a Shaft of Light."

It is the opening quatrain of the *Rubáiyát of Omar Khayyám,* quoted from the Second Edition of the famous translation by Edward Fitzgerald.

What is the essence, substance, or distinctive quality of this passage? A pregnant question, indeed!

Hints: Page 163.   Resolution: Page 171.

2 BEYOND THE LAW

Penetrating beyond language has many aspects. One of them is piercing the façade of grammar to find out what lies behind it.

Our language has a good many words ending in -CEDE, -CEED, and -SEDE. Those textbooks of English dealing with the subject provide us with a clear, simple rule for determining which of these three endings any particular word uses: one word, SUPERSEDE, ends with -SEDE; three words, EXCEED, PROCEED, and SUCCEED, end with -CEED; all other words end with -CEDE.

Oh, if life and language were but that simple! They are not. Can you give us two additional English words ending in -CEED, and two additional words ending in -SEDE? In selecting appropriate examples, you should exclude mere compounds of the examples already mentioned, words such as RESUCCEED, REPROCEED, and SUPEREXCEED. These compounds are legitimate dictionary words but do not represent a true conquest of the problem posed.

The problem brings a number of other questions in its wake, and we should like to have you answer these, too, if you can:

1. If you set out to compile a list of words ending with specific letter combinations, to what reference books would you turn?
2. What are the relative merits of the principal such works?
3. What is their common failing, and how can you overcome it?

Hints: Page 146.   Resolution: Page 295.

3 SYMBOL OF THE SUN

Pictured at the right is a symbol known and used all over the world, from time immemorial.
Give us 25 English names for it!

Hints: Page 157.   Resolution: Page 291.

4 CHARMING SPELLING

Anyone proposing to use language, or to delve into the regions that lie beyond language, must know how to spell words. This fact of life prompts us to offer you our version of a spelling quiz. A list of English words follows:

1. Cryptogam	7. Acter
2. Therefor	8. Contect
3. Windrow	9. Orignal
4. Galop	10. Viraginity
5. Harras	11. Merengue
6. Poisson	

One word in this list is misspelled. All other words are correctly spelled. Can you find the one error?

Keep in mind that there are no proper nouns in the list; all entries in it are words, not names. Keep in mind, also, that all of the words are English, according to Webster; not a single foreign word has been included.

Obviously, you can solve this problem without much mental strain by looking the words up in the dictionary. Aside from the fact that this would defeat the purpose of measuring your knowledge of English spelling, it is also *impossible*. Can you figure out why?

We have deliberately made this problem so easy that *anyone* can solve it, including a foreigner who has never had the slightest contact with our language, using purely *a priori* considerations. Can you tell us how?

Hints: Page 159.   Resolution: Page 283.

5 *EMINENT AMERICAN PALINDROMIST?*

One of America's outstanding poets and short-story writers, Edgar Allan Poe, is known for his interest in amateur cryptography, revealed in his prize-winning tale, *The Gold-Bug*, a development of Poe's earlier essay, *Cryptography*.

Not so widely known is the fact that Edgar Allan Poe was also keenly interested in palindromes. What evidence of this interest can you find in his works, without engaging in a great deal of research?

There is *something* about the title chosen for this problem, something you should spot. What is it?

Hints: Page 162.   Resolution: Page 269.

6 *JAYS THAT AREN'T*

The Generalissimo was slightly disturbed. A rumor had just reached him that enemies of his régime were planning to march on his capital. He stared at the map spread out on the table before him, and started doodling along its edges.

After a time, the Generalissimo began reading his doodles. He noticed his date of birth, a date in the last quarter of the year. It occurred to him that the year of birth was in the same lustrum with those of the only two "titlesakes" of his that he had ever heard about. He also noticed his name, written out in full. His eye was caught by his two-part surname, one of which he was proud. Scanning his name, he stopped on seeing the six-letter one—naturally!

Roaming along the edges of that map, his eye was again caught by a two-part name, this one the name of his nation. Directly next to it he had doodled yet another two-part name, this one the name of his capital. In utter disbelief, he counted the letters in it. Twelve alphabetic characters! But how could *he*, the head of his nation, he of all people, have jotted that name down?

He pondered about his now imperiled capital. Twelve characters—no more, no less—no matter how you counted them. Incredible!

From the story you have just read, you should be able to tell us the name of the Generalissimo, the name of his country, and the name of his capital. You should also be able to identify his two "titlesakes." Finally, you should be able to discern the three separate connections between our title and our plot.

Hints: Page 144.   Resolution: Page 306.

7 THE GREAT PRETENDER

Who was William Shakespeare?

An easy question . . . much, much too easy, compared with other problems in this neck of the woods. You are cautioned to think before replying.

Hints: Page 145.   Resolution: Page 288.

8 E PLURIBUS UNUM

Seán O'Downer, a resident of Newtownmountkennedy, in County Wicklow, Ireland, was visiting his cousin, Eoin O'Worden, in Baile Átha Cliath, a seaport in County Dublin. Eoin, a wordy chap, decided to tease Seán with this poser: "How do you make one word out of the two words NEW DOOR?" Seán, no schnook at words himself, recognized the problem immediately and gave the expected reply: "You turn NEW DOOR into one word by rearranging its letters to form ONE WORD."

Delighted, Eoin shouted: "You're wrong, absolutely and completely wrong!" This baffled Seán, and also baffled us, until we started studying the problem and gained new and startling insights into its nature. So that our efforts will not have gone for naught, we ask you to analyze the problem just as exhaustively, centering your attention on these questions:

1. Why is the ONE WORD solution indefensible?
2. There are four legitimate solutions to the NEW DOOR problem. Name them and discuss their relative merits. Which one exhibits the greatest degree of originality?
3. There is something very peculiar about the first and the last names of our heroes. Elaborate, please.
4. There are commensurately outré aspects to the names of the communities in which our protagonists live. Identify these aspects, if you will.
5. The title that adorns (uglifies?) our problem is related both to the "trick" solution already mentioned, and to one of the bona fide solutions we want you to discover, but in opposite ways. Can you explain?

Hints: Page 164.   Resolution: Page 264.

9 *SUPERCALIFRAGILISTICEXPIALI-DOCIOUS!*

One of the many realms beyond language—beyond the language we speak—is that of word origins. For reasons difficult to fathom, men seem to be driven to discover the source or sources of the words they use. Possibly, the search is akin to another activity of dubious value, that of tracing rivers to their ultimate headwaters.

Be that as it may, we have assigned to you the project of establishing the etymology of the word SUPERCALIFRAGILISTICEXPIALIDOCIOUS, the title of a hit song in the motion picture *Mary Poppins*. The etymology of the word will enable you to define it properly. The song itself refers to the word as "the biggest word you've ever heard". Aside from the fact that we don't believe this statement—we've heard bigger words—a definition of that sort leaves something to be desired, and we prefer a more conventional definition.

Most people, including Walt Disney, the motion picture producer, and Julie Andrews, the singer, apparently thought that SUPERCALIFRAGILISTICEXPIALIDOCIOUS is a nonsense word. We, in sharp, shocking contrast, cannot force this conclusion upon ourselves, and count on you to extract the real meaning of the word from its roots.

Please report back to us as soon as success is yours.

Hints: Page 166.   Resolution: Page 272.

10 *THE SHELL-AND-KERNEL GAME*

Don't be fooled by the military sound of our title. This is a very peaceful problem, requiring calm reflection on your part to penetrate. (Military title? Why, yes—shells are artillery projectiles, and a colonel is a commissioned army officer!)

Listed below are 25 twelve-letter words, grouped into eight categories. Please examine the list attentively:

(1) COLLATERALIS

(2) ASSEMBLEMENT

(3) SURRENDEREST
    UNTRAVESTIED

(4) CARDSHARPING

(5) CHOLESTERATE
    COMMUTUALITY
    MONORCHIDISM
    NONFISHERMAN
    NONTRIBESMAN
    OUTBRANCHING
    OUTPOCKETING

(6) FADMONGERING
    LABORATORIAL
    NONCUSTOMARY
    NONMOMENTARY
    NONSIPHONAGE

(7) INTRACISTERN
    LIPOBLASTOMA
    MISPOSSESSED
    MISREHEARSAL

(8) CARLOVINGIAN
    RECORDERSHIP
    RESIDENTSHIP
    UNISILICATES

These 25 words have a special quality that sets them apart from most other twelve-letter words, but they possess that quality in varying degrees, represented by the eight subgroups into which they have been ordered. Group (1) is furthest from our ideal; Group (8) is the only one that realizes it fully. The six intermediate groups are successive stages of refinement on the road to our ideal, moving progressively closer to it.

We should like to see you duplicate our train of reasoning by giving us the correct answers to these five questions:

1. What is the fundamental characteristic of all 25 words?
2. Define the eight successive stages.
3. We have chosen stages (5) to (8) inclusive in accordance with a certain principle. We could have resorted to a different principle. Explain!
4. The word NONSIPHONAGE, in Group (6), could have been placed in Group (5) with equal logic. How come?
5. Our title serves two diametrically opposite functions. Can you identify both of them?

Hints: Page 151.   Resolution: Page 210.

11 *SHADCHONIM WANTED!*

We assume that you have traveled on, and are familiar with, the highways of English. On the other hand, there is reasonable doubt in our minds as to the extent of your acquaintance with the byways of our language. To put the matter to a test, we are listing ten unusual words at the left below, and their definitions at the right. Your problem is to match the two columns up properly, fitting each definition to the word that owns it:

(1)	hnau	(a)	people
(2)	votchez	(b)	father
(3)	gawrey	(c)	a flying woman
(4)	quinba	(d)	female
(5)	grildrig	(e)	manikin
(6)	gy	(f)	woman
(7)	Hiya	(g)	She
(8)	ngooka	(h)	life
(9)	klock-klock	(i)	village (?)
(10)	numa	(j)	lion

Since this is the most unusual vocabulary quiz you are ever destined to take (you have our word for that!), there are some special questions attached to it, for you to puzzle over:

1. In preparing this test, we violated a natural assumption of yours. To explain what is amiss will require you to give a 10-part reply. Proceed.
2. There is a second assumption, equally instinctive, that we also crossed up, resulting in the fact that our title contradicts the actual state of affairs. Explain.
3. Why is there a question mark after the word "village"?
4. Why are the words "Hiya" and "She" majuscular in style?
5. How else could we have spelled the word "Shadchonim"?
6. What is the best day of the calendar year on which to take this vocabulary quiz?

Hints: Page 148.   Resolution: Page 214.

12 MABEL A. FUNK (1739-1937)

There is a remarkable connection between our title, the picture given at the right, and a recent best seller. Can you identify the book in question? Further, what is the paradox residing in the picture? And what is the paradox in our title?

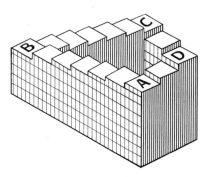

Hints: Page 168.

Resolution: Page 201.

13 HOMONYMIC HUMDINGERS

Some words, differing in spelling, are pronounced alike. Words of this type are called homonyms. Thus, WRITE, RITE, RIGHT, and WRIGHT are homonyms, as are ROAD, RODE, ROWED, ROED, and RHODE (in "Rhode Island").

English, remarkable language that it is, affords examples of as many as ten different words and/or names pronounced alike. An instance:

1. OH – an exclamation of surprise or of sudden emotion.
2. O – an exclamation used in earnest or solemn appeal.
3. OWE – to be in debt.
4. EAU – water, as in "eau de Cologne".
5. EAUX – waters, as in "eaux de vie" (brandies).
6. AU – after the style of, as in "au naturel" (in the nude).
7. AUX – to the, as in "aux armes!" (to arms!).
8. OE – a violent whirlwind off the Faroe Islands.
9. OU – a dialectal form of the interjection "oh".
10. OW – reformed spelling of the verb "owe".

To heighten your homonymic sensitivity, we have worked up another group of ten mutually homonymous English words, but are not revealing them to you directly. We are giving you their dictionary definitions, expecting you to deduce the words from the definitions. Because the words sound alike, finding one or two of them will enable you to guess many of the rest, or at least to look for them intelligently. Consequently, it has been incumbent upon us to select definitions difficult to recognize, and we have not shirked our duty. If this sounds apologetic, it was meant to be precisely that. The definitions:

(1) rather than.
(2) utterance abroad.
(3) the Saxon and Bavarian name for the Teutonic god Tiwaz.
(4) in any conceivable way.
(5) a court of circuit judges.
(6) a.
(7) a town in Massachusetts.
(8) a town in Scotland.
(9) a point on the Isle of Man.
(10) that which is produced: a term used by Shakespeare.

The typography for these definitions has skillfully been modified to conceal the differentness of one of the ten terms, in two respects. Can you identify the term and point out the two typographical features involved in this deception?

Hints: Page 154.   Resolution: Page 181.

14 SCRABBLE!

In recent years, a popular word game resembling anagrams, played with letters printed on small, flat blocks and with a game board, has been the game of Scrabble, put out by the Production and Marketing Company of Newtown, Connecticut. Included with the game is a booklet entitled, "Rules for Playing Scrabble".

According to this booklet, a total combined score (the sum of all individual scores) of 700 or more is excellent. This means that, if the game is being played by only two persons, an individual score of 350 or more is excellent.

Just how high can an individual score go, in a game played by two? This problem has absorbed the attention of some highly competent logologists, and astonishing scores have resulted. If you would like to match your skill with those of the experts, test yourself on the following points:

1. What is your estimate of the highest score one player can actually reach during the course of one game, playing strictly in accordance with the official rules and using Webster's Second Edition as the sole dictionary authority?
2. Can you produce an actual game, move by move, showing the successive words formed by both players, that bears you out?
3. What is the highest score, in your opinion, that can be achieved in one individual move during such a game?
4. Again, can you prove your point with a concrete example?
5. The screamer, or note of admiration, punctuating our title indicates that the title has a hidden meaning, singularly appropriate to the problem. What is it?

In our "Hints", we give you the figures attained by Mrs. Josefa H. Byrne, a logologist in San Francisco, California. In our "Resolution", we show you the actual game. Remember that what you will see there is not the absolute maximum, but merely what has already been achieved. The real challenge posed by this problem is to top Mrs. Byrne's champion game. It can and will be done, by someone, sooner or later. You, perhaps?

Hints: Page 156.   Resolution: Page 217.

15 "THE"

Whether consciously or subconsciously, you have undoubtedly noticed that the names of some countries are generally preceded by the definite article: the Congo, the Sudan, the Ukraine, the Yemen, the Transvaal, the Yukon, the Punjab, the Crimea, the Hejaz, the Netherlands, and others.

All sorts of explanations for this phenomenon can be advanced, in relation to particular cases. It can be argued, for instance, that the article is justified for Holland because its present name is a synonym for "*the* lowlands". For the Arab nations, the excuse is that an article is prefixed to the names of the countries in Arabic. This is not a particularly convincing explanation, for the same practice is followed in French, but we don't speak of *"the* France". The Congo and the Yukon happen also to be the names of rivers, but this is an equally weak explanation, as we do not refer to the distinguished Senators from the Ohio and the Illinois.

What is needed is a general theory that will account for virtually all of the "the" countries. Such a theory has been formulated. Do you have the acumen, the perspicacity to figure it out for yourself? If not, you can always choose the easy way out, referring to our "Resolutions" section, and no one, but *no one*, will be the wiser!

Hints: Page 142.   Resolution: Page 234.

16 *A PERI'S SAD LOT*

Poetry has been described as vocal painting. Let us paint today:

> "Instant without disturb they took alarm,
> And onward move embattled; when behold
> Not distant far with heavy pace the foe
> Approaching gross and huge; in hollow cube
> Training his devilish enginery, impaled
> On every side with shadowing squadrons deep,
> To hide the fraud. At interview both stood
> A while, but suddenly at head appeared
> *Satan:* And thus was heard commanding loud."

How many of the following questions concerning this passage can you answer:

1. From what important work of poetry have we quoted it?
2. One of the great military victories of history was won by putting into practice the new mode of warfare described in the lines quoted and in following lines of the poem. Please elaborate.
3. Our title makes this problem much too simple for you. In what way?
4. We have improved on the original poem. How?

Hints: Page 152.   Resolution: Page 207.

17 *THE SCACCHIC SCOOP*

One of the most important aspects of chess is knowledge of the various standard combinations or sequences of moves used by proficient players in beginning a game. Depending on their nature, these combinations or sequences are called openings, gambits, attacks, defenses, games, gambits declined, Queen's side developments, fianchetto openings, and so forth.

Among these commencement maneuvers there is one kind designated as a *countergambit*. To learn what a countergambit is, let's consult the dictionary.

Both the First and the Second Editions of *Webster's New International Dictionary of the English Language*, first published in 1909 and in 1934 respectively, define the term thus:

"*Chess.* A gambit played in return to a gambit offered by the first player."

Webster's Third New International Dictionary of the English Language, first published in 1961, makes a slight change in the wording of the definition but leaves its meaning intact:

"A chess gambit played in answer to a gambit offered by the first player."

The definitions of "countergambit" given in all three of these dictionaries are incorrect. What is wrong? How should the definition read? En passant, what is remarkable about the title of this problem?

Hints: Page 144.   Resolution: Page 297.

18 *THE WITCHES' PRAYER*

Joseph Addison, English essayist, 1672–1719, mentions an epigram called the "Witches' Prayer", that is said to have fallen into verse when it was read either backward or forward, "excepting only that it cursed one way, and blessed the other".

To test your ability as a researcher, we now ask you to locate a copy of the text of that prayer. Good luck!

Hints: Page 163.   Resolution: Page 269.

19 ONE IDA: AN ONEIDA?

In 1863, an interesting reference work burst forth upon the language scene—Charlotte Mary Yonge's *History of Christian Names*. Since Miss Yonge died in 1901 and her work has been out of print for many years, it is a little late to plug this dictionary of names. Still, it is a fact that the dictionary is a veritable mine of curious information, tempting us to dip into it.

One of the gems that greets the browser is the little-known vignette of GWALLAWG ("hawk" or "stammerer"), more fully GWALLAWG AP LLEENAWG, a champion in old Welsh poems fighting IDA, 6th-century monarch of Bernicia, a country on the coast of the North Sea. That GWALLAWG was two-faced is obvious, but it is a little less evident why history books do not mention any queen as having reigned over Bernicia in the sixth century. We consequently turn to you for help. Can you answer these questions:

1. Why do we call GWALLAWG two-faced?
2. Why is there no mention of the Queen of Bernicia in history texts?
3. Our problem laid three psychological traps for you. Do you recognize them now?
4. What is the significance of our title?

Hints: Page 149.   Resolution: Page 289.

20 GROUP THEORY

Many mathematicians are enamored of a branch of their craft called the Theory of Groups. To cater to these gentlemen, we shall now delve into a linguistic analogue to Group Theory.

Listed next are four groups of words. Please examine them with care;

	(1)		(3)	(4)
(1) aa	skiing	(3) barroom	(4) buzzing
access	snarleyyow	granddaddy	flivver
coordinate	suggest	keenness	hajji
duumvirate	withhold	roommate	zaqqum
ex-xylophonist		self-flattery	
misshapen	(2) dumbbell	toolless	
postthoracic	glowworm	uppull	
reenter	jackknife		

If your analysis of these word lists is correct, you will be able to answer each of the following questions:

1. If we take all of the words in the four lists and mix them together, they constitute a group possessing a very specific characteristic. What is that characteristic?

2. Exclude the four words in group (4). The remaining words, those in the first three groups, indiscriminately combined, represent a group of a higher order, a group the characteristic of which is of a higher degree of specificity. What is that characteristic?

3. Exclude the 11 words in groups (3) and (4). The remaining words, those in groups (1) and (2), jumbled together, are a group with an even higher, still more refined, degree of specificity. What is the controlling characteristic of this group?

4. Exclude all words except those in group (1). The twelve words in that first group are the most exclusive, most specific set of all. Do you recognize their common bond?

5. The words of group (3) have an irrelevant, distracting feature built into them, out of pure malice. What is it?

6. Of all the words in the four lists, there is one word with a degree of balance unmatched by any other. Identify the word and explain what makes it unique.

Hints: Page 143.   Resolution: Page 282.

21 *THE SINISTER SEVEN*

Higher powers have served us with an ultimatum insisting that we pass on to you a problem involving seven ominous words. Bowing to this peremptory demand, we list the fateful heptad here:

TANGIER	HOME	POLISH
SALAMIS	CHOU	SINGER
	LAME	

What is the common denominator underlying this word group? We are permitted to divulge the fact that its nature is triune, touching simultaneously on the meaning, the sounding, and the spelling of the words.

Our "Hints" are purely pictorial. Relate the picture to the problem, and expose its conflict with the problem!

Hints: Page 165.   Resolution: Page 195.

22 SHAKESPEARE AND CERVANTES

William Shakespeare, greatest of all English dramatists, died April 23, 1616. Miguel de Cervantes Saavedra, greatest of all Spanish novelists, also died April 23, 1616. This astonishing coincidence is an example of synchronized nonsimultaneity, for Shakespeare and Cervantes did not die on the same day at all.

Stimulated by this discovery, we now ask you to provide answers to a series of questions:

1. How do you explain the facts just recited?
2. There is a second, equally remarkable coincidence involving the date of Shakespeare's death. What is it?
3. Why is this second coincidence another example of synchronized nonsimultaneity?
4. It happens that the full names of both Shakespeare and Cervantes may be turned into first-rate anagrams, aptly descriptive of those masters; another thought-provoking coincidence. Try your hand at developing these anagrams.
5. Pursuing the subject of coincidences just one step further, what is the coincidental relationship between the life of Shakespeare and the King James Version of the Holy Bible?

Hints: Page 147.   Resolution: Page 291.

23 SEQUELS TO ALEPH

You are taking an I.Q. test. One section of the test presents you with number sequences, each of which you must analyze to establish the underlying rationale, in order to determine the number in the sequence that immediately follows the last number given.

The first number series is an easy one:

$$1 \quad 2 \quad 4 \quad 7 \quad 11 \ldots$$

You quickly grasp that the successive differences between consecutive numbers in this series are 1, 2, 3, 4. Evidently, the next difference will be 5, making the next number $11 + 5$, or 16.

The second number sequence is a more challenging one:

$$8 \quad 5 \quad 4 \quad 9 \quad 1 \ldots$$

Study this series and then answer the following questions:

1. What is the "obvious" next number? Why?
2. What are the *two* reasons each of which, taken by itself, is sufficient to make that choice incorrect?
3. What is the true next number? Why?
4. It is possible to arrive at the true next number by means of faulty reasoning. How?
5. At what point in this sequence will the number 0 occur?
6. What is the connection between ALEPH and this problem?

Hints: Page 145. Resolution: Page 247.

24 A PONDEROUS POSTAL PROBLEM

The function of language is to communicate. Communication may be either oral or written. One of the forms that written communication takes is that of the letter. Every day, millions and millions of letters are in transit around the country. They are sped to their destinations by the United States Post Office. Consequently, anyone who uses language in writing a letter must concern himself with postal affairs.

Observation over the years indicates that the United States Post Office is almost habitually operating with a deficit, and that rates of postage are periodically increased in a necessarily futile effort to keep up with growing postal expenses. No one likes postal rate increases. As public-spirited citizens, we are obliged to think of a way to increase postal revenues materially without permitting a rate increase. Specifically, a means must be found of increasing the revenue from first-class mail without raising the present rate of five cents per ounce.

With the welfare of the nation at stake, we have spent many sleepless nights revolving this problem in our minds, and have found a solution that accomplishes the seemingly impossible. Are you sufficiently ingenious to duplicate that solution, or to discover an alternate one?

Hints: Page 159.   Resolution: Page 285.

25 DESPERATION

The world is full of languages the layman seldom, if ever, hears about. Glancing through A Dictionary of Linguistics by Mario Pei and Frank Gaynor, we ran across languages such as ESKUARA, spoken in the Pyrenees, IVRIT, spoken in Israel, and MAGHI, spoken in Burma. These names don't even look like language names, most of which end with suffixes such as -ESE, -ISH, -IAN, and -IC or -ICAN.

To familiarize you with more of these odd-looking language names, we are listing ten of them, in alphabetical order:

ARULO	MYRANA
BALTA	OMNEZ
BLAIA ZIMONDAL	OPTEZ
CABE ABAN	SOLRESOL
MONARIO	SPELIN

Our list creates problems that we should genuinely like to see you resolve for us:

1. Can you identify these languages properly?
2. It is not customary to list them alphabetically. How should they be arranged, to be conventional?
3. Inability to answer our first two questions might, conceivably, bring you into a state of desperation, but that is insufficient reason for labeling this problem DESPERATION. Can you discern a much more compelling reason for our title choice?
4. In retrospect, those language names we first cited—MAGHI, IVRIT, and ESKUARA—are stranger than you may have realized. Each is an uncommon

designation for a reasonably well-known language. Can you identify the three languages by their more usual names?

5. Going back to the title of our problem and hewing to the same line, how else might we have entitled this problem?

6. Give us eight generic names for the group of ten languages under discussion.

Hints: Page 158.   Resolution: Page 208.

26   *A MAGIC CIRCLE*

Pictured at the right is a magic letter circle. If you care to do so, we suggest that you answer a number of questions in regard to it.

1. Mathematically, the figure shown belongs to a class possessing a specific designation. What is the designation that applies to it?
2. Prove that the letter circle has the characteristic expected of it.
3. This particular circle has a much more encompassing characteristic of the same sort. Elucidate.
4. Where would you look for the mathematical background of this word problem?

Hints: Page 169.   Resolution: Page 215.

27   *STATELY SOBRIQUETS*

To let you relax for a while, we are switching to a simple, old-fashioned quiz, one concerning itself with state nicknames. All of us are familiar with the popular nicknames for the various states: New York, the Empire State; Indiana, the Hoosier State; Arizona, the Grand Canyon State; and so on. In the quiz that follows, fifty such sobriquets are assembled, one for each state. Your problem is to identify the states to which the nicknames apply.

Simple quiz? Old-fashioned quiz? You may differ with these evaluations after testing yourself on it. Actually, the quiz is designed to measure how far beyond the reach of general information your familiarity with the colorful nicknames of our states extends. Accordingly, we warn you not to look these designations up in current almanacs, for you will not find even one of them in such publications.

As an indication of the difficulty of this quiz, we suggest the following score levels: 5, good; 10, excellent; 15, unbelievable; 20 or more, impossible!

One of our fifty sobriquets lays a peculiar trap for you. Can you spot that trap? Can you explain it?

1. The Terrapin State
2. The Red Mud State
3. The Hot Water State
4. The Snake State
5. The Basin State
6. The Lizard State
7. The Hoop-Pole State
8. The Antelope State
9. The Saddle Horse Capital of the World
10. The Valley of Humility Between Two Mountains of Conceit
11. Uncle Sam's Pocket Handkerchief
12. The Land of the Rolling Prairies
13. The Land of the Delight-makers
14. The Captain-General of Resistance
15. The Modern Mother of Presidents
16. The Banner State of the South
17. Up Over
18. The Cyclone State
19. The Lion's Den
20. The Grape State
21. The Syringa State
22. The Holy Experiment
23. The Ocotillo State
24. The Water Wonderland
25. The Top of the Nation
26. The Soreback State
27. The Gateway of America
28. America's Loggerhead
29. The Cattlemen's Commonwealth
30. The Live Oak State
31. The Hospitality State
32. The Pickerel State
33. The Zephyr State
34. Wahoo
35. The Stubtoe State
36. Super America
37. The Mining State
38. The Future State
39. The Lively Experiment
40. The Boomer's Paradise
41. The Mother of Rivers
42. The Arsenal of the Nation
43. The Dark and Bloody Ground
44. The Empire State of the West
45. America's Dairyland
46. The Sportsmen's Paradise
47. The Theater of Seasons
48. The Everglade State
49. The Cradle of Liberty
50. The Land of Hard Cases

Hints: Page 151.

Resolution: Page 266.

28 DISCOVERED BY HERSCHEL!

Think of William Shakespeare. Think of his comedy, A *Midsummer Night's Dream*. You are reading a portion of Act III, Scene 1. Titania, imperious Queen of the fairies, is speaking to Bottom the Weaver:

"Out of this wood do not desire to go;
Thou shalt remain here whether thou wilt or no.
I am a spirit of no common rate,—
The summer still doth tend upon my state;
And I do love thee: therefore, go with me,
I'll give thee fairies to attend on thee;
And they shall fetch thee jewels from the deep,
And sing, while thou on pressed flowers dost sleep:
And I will purge thy mortal grossness so
That thou shalt like an airy spirit go.—"

A penetrating analysis of this passage shows us that Shakespeare was a word puzzler at heart, using his plays as a medium to disclose that fact to the world. Can you tell us why? Can you also tell us how Herschel got into the act?

Hints: Page 163.   Resolution: Page 279.

29 BALANCE AND BEAUTY

To gain a wholesome, refreshing, and unbiased perspective in our verbal musing, we must look at language not as the linguist sees it, but as does the mathematician.

For the mathematician, every formula and every equation is a thing of beauty, distinguished for the quality of balance intrinsic to it. Similarly, a word can appeal to the number expert only if it, too, is in balance.

In relation to what can we balance a word? In relation to the alphabet that spawned it, of course. Since the English alphabet has 26 letters, its midpoint, halfway between M and N, with 13 letters preceding it and 13 following it, and with the letters numbered sequentially from 1 to 26, has a numerical value of $13\frac{1}{2}$. To be balanced, the average numerical value of all the letters in a word must be precisely $13\frac{1}{2}$.

To illustrate, let's take one of the most important words in our language, the word LOVE. The numerical values of the four letters in LOVE are 12, 15, 22, and 5 (these are the numbers that define the positions of the letters in our alphabet: L is the 12th letter, O the 15th letter, V the 22nd letter, and E the 5th letter). Add the four values, and you find that their sum is 54. Divide that sum by 4 (the number of letters in the word), and you have their average value, $13\frac{1}{2}$. This shows that LOVE is a balanced word. By appropriate contrast, HATE is not a balanced word: the individual values of the four letters comprising HATE are 8, 1, 20, and 5, with a sum of 34; dividing this sum by 4 gives us an average value of $8\frac{1}{2}$. This demonstrates that HATE is unbalanced, a fact we've known all along.

Balanced words—alphabetically balanced combinations or collocations—are known as ABC's for short. This, then, is your introduction to the ABC's of today, a breed entirely different from the ABC's that were taught to you in elementary school.

To gauge your awareness of the ABC's, your sensitivity and responsiveness to them, we have prepared a questionnaire dealing with the ABC's, and ask you to fill it out. The questionnaire is reproduced below. Score yourself by checking your answers against those we are providing.

As you go into this exercise, remember the time-honored adage to the effect that "balanced words reflect a balanced life".°

1. What are the three shortest common ABC's?
2. What are the longest known ABC's?
3. Why is it impossible for a word with an odd number of letters to be an ABC?
4. For some as yet undetermined reason, most ABC's show a preponderance of letters from the last half of the alphabet. Thus, if we are working with 8-letter ABC's, the chances are that only 2 or 3 of the 8 letters will be first-half letters. For instance, the ABC's PROPOSED and NOTATION use only two first-half letters apiece, and the ABC's BROWNISH and FROSTING use only three first-half letters apiece. Consequently, it becomes a challenge to discover ABC's that run counter to this trend. Can you name any 8-, 10-, or 12-letter ABC's in which first-half letters preponderate?

° A free translation from the original Armorican text, quoted by Professor Cloudesley in *Boustrophedonic Reveries*, Quéfanôn Reprint Edition, Volume 8, Page 17.

5. Name some 8-letter ABC's that exhibit an even higher order of balance than ordinary ABC's, with equal numbers of letters drawn from the two halves of the alphabet, and with the further condition that: (a) all four of the first half letters occupy the *first* four positions in the word; (b) all four of the first-half letters occupy the *last* four positions in the word.

6. The letters of the alphabet can be paired in balanced fashion: A-Z, B-Y, C-X, D-W, E-V, ... M-N. If we scramble several such pairs with sufficient skill, we find ABC's that belong to a yet higher class, those that can be resolved into the balanced pairs out of which we originally shaped them. A 6-letter ABC of this kind is the word RIGHTS, which can be analyzed into the three balanced pairs G-T, H-S, and I-R. How many 8-letter ABC's of the same sort can you find? Any "tens"?

7. Ascending another rung on the ladder to the stars, diligent searching reveals some ABC's of the sort just described which arrange their component balanced pairs not in haphazard, random letter order, but according to a special pattern. Examining 6-letter ABC's with showmanlike wizardry, we hit upon the word WIZARD, constructed from the balanced pairs A-Z, D-W, and I-R. Instead of disporting themselves in random order, the six letters have drawn themselves up in a concentric arrangement:

Our love for orderliness carries us onward, to the word BY-LOVE (a corollary form of love). Here, the balanced pairs (B-Y, E-V, and L-O) have arranged themselves in sequential instead of concentric style:

Your problem? To find analogous, 8-letter, dictionary-sanctioned ABC's!

8. There is more than one way to reach skyward in the land of the ABC Himalayas. We can try for the opposite extreme, a long word that contains not even a single balanced pair of letters, yet is an ABC. 8-letter examples include SPARTANS, PREOPENS, and OPINANTS. It is now your turn, and your assignment is to submit a comparable, 12-letter ABC.

9. In our drive toward the dizzying heights, we must point out a defect in the specimens of the preceding section: all of them contained repeated letters. Esthetically, there is more satisfaction derived from ABC's that do

not repeat any letter, using each one only once. Examples of 8-letter ABC's that use no letter of the alphabet more than once and which include not even a single balanced letter pair: OPERANTS, PARSONET, PATERSON, PRONATES, PROTEANS. Curiously and parenthetically, these five words are transpositions of one another and of the French word REPOSANT ("restful, refreshing"). For a restful, refreshing diversion, we are setting you the problem of finding or devising a 12-letter ABC with exactly the same characteristics.

10. There are many facets to the concept of balance, and correspondingly many ideas of the beautiful. One school of thought holds that an ABC is not a true model of balance unless it shows a balance of vowels and consonants—equal numbers of the two, arranged alternately. To satisfy exponents of this theory, you are requested to supply some 8-letter specimens of ABC's consisting of 4 consonants and 4 vowels, placed alternately.

11. Another school of thought espouses the view that, to be genuinely worthwhile, to represent KALON, an ABC must have a meaning in the field of language or of wordplay. How many ABC's of this type are at your beck and call?

Hints: Page 167.   Resolution: Page 257.

30 *FRONTIER DAYS*

Most of us spend our lives sheltered by the enormous number of English words that constitute our verbal environment. Seldom does it occur to us that others are less fortunate, engaged in a never-ending struggle to express thoughts for which no words have yet been found. It is our bounden duty to rescue these unfortunates from their miserable plight, by creating some of the words they need but do not have. Come, join us as we patrol the "New Frontier", the hitherto unexplored areas of language, making up words for the New Thoughts we encounter in our probing.

Most urgently needed, perhaps, is a medical term for the state produced in female children, usually between the ages of 11 and 13, by crude rhythm or pop music. Without straining our brainpower beyond the breaking point, we come up with apt words such as ADULESCENCE, BEATOLESCENCE, ELVISOMANIA,

HEPILEPSY, HEPNOTISM, HEPSTERIA, HIPPOSIS, MADOLESCENCE, POPOCATALEPSY, POPSTASY, POPSYCHOSIS, RAVIES, RINGORRHEA, and ST. NINNY'S TRANCE.

See how easy it is? Very well, then: we are giving you the opportunity to become frontiersmen, too, by devising suitable words to express the thoughts in the eight definitions that follow:

1. To make a sound like escaping bath water.

2. An unreal person; one who talks in an unreal, exaggerated, or unnatural fashion, like a character in a television commercial.

3. To pursue an excessive standard of living; to "keep up with the Joneses".

4. To drive a small, old car in the middle of the road with an air of virtue.

5. Having the appearance of affluence, while actually living on credit.

6. The technique of erecting standard cubical structures (offices, apartments, etc.), a technique which supplanted architecture some years ago.

7. The crime of killing with an automobile.

8. One who compensates for a lack of creative and critical ability by an exaggerated enthusiasm for anything new, difficult, or shocking.

The meanings just listed ought to be in the dictionary, but they aren't. How can they be, when the words whose definitions they are haven't been invented yet? The time to erase this blot on language is NOW!

Hints: Page 165.   Resolution: Page 243.

31 CRACKING THE "Q" CODE

Known only to initiates into the "arcanum arcanorum" of word lore, there exists a code or cipher for transmitting communications with absolute secrecy, one in which each word is represented or replaced by a single letter of the alphabet. In this code, each letter is found, upon intelligent examination, to be a form of highly compressed English, standing for a whole word; or, in rare instances, even for a full phrase. Since the use of this code would be a boon, not only to cryptographers but also to brachygraphers and tachygraphers°, we have reluctantly decided to release its details to the world at this time.

° Stenographers, to put it more simply.

Whether our action will turn out to have been an ill-advised one, only future events can determine.

There are a number of different principles that enter into the construction of this fabulous code. We are going to explain these principles, using many different alphabetic letters for illustrative purposes, but avoiding that most refractory of all letters, the letter Q. Your problem will be to demonstrate your understanding of our expository material by devising at least one Q code corresponding to each of our methods. Fair enough?

(1) The first and most basic form of our code—a code sometimes referred to as the "letter rebus", incidentally—involves looking at the letter that is to be the code letter, and so describing that letter as to make the description form an English word when all the letters in the description are placed next to one another (interrupted by word breaks, in the case of a phrase). For instance, if we see a solitary B, we can speak of *"a B alone"*. Taking the seven letters in this phrase and eliminating the spaces between them, we find that they spell ABALONE, the name of an edible mollusk with a flat shell. In the same way, we may express astonishment at encountering a D by ejaculating, *"Lo! A 'D'!"*, at the same time converting that D into a code letter for the word LOAD.

There seems no limit to the many ways in which a letter may be thought of that result in one-letter codes. Some additional examples:

E — *"The E"* = THEE
L — *"L, I ken!"* = LIKEN
M — *"M is placed!"* = MISPLACED
N — *"N once"* = NONCE
O — *"Perfect O"* = PERFECTO
P — *"A 'P' perceived"* = APPERCEIVED
S — *"Lo! An S!"* = LOANS
T — *"T, actually!"* = TACTUALLY
W — *"One 'W' here!"* = ONEWHERE (in one place only)
Y — *"Ever Y!"* = EVERY
Z — *"Ha! Zed!"* = HAZED

(2) A variation of the first technique is to pass off a comment which is not an abstract one but addressed to a listener. Thus, if we observe a D, we may tell our listener, *"See the D!"*, a remark that turns the D into a letter rebus for SEETHED. Other specimens of a like order:

G — *"Bring in G!"* = BRINGING
S — *"Read just 'S'!"* = READJUSTS
Y — *"Read Y!"* = READY

(3) Another variation of the first technique is to have the letter speak for itself, telling us about itself; a form of personification or prosopopoeia. For instance, the letter B proclaims to all the world, *"I am B!"*, forming the word IAMB (a metrical foot). Others:

D — *"A 'D', I pose!"* = ADIPOSE
P — *"I'm P!"* = IMP
S — *"S I am!"* = SIAM

(4) Totally different in its approach is the "negative" rebus, which notes both the letter that is present and one or two others which must sadly be conceded as absenting themselves. Thus, when looking at an A, we may think to ourselves that a T could also be present, but isn't. This thought may inspire us to comment, *"No T, and A"*, which just happens to be a rebus for NOTANDA (memoranda). Other examples:

B — *"B; Y gone!"* = BYGONE
H — *"No 'A'; 'H' "* = NOAH
R — *"R; a G out!"* = RAGOUT

(5) Yet another technique introduces phonetics, the sound of words as they are pronounced. To illustrate, the letter C can be described as *"a C"*, which phrase is homonymous with the word ASEA. This makes the letter C a phonetic rebus for the word ASEA. Other phonetic rebuses:

E — *"I see E!"* = I C E = ICE
G — *"Oh, G!"* = O G = OGEE (an S-shaped molding)
X — *"An 'X' "* = ANN X = ANNEX

(6) The science of the letter rebus reaches its culmination in the form known as the "enigmatic" rebus. This type of rebus is certainly the most intriguing and challenging one, exhibiting greater ingenuity and variety than any other. It is almost impossible to define, so we shall proceed directly to exemplifying it.

D = *"End o' 'card' it is!"* = ENDOCARDITIS

(How indisputably true that D is the end of CARD . . . but how unfortunate that it reminds us of an inflammation of a membrane lining the chambers of the heart!)

E = *" 'Sense' less 'ness' "* = SENSELESSNESS

(Take the letters in SENSE and remove those in NESS. What you have left is a lonely E.)

H = *"H, as H, is H"* = HASHISH

(Here is a profound philosophical statement which tells us that the letter H, considered simply as an H, must truly be regarded as an H. If this seems like a pipe dream to you, you've probably been smoking HASHISH, that intoxicant also known as BHANG and as CANNABIS.)

K = *"See K; no further!"* = SEEK-NO-FURTHER

(This rebus lands in the category of the enigmatic on the strength of its ominous warning to us not to go beyond the letter K. The SEEK-NO-FURTHER is a variety of winter apple, another sinister facet of the rebus—we all know of the poisoned apple in the folk tale *Snow White!*)

L = CENTER OF OSCILLATION

(The word OSCILLATION is spelled with 11 letters. The middle one, the sixth letter, is an L. The phrase CENTER OF OSCILLATION is a technical term in physics.)

M = *"M is in formation"* = MISINFORMATION

(This time, we are viewing the letter M as consisting of a number of independent lines which have drawn themselves up in formation so as to create the shape of an M.)

O = A CIRCULAR LETTER

(A double-entendre, more correctly double entente: taken literally, O is a letter circular in shape; taken figuratively, we are referring to a printed letter intended for general distribution. Of course, there is something awry here . . . the O isn't *really* circular—it's oval or elliptical!)

O = *"Con 'naught'!"* = CONNAUGHT

(The letter O, written as a capital letter, is identical with the numeral representing zero. "To con naught" means to peruse or study the zero carefully, in order to realize its identity with the O. CONNAUGHT, or CONNACHT, is a Province of western Ireland.)

T = *"T in type"* = TINTYPE

(We are considering the letter T, not from a layman's standpoint, but as it appears to a typesetter. Result: a TINTYPE, or kind of photograph also called a FERROTYPE.)

V = CENTER OF GRAVITY

   (This is the same species of enigmatic rebus encountered under "L". This
   time, the letter V is at the exact center of the word GRAVITY. The phrase CENTER
   OF GRAVITY is another term plucked from the pages of a textbook on physics.)

X = "*Crossed I's*" = CROSSED EYES

   (This is a phonetic rebus. Its enigmatic quality derives from regarding the letter
   X as consisting of two I's lying athwart each other.)

Altogether, we have shown you forty examples of one-letter rebuses,
classified in six general categories. A number of letters are not covered by the
foregoing specimens: F, I, J, Q, and U. As a remedial measure, we adduce
another few examples:

   F — "*F is sure!*" = FISSURE
   I — "*Real 'I'—st!*" = REALIST
   J — "*A 'J', a 'J', a . . .!*" = AJAJA (a spoonbill)
   U — "*A 'U' to type*" = AUTOTYPE (a facsimile)

With all alphabetic letters except the Q now properly accounted for, there is
nothing to distract you from the task at hand: to construct rebuses of various
kinds using the single letter Q as a fully satisfactory representation of the word
or phrase being coded.

   The task is urgent and difficult, the time is short and precious. You have
not a moment to lose. Our final word of advice to you is the final word of
Episode 7 in Section I of *Finnegans Wake* by James Joyce: QUOIQUOIQUOIQUOI-
QUOIQUOIQUOIQ! (It's the only word in English spelled with eight Q's.)

Hints: Page 158.   Resolution: Page 260.

32 *SOCRATES AND SERENDIPITY*

Napoleon I, known as the "Nightmare of Europe" at one time, was born
on the Mediterranean island of Corsica. Yet, in a sense, his origin may be sought
with equal logic in another island, Ceylon.

   How come?

Hints: Page 153.   Resolution: Page 241.

33 DOPPELGÄNGER!

The May 7, 1955 issue of the *Competitors' Journal,* a London newspaper, carried an article by the English journalist, J. A. Lindon, including this piece of verse:

> "As I was passing near the gaol
> I met a man, but hurried by:
> His face was ghastly, grimly pale;
> He had a gun. I wondered why
> He had. A gun ? I wondered . . . why,
> His face was GHASTLY! Grimly pale,
> I met a man, but hurried by
> As I was passing near the gaol."

The poem just quoted raises a number of questions, among them these:

1. The English word GAOL, a variant of the American word JAIL, has two peculiarities. Name them, if you dare!
2. What is the distinguishing characteristic of this poem, one that sets it apart from virtually all other poetry?
3. What was the probable subject of Mr. Lindon's article?
4. Can you compose a verse of the same sort, but an appreciably longer one?
5. The title of this problem is related to it in two ways. One should be apparent to you now, the other after you have compared your answer to Question No. 4 with ours. Can you find both connections?
6. In view of the preceding, how else might our problem have been entitled?

Hints: Page 168.   Resolution: Page 293.

34 THE BLACK ISLAND

Our state legislatures sometimes engage in activities of a curious nature. In 1965, for instance, North Carolina's Senate received a bill to designate the bedbug as the State insect, and Florida passed a law prohibiting chimpanzees from driving cars.

Going back in time, we find that, in 1923, the Legislature of the State of Illinois enacted a law prohibiting the use of English as the official language of the State. With what language was English replaced in Illinois?

What and where is the Black Island? What is its connection with the *Atlas of America?*

Hints: Page 164.   Resolution: Page 171.

35 *ETYMOLOGICAL ECCENTRICITIES*

One of the many ways in which we reach out beyond language is through etymological studies, aimed at tracing the words we use back to their ultimate sources. Those who undertake these studies, etymologists, sometimes chance upon queer things. Thus, at the meeting of the Linnean Society of New South Wales, on August 27, 1890, some etymologists maintained that, in the dialect of the Australian natives living along the Endeavor River, the word KANGAROO meant "I don't know".

Dispensing with such frivolousness, the etymologists have slowly been accumulating words with redundant etymologies—words derived from two older words identical or nearly identical in meaning. Professor Cloudesley, intervening on our behalf, has made it possible for us to release some of the precious hoard to the world at this time. Seven superb examples of etymological redundancy follow.

1. OUIJA (a board device used to spell out mediumistic communications at a séance). This word is derived from the French OUI and the German JA, both of which mean YES.

2. FISNOGA (calf's-foot jelly). Derived from the German FUSS and the Russian NOGA, both meaning "foot".

3. DEMISEMI (an adjective used in music to indicate "one quarter"). From the French DEMI- and the Latin SEMI-, both meaning "half".

4. REINDEER (a kind of deer). From the Old Norse HREINN, meaning "reindeer", and the Old Norse DȲR, meaning "deer".

5. LASPRING (the young salmon). From the Old English LEAX, meaning "salmon", and the dialectal German PINKE, meaning "small salmon".

6. CHERSONESE (a peninsula). From the Greek CHERSOS, meaning "dry land", and the Greek NĒSOS, meaning "island".

7. PILLICOCK (the coles or tentum). From the dialectal Norwegian PILL, and the English COCK, both with the same meaning.

Occasionally, etymological redundancy affects only part of a word, being attached to another, nonredundant element. Sometimes, the redundancy is not merely a two-part affair, but one of three parts. Both of these situations are illustrated by the next case.

Let's take the word ULTIMA, the name for the last syllable of a word. By changing it slightly, we obtain the adjective ULTIMATE, referring to that syllable. By prefixing "pen-", we obtain PENULTIMATE, an adjective designating the syllable that precedes the ultima. Adding a second prefix gives us ANTEPENULTIMATE, an adjective for that syllable of a word third from the end. Adding a third prefix, we wind up with PREANTEPENULTIMATE, the adjective used in speaking of the syllable fourth from the end of a word.

All three of the prefixes used are Latin in origin. In the context provided by the meaning of the words formed, all three prefixes may be construed as meaning "before" or "preceding".

We have shown you how it is done, and it is your turn to demonstrate your etymological skills by solving two simple problems:

1. Finding a word or name that exhibits a pure, quadruple redundancy, consisting of four elements identical in meaning.
2. Finding a word or name in which there is also a quadruple redundancy, but limited to a portion of the word, the entirety of which includes a fifth, unrelated element.

The stage is yours.

Hints: Page 160.   Resolution: Page 204.

36 *THE WITCHING HOUR*

Among his many and varied accomplishments, Professor Ravenscroft J. Cloudesley boasts that of armchair traveler par excellence. It is not to be wondered at, therefore, that the good Professor has discovered a way of traveling from Yukon Territory, Canada, to Alaska, and on to Norway, *without* moving from one land to another.

How can this bit of magic be accomplished? How does our title provide the fateful clue to resolution of the mystery? Can you provide documentary proof that the Professor's method is valid?

Hints: Page 162.   Resolution: Page 229.

37 *H O N*

In this problem, you are being thrown to the wolves! After you have resolved it to your satisfaction (and, parenthetically, to ours), tell us why.

Gathered together for your amusement and amazement are four designations of a most curious variety:

> AN CRAOIBHIN AOIBHINN
>
> CATHLEEN NI HOULAHAN
>
> ROISIN DUBH
>
> SHAN VAN VOCHT

Of what or of whom are these designations? What sort of designations are they? What do they mean?

In a sense—a most erroneous one, however—our enigmatic title discloses what the four names have in common. In a different sense, our title signifies total exclusion of the four names. Can you read both meanings into H O N?

Hints: Page 169.   Resolution: Page 233.

38 *ANTIPODAL IDENTITIES*

Give some thought to the following list of words (not too much thought, of course, for you might then see through them, and that would spoil the fun!). The words have been grouped in twos and threes:

(1) SKIN — FLESH — BONE
(2) SEED — ROOT
(3) TABLE — STAND
(4) OVERLOOK — SCAN — OVERSEE
(5) WITH — FOR
(6) ALMSMAN — HELP
(7) LEASE — RENT — LET

The words forming each group are either synonymous or closely connected in meaning. Skin, flesh, and bone are almost proverbially associated: "nothing left but bone and skin"; "the nearer the bone the sweeter the flesh"; etc. A developing seed acquires a root. A stand is a small table. To overlook, scan, and oversee all mean to examine or inspect. To be with someone, in one sense, is to be for him. An almsman is one who receives help in the form of charity. To lease, rent, and let all mean to permit premises to be occupied in return for compensation.

Related or synonymous as these words are, they can be arranged so as to produce two columns of definitions, with each pair of corresponding definitions exact opposites of each other. Although the number of words in our list is odd, the desired regrouping can be effected without deviating from purely *paired* definitions, and without leaving any word unused. See if you can achieve this arithmetical miracle. There are very many rearrangements that comply with our conditions. What is the smallest number of word moves in which you can accomplish the juggling act suggested?

Hints: Page 150.   Resolution: Page 224.

39 *BEAUTY IN UGLINESS*

He who penetrates the outer shell of words finds meanings hidden in them that lie beyond the vision of a less percipient observer. How many, for instance, know that the word BLACK really means WHITE?

Dictionaries define words in terms of other words. If we look these other words up, we are treated to yet other words; and so on. This permits us to build a chain of synonymous words. If we do this carefully and schemingly, unforeseen results are likely to ensue; unforeseen to the ordinary dictionary consultant, anyway. Consider the case of BLACK. Dictionary investigation yields a series of equations showing us that black is actually white.

$$Black = Dark$$
$$Dark = Obscure$$
$$Obscure = Hidden$$
$$Hidden = Concealed$$
$$Concealed = Snug$$
$$Snug = Comfortable$$
$$Comfortable = Easy$$
$$Easy = Simple$$
$$Simple = Pure$$
$$Pure = White$$

The turning point in the series is, of course, the pairing of CONCEALED, a negative attribute, with SNUG, a positive attribute. Since dictionaries equate the two words, so do we.

You must feel as inspired by this revelation as we feel, and be chafing at the bit to make comparable discoveries of your own. It devolves upon us to help you, by suggesting another pair of opposites that are really the same. That is why we are asking you to prove that what is UGLY, when viewed in the proper light, is truly BEAUTIFUL. The transition from ugliness to beauty can be accomplished in as few as nine successive equations.

If you can duplicate the series, just where does the switch from negative thinking to positive thinking take place?

Hints: Page 157.   Resolution: Page 191.

40 *JOCKEYS AND YANKEES*

JOCKEYS, YANKEES, ZANIES, and all others need plenty of JACK to keep hitting the JUG or the bottle. What is the hidden link between the five words in capitals?

The relation of our title to our problem is apparent—or is it? Come to think of it, there is an obvious, yet concealed, connection between the title and the problem. Can you uncover this hidden link as well?

Hints: Page 142.   Resolution: Page 228.

41 *KIPLING REVISED*

Daniel Z. Ross, that intrepid, latter-day Marco Polo, making his way across America, subsequently reported coming upon a signpost with the legend, "This is the easternmost point in the United States."

Meager as the data just given may seem, they should enable you to answer these questions:

1. In which of our 46 States, and precisely where within that State, did our traveler see that signpost?
2. Why is it impossible for him to have seen such a signpost?
3. Had there been such a signpost, why would the message on it have been untrue?
4. What message would there have been on the back of the signpost?
5. How can the name of the State involved be deduced directly from the name of our traveler?
6. What is the "Kipling" problem, and how is it most simply and elegantly solved?
7. Why does the first question refer to 46 States, rather than to 50?
8. What makes the subject of this problem singularly appropriate for inclusion in this book?

Hints: Page 153.   Resolution: Page 237.

42 *BAMBOOZLING THE "BAMBINO"*

With all due respect for "Babe" Ruth and the New York Yankees, it is our unswerving conviction that the Sultan of Swat never hit a single home run.

There are two separate, unrelated reasons for our contention. Can you infer both of them from what you have just read?

Hints: Page 145.   Resolution: Page 244.

43 *THE GAME OF CROSS-REFERENCE*

Anyone who presumes to travel through and beyond the realm of language must know how to use a dictionary. One of the features common in almost all dictionaries is the cross-reference. A cross-reference is a note or statement directing a reader from one part of a book or index to another part. Suppose, for example, that you want to know what the word MATACO means. You look that word up in the Second Edition of Webster's unabridged, and confront the definition: "The apar." Unless you are a devotee of the crossword puzzle, chances are that you don't know what APAR means any more than you knew what MATACO meant, so you refer to the word APAR. Here, you find the information you were seeking: a mataco or apar is a three-banded, South American armadillo. Under MATACO, you were given a cross-reference to APAR; under APAR, you were given the definition.

Cross-references are an essential device in present-day dictionaries and encyclopedias, enabling editors to compress a large volume of information into books of manageable physical size and of reasonable price. What has not, however, been fully realized yet is the role that the cross-reference plays as a test of will between the lexicographer or dictionary editor and the user of his publication. It would be easy to write a book exploring the subject of cross-references as a game played between editor and user, pitting the knowledge, experience, and resources of the former against the patience, determination, and single-minded dedication to purpose of the latter. Our intention here is merely to give you a glimpse of the enchanting world of the cross-reference.

Within this limited framework, we are introducing you to a term most probably unknown to you: BIRD'S-HEAD TYPE. We want you to look the word up in a dictionary, telling us: (1) in what dictionary you found it; (2) what it means; (3) what you went through to obtain its definition.

Hints: Page 161.   Resolution: Page 278.

44 *THE COLLECTIVE FARM*

The November 14, 1965 issue of *Book Week* Magazine, as included in the *Washington Post* of the same date, carried the following delightful poem by Felicia Lamport, in its "Similes & Metaphors" section:

COLLECTIVE FARM

In the best collective use,
>   Geese afoot are *gaggles*
(Even when one goose gets loose,
>   Falls behind and straggles);

Skein's the word for geese in flight.
>   Turtledoves form *dools.*
Barren's right (though impolite)
>   For a pack of mules.

Starlings join in *murmuration,*
>   Pheasants in a *rye,*
Larks in lovely *exaltation,*
>   Leopards, *leap* (they're spry).

Ducks in flight are known as *teams;*
>   *Paddings* when they swim.
Herrings in poetic *gleams*
>   Please the wordsmith's whim.

Cats collect into a *clowder,*
>   Kittens make a *kindle.*
Sloths of bears growl all the louder
>   As their forces dwindle.

Lapwings gather in *deceit,*
>   Apes convene in *shrewdness,*
Mares in *stud* (an odd conceit
>   Bordering on lewdness).

Foxes muster in a *skulk,*
>   Squirrels run in *drays*
While collectives in the bulk
>   Make up word bouquets.

We want you to examine this poem from the standpoint of Advanced Language, and answer four questions:

1. Five of the collective designations for animals, as shown in the poem just quoted, are incorrect. Identify and explain the errors.

2. A sixth collective designation may be erroneous. Please elucidate.
3. Hidden in the text of the poem are an additional two collective terms, one for peacocks and one for pheasants. Can you spot them?
4. Can you name at least one exact synonym for each of the 19 italicized nouns of multitude in the poem?

Hints: Page 154.   Resolution: Page 212.

45 THE NEW CHEMISTRY

How do you FORM ICE, languagewise?

Hints: Page 148.   Resolution: Page 221.

46 MEMORY HOOKS

Professor Ravenscroft J. Cloudesley, semantic savant supreme, has been working on a pet project, that of memory hooks, for most of his adult life. A memory hook is a gimmick for remembering the essential difference between two very similar words, or a salient fact about something, based on spelling. A few examples will show you what the Professor has been doing and dreaming.

The name of the color produced by mixing black and white is spelled GRAY in the United States, GREY in the British Isles. We can remember which is which by noting that GREY, is the English spelling, GRAY the American spelling. In the same fashion, it becomes easy to remember that STALACTITES hang down from the ceiling of a cave while STALAGMITES loom up from its ground; that the TITANIC was sunk by an ICEBERG; and that the ERIE Canal ran from EAST to WEST, not from North to South.

Ingenious as these memory hooks may seem when you first encounter them, they represent the one great failure of Cloudesley's professional career. It happens that, just before his abrupt retirement in 1961, Cloudesley decided to test the alertness and resourcefulness of his Advanced Logology class by presenting to it the four situations enumerated above, and asking the students to devise memory hooks of their own to fit. The suggestions turned in by

Cloudesley's class were so outrageously at variance with the facts that a good many of Cloudesley's closest friends believe that the shocking performance of the class was directly responsible for his suddenly leaving the limelight, as it were, and going into ascetic seclusion.

Whatever the truth may ultimately turn out to be, *we* are going to test *your* resourcefulness, *your* mastery of word and of thought, by asking you to duplicate the astounding perversion of truth in which Cloudesley's class indulged. How many alternate, wholly fictitious, memory hooks can you create for the four situations we have discussed?

Hints: Page 142.   Resolution: Page 202.

47   *BOWDLERIZED ENGLISH?*

Some of the most common and most important terms in modern English— there can be no doubt that you have met them many times in your reading— have never appeared in any dictionary of our language, and are not likely ever to do so. Among the terms we have in mind are LIBE, CASTIR, RAYN, and HYDROZ.

Since these terms are quite familiar to you, we request you both to identify them and to tell us the character of the group to which they belong. Should you be so imprudent as to take a peek at our "Hints", you will also assume the obligation of explaining what you find there.

Hints: Page 150.   Resolution: Page 210.

48   *KNOW YOUR COLORS!*

You are a contestant on one of the big television quiz shows. Your category is geography, a subject on which you are, indeed, an expert. You have already won $5,000, and have decided to try for the $10,000 plateau. If you answer the next question correctly, the $10,000 is yours; if you miss, you receive the consolation prize: a ten-year supply of dog food!

In his best graveside manner, the quizmaster intones your next question: "Picture a flag rectangular in shape and consisting of two horizontal stripes equal in width, the upper stripe red, the lower stripe white. Can you identify that flag?"

Although the question is peripheral to your real interests, you instantly sift the data in your mind subject to total recall, and come up with this answer: "The flag described is the national flag of Indonesia, more fully entitled 'The Republic of Indonesia'. The colors of its flag are those of a 14th- and 15th-century Hindu empire centered on the island of Java and known as MAJAPAHIT (also spelled MADJAPAHIT or MODJOPAHIT), a name translated as 'Bitter Fruit'. For Majapahit, the colors red and white stood for courage and honesty. Combined, they represented freedom, as also today they do for Indonesia."

Pleased with your ability to answer a tough question in greater detail than had been requested, you complacently await the quizmaster's congratulations and the adulatory applause of the audience. Naturally, you are stunned when the emcee commiserates with you on your failure to answer his question correctly, and sends you home with your consolatory canine comestibles.

What was the explanation provided by the emcee? Can you reproduce it in detail similar to the detail of your own reply to the original question?

Hints: Page 159.   Resolution: Page 262.

49 *MINORCA DIDN'T QUITE MAKE IT!*

Let's investigate three words and/or names normally regarded as quite ordinary:

EUCLID   HERALD   MEDUSA

Imagine that someone asks us what essential feature the three words have in common that sets them apart from the vast majority of other words. Thinking about the words, all sorts of likenesses occur to us:

1. Each is a noun.
2. Each is a six-letter word.
3. Each word consists of six different letters.
4. Each word contains the two letters D and E.
5. Each word can have its letters juggled to produce another word or name (Il Duce; harled; amused).

Since there are thousands of words and names that fit each of these characterizations, that which has been asked for must be something else, something nearly unique in status.

Assuming that you are a charitable individual, we beseech your help in getting us out of the muddle we're in, by answering a number of questions:
1. What is the singular quality shared by these words, but by very few others?
2. Can you name four or five other words that are also members of the clan?
3. Do you know any longer words of like caliber?
4. What in the world has our title to do with all this?

Hints: Page 162.   Resolution: Page 287.

50 *THE SILENT HOST*

We have been examining booklets designed to acquaint small children with the alphabet. Such booklets usually have entries along the lines of "A is for Apple; B is for Boy; C is for Cat; . . . Z is for Zoo." Aside from the obvious unimaginativeness of this fare, it is misleading, for ordinary English words use silent letters. It would certainly be more realistic and more instructive to teach children an alphabet such as "A is for Hoarse; B is for Limb; C is for Czar; . . . Z is for Pince-nez."

To remedy the situation, we are launching a nationwide "Mots for Tots" campaign. Your part in this campaign—you *do* wish to play a role in it, we feel certain—is to make up a complete alphabet of the sort required, one in which each of the 26 letters of the alphabet, in its turn, takes the vow of silence.

Our future lies in our children. You owe it to them and to yourself to do a dazzling job. On with the task!

Hints: Page 167.   Resolution: Page 219.

51 *THOUGHTS FOR TODAY*

A series of unusual statements is subjoined. What quality do these statements share?

(1) This sentence is not true.
(2) I am now adream.
(3) Do not obey me!
(4) I have forgotten that today is Saturday.
(5) The Devil does not exist.
(6) Never give credence to what you hear.
(7) The statement I am now making is in code.
(8) I always forget to speak.
(9) Pay no attention to any statement whatever that I make.
(10) All of these ten statements are lies!

Prove that the statements just listed do *not* have the quality imputed to them.

Hints: Page 155.   Resolution: Page 182.

52 *SYNONYM SETS*

For some time, we have been bemused by groups of mutually synonymic words all of which have the same number of letters. Thus, we look appreciatively at three nine-letter synonyms for the eggplant: AUBERGINE, BERENGENA, and MELONGENA; or at three eight-letter names for a ptysma receptacle: CUSPIDOR, SPITTOON, and CRACHOIR. Proportionately more meritorious are groups of four equiliteral synonyms, such as the five-letter names for the jack in cards (KNAVE, MAKER, NODDY, and BOWER), or the six-letter names for the flying lemur of the East Indian regions (COBEGO, COLUGO, KAGUAN, and KUBONG). Of course, there is a nightmarish aspect to such groups—imagine being faced with choosing from them in solving a difficult crossword puzzle!

Here is another four-member synonym set, handed to you without any clue as to the meaning that these four words have in common: CLOUD, TROOP, EARTH, and SKULK. Each of these words is both a noun and a verb, and each boasts a multiplicity of meanings. Can you discover the one meaning shared by all?

Offhand, this seems like a problem in dictionary research. We must warn you that it is not; you can deduce the general nature of the connection between our mystery words directly from what you have just seen, permitting you to particularize that relationship in an easier way than by reading countless dictionary definitions.

Hints: Page 164.   Resolution: Page 276.

53 *OF RULERS AND SUBJECTS*

Have you ever wondered about the relationship between sovereignty and government?

According to dictionaries, that relationship is a simple, uninspiring one: sovereignty (supreme authority) is an attribute or function of government (a governing body). The true relationship, of course, goes much deeper and is of a far more novel and stimulating nature. Rather than merely advising you of the facts, a tactic that might astonish you but would do little or nothing in the way of developing your own ability to ferret out such information, we ask you to unshackle your mind, to release it from the narrow, worn channels in which it customarily moves, and to let it roam freely along the borderlands of Language and of the Great Beyond. Only after you have completed your own survey are you to examine and assimilate our findings. Good hunting!

Hints: Page 160.   Resolution: Page 281.

54 *DECUSSATE DELIBERATIONS*

Quick as a flash—name fifteen communities in the United States whose names begin with the letter X!

What automatic, subconscious assumption must you discard to succeed? What does "decussate" mean?

Hints: Page 143.   Resolution: Page 239.

55 *PERMUTATIONAL LANGUAGE*

It was Professor Ravenscroft J. Cloudesley° who first pointed out the absurdity of the rules devised by grammarians to regulate word order in a sentence. As Cloudesley so sagely observed, while it may be true that the ordinary user of language is unable (or unwilling) to fashion his sentences in such a way that the words of which they consist may be shuffled around every which way without disturbing clarity of thought, the more careful and interested speaker or writer makes language his servant, demonstrating his mastery of words by choosing those which permit unlimited transposability at no sacrifice in comprehensibility.

Since permutable language is one of the semantic domains beyond the pale of everyday language, it is important for you to acquire a grasp of the principles involved, of the modus operandi, giving this problem its raison d'être.

First, let's examine a "normal", defective sentence, "I was there." Three words—or three objects of any sort—may be permuted or arranged in six different ways. If we designate the three by means of letters (A, B, C), the six arrangements mathematically possible are ABC, ACB, BAC, BCA, CAB, and CBA. Applying this scheme to our test sentence, we observe the following results:

1. I WAS THERE. A simple, clear statement, one that needs no amplification.

2. I THERE WAS. A very stilted sentence, not measuring up to our exacting criteria. With some imagination, we could repunctuate it "I, THERE, WAS!", interpreting it as "I, the individual who is over there, existed!"

3. WAS I THERE? Another very straightforward sentence; this time, a question.

4. WAS THERE I. It seems beyond the power of human thought to read a logical meaning into this word combination, faulting our test sentence as a nominee for the exclusive realm of permutational language.

5. THERE I WAS. Excellent English.

6. THERE WAS I. There, rather than some other place; or, I, rather than someone else; depending on the inflection of the speaker's voice, or on the word underlined in writing.

°*An Analysis of Anacyclics*, Fifth "Oxoboxo" Edition, Volume III, pp. 2179–2207.

So much for ordinary English. Now that you understand the nature of the problem, you are invited to exercise your budding skills as a permutator by tackling these questions:

1. What is the underlying technique that permits one to construct permutable sentences?
2. Using that technique, construct one, and compare your effort with ours. A three-word sentence will do.
3. Explain the meaning of each of the six variations of your sentence, comparing the style of yours with the facile glibness of ours.
4. If you wanted to construct a permutational sentence of four or of five words, how many sentence variations would you have to prove yourself capable of supplying?
5. How is the number of possible variations computed?
6. Can you illustrate a permutational sentence of four words with an actual sample?

Hints: Page 161.   Resolution: Page 255.

56 ASPHALT, CLIFF, AND RAVEN

Most of our states are divided into counties. A few states choose to be different; thus, Alaska is partially divided into boroughs, and Louisiana entirely into parishes.

Since counties are subdivisions of states, each county in the United States is in a state. One county, however, is unique, for not only is the county in a state, but the state in which it is also happens to be in that county.

What is the state, and what is the county, involved in this strange paradox? How do you explain that paradox? Shifting ground, in what way does the fact that the state is in the county prove that the county is in the state? Assuming that the title of our problem is relevant, can you establish its connection with the problem?

Hints: Page 149.   Resolution: Page 274.

57 APPLE AND ARROW

Question: who was William Tell?

We refer, you understand, to that sharpshooting archer who successfully picked an apple off his son's head. Can you place the man in space and in time, and fill in some of the pertinent details?

If our inquiry looks too simple, be certain that it is nothing of the kind. In fact, you may wish to skip this and go right on to the next offering!

Hints: Page 163.   Resolution: Page 197.

58 SIGHT AND SOUND

This lesson in the logic of language concerns its two parallel aspects: how it is written, and how it is pronounced. We are challenging you to prove your mastery of English—a prerequisite to any exploration of what lies beyond —by composing two perfectly grammatical and perfectly sensible sentences. In one, all words are to begin with the same sound, although no two begin with the same letter. In the other, all words are to begin with the same letter, although no two begin with the same sound. Suggested length: about six words each.

Hints: Page 148.   Resolution: Page 204.

59 MINISTERIAL MEDITATIONS

The son of a neighbor of ours took a history test in school the other day. One of the questions included in the test read as follows:

"Who was the prime minister of Great Britain during World War II?"

The student answered the question, "Winston Churchill". His teacher marked that answer wrong.

Can you give two reasons why the answer was wrong? Also, why was the question improperly worded?

Churchill was the author of a good many books. What was his alphabetical idiosyncrasy as a writer?

Hints: Page 144.   Resolution: Page 273.

60 *A STUDY IN FRUSTRATION*

Some of the problems in this book concern that frontier of language which faces the world of numbers. In this problem, we are asking you to explore a different language frontier, the one that overlaps the world of pictures. Every picture has a name, and a name is a word, making the identification of unfamiliar pictures a periodic problem for the word expert.

Shown below are four pictures featured in a recent prize contest. Participants were told that these were views of American cities and asked to identify the cities. Fifteen days were allowed in which to do so. One contestant succeeded in identifying all four pictures correctly; four others recognized the first three pictures, but failed to identify the fourth one.

Here are the pictures:

No. 1   No. 2

No. 3   No. 4

What we want you to do is to identify the four cities, and to tell us how you did it. More specifically:

1. What are the four cities?
2. From what printed source were the pictures copied?
3. From what ultimate sources are these pictures derived?
4. How can the pictures be identified without knowing their source?

Hints: Page 147.   Resolution: Page 299.

61 *THREE-DIMENSIONAL THINKING*

Residents of "Flatland", a hypothetical two-dimensional world, construct word squares, in which a given set of words can be read both horizontally and vertically. We, in our superior three-dimensional continuum, devise word cubes, in which each word can be read in each of the three dimensions. Since the page you are reading is two-dimensional, the easiest way of illustrating a word cube is by showing its two-dimensional sections successively. Thus, a word cube of the fourth order is dissected into four consecutive word squares of the fourth order. Observe:

C O R D	O V E R	R E N O	D R O P
O V E R	V I V A	E V E R	R A R E
R E N O	E V E R	N E S T	O R T S
D R O P	R A R E	O R T S	P E S T

Because these are the successive sections of a cube, the four letters in the upper left corners of the squares are C, O, R, and D. If you use children's letter blocks and erect the cube, those four letters will spell the word CORD in the third dimension. Similar reasoning holds for the other corresponding positions in the four sections shown.

Fourth-order cubes are for children. Since our readers are adults, it is only fair that you demonstrate your command of cubes by constructing one of the sixth order, shown on paper in the form of six successive sections, each of which is a 6 × 6 word square in its own right.

Hints: Page 141.   Resolution: Page 230.

62　*ITALIAN GENIUS*

It is said that, in Europe, someone may not know you well enough to call you by your first name, or even to know what your first name is; but that in America, a stranger may only know your first name, not being well enough acquainted with you to be aware of your last name.

Whatever the extent to which this observation may be justified, it is paradoxical to note that some of the greatest figures in the intellectual life of Europe are familiar to us by their given names, not by their surnames. To prove our point, we are listing four Italian geniuses of the past, as they are generally known to the world:

> DANTE, the poet
> GALILEO, the astronomer
> MICHELANGELO, the sculptor
> RAPHAEL, the painter

For how many of the four can you supply the correct surname?

There is more to this problem, as there usually is.

1. The surnames of two of the four have a dual aspect, but in different senses. Can you explain?
2. Two of the four have a special relationship to each other and to William Shakespeare. What is it?
3. Two of the four have a special relationship to each other and to the Patriarch of the West. How come?
4. One of the four has a dual relationship to Sir Isaac Newton. Define it.

Hints: Page 143.　　　　　　　　　　　　　　　Resolution: Page 212.

63　*A SINGULAR PLURAL*

Pretenders to word wisdom are fond of citing the plural word CARES, which is converted into the singular word CARESS by adding an S. Since the addition of an S to a word normally changes it from a singular into a plural, this is an inversion of the usual procedure, making it noteworthy.

The trouble is, the CARES-CARESS pair is by no means the only one of its kind in English. Can you name half a dozen other word pairs falling into the same category?

Some such pairs follow a specific pattern, in which the shorter plural word is masculine, and the longer singular word is the corresponding feminine form: PIRATES-PIRATESS, for instance. Try to come up with half a dozen similar pairs.

Although these plurals are unusual, they are not singular or unique, since we have a proliferation of them. To expand your understanding of those profound philosophical ideas, Unity and Plurality, we are setting you a more difficult problem, the solution to which does appear to be singular. Find a word plural in meaning but not ending in an S. Add an S to it, making it singular. Shift ground, assigning a plural meaning to the same word. Add a second S to it, turning it singular again. What we propose can be done, and has been done. We ask you only to follow in the footsteps of the masters.

Both the literal meaning of our title, and its punning quality, are quite obvious. Accordingly, we are giving you a more challenging, third interpretation to seek in that title. Properly defined, a "singular" *is* plural. What is the definition that fills the bill? Curiously, the required definition has a remarkable connection with the problem of the previous paragraph: the starting plural word in the preceding paragraph, considered orthographically, is the first half of the key noun in the plural definition of "singular" sought in this paragraph; the last half of that key noun is included both in SINGULAR and in PLURAL, though frontwards in one and backwards in the other. Figure it out.

Hints: Page 155. Resolution: Page 219.

64 *A SYLLABUB OF SYLLABLES*

Once upon a time, someone made a sensational discovery. Take the one-syllable word SMILE and insert an I into it; the result is SIMILE, a three-syllable word. By adding one letter, you have added two syllables.

The slothfulness of the human race being what it is, the discovery has stood the test of time, unsurpassed and unequalled. Yet, it is a fact that there are many transformations of this sort possible in English, and the letter added does not have to be on the inside. We can add it at the front, as in the case of VEAL-UVEAL, or at the back, as with ROME-ROMEO.

Inspired one day, we found a substantial number of "syllable" words, jotting down the definitions both of the shorter and of the longer word. Through an oversight, we forgot to record the words themselves, however, and have only a jumbled list of definitions. We are going to entreat your assistance, therefore, by listing our definitions. You are to find the words matching these definitions and then to group them as the syllabic duads that they are. This will be a great boon to us, releasing our time for exploring new pathways in the science of words. Here are the definitions; the number of letters in the word defined is shown in parentheses immediately following the definition:

1. Feminine or female. (6).
2. A contest at birling logs. (5)
3. To depart from a straight line or course. (4)
4. A replica of a pattern or archetype. (4)
5. A market place where cattle are collected. (5)
6. Any of several colors varying in hue from bluish-red to yellowish-red. (5)
7. The spleen. (4)
8. The principal fissure in shaken timber. (4)
9. A helmet or casque. (5)
10. Pertaining to fixed and immovable property. (4)
11. A nymph of the mountains and hills. (5)
12. Northern. (6)
13. A serious violation of law or morality. (5)
14. To promote the success of. (3)
15. A precious stone of peculiar depth or brilliancy. (4)
16. Time or pains expended upon a thing. (5)
17. An urgent entreaty or request. (4)
18. Existed as a result of circumstances or causes. (4)
19. Food or sustenance. (5)
20. Converts to one's service again. (6)
21. The rind or husk of a fruit. (4)
22. A payment at certain stated intervals. (4)
23. An Ethiopian slave of Amneris, daughter of Egypt's king. (4)
24. A bird laying its eggs in holes in sandy beaches. (5)
25. Pertaining to an open space in a building. (5)
26. To understand musical notation. (4)
27. A Swiss river emptying into the Aar River. (5)
28. Profits, benefits, advantages: the verb. (5)
29. The dewlap or throat-wattle of a turkey. (5)
30. The love-feast of the primitive Christians. (5)
31. The nasua or tejon. (5)
32. A Muscovite chersonese. (6)
33. Controlled imperiously or oppressively. (4)

34. Brimless felt caps worn during the Roman Saturnalia. (5)
35. Pertaining to an ancient country of the Greek Peloponnesus. (5)
36. A governor-general of the Philippine Islands. (3)
37. Any assumed character or function. (4)
38. A pyramid, or anything that is pyramidal. (4)
39. To transfer, as property or ownership. (5)
40. The "man with a crook" accompanied by the Canes Venatici. (6)

Hints: Page 169.   Resolution: Page 181.

65   UN-FRENCH FRENCH

We use all sorts of words and phrases in English that have been borrowed from French, and we delude ourselves into thinking that this upgrades our speech. The funny thing about this is that, often, the "French" words we use are *not* used by Frenchmen, or at least not with the meanings we assign to them. For example, we shout, VIVE!; meaning "long live!" To the Frenchman, a VIVE is an edible fish, the weever. What is the French equivalent for our "long live!"? Either HOURRAS!, or BRAVO!, or VIVAT!; but *never* VIVE!

Here are another seven terms, supposedly French but not used in French as we use them in English. Can you translate them into French correctly?

1. BRASSIERE
2. DOUBLE ENTENDRE
3. ENCORE!
4. LINGERIE

5. MENU
6. MORALE
7. NOM DE PLUME

Hints: Page 164.   Resolution: Page 230.

66   THE MATHEMATICAL MINIMUM

Here is a list of names assembled for your pleasure and bafflement:

Earth	Pluto
Mars	Saturn
Mercury	Venus

Questions: What is the minimum number of names omitted from our list? Where can you find all six of the names enumerated?

Hints: Page 163.   Resolution: Page 236.

67 THE OTHER ONE

Much has been written about Napoleon Bonaparte, the *Man of Destiny*. By all logical criteria, the most astonishing statement ever made about Napoleon is this one:

"Napoleon, the destroyer of whole cities, was the lion of his people."

Tell us why. In addition, explain the pertinence, if such there be, of our title.

Hints: Page 157.   Resolution: Page 242.

68 TRUE AND FALSE

Most likely, there are some things in this book with which you find yourself in disagreement: facts you would like to dispute, or modes of reasoning that seem . . . uh . . . well . . . strained. There is a sound reason for this, of course.

In his epic work, *A Primer of Janus Logic,* Professor Ravenscroft J. Cloudesley has given two mathematical proofs of the equivalence or identity of truth and falsity, by showing that (a) two things not equal to each other really are equal to each other, and that (b) what is positive is really negative, and vice versa.

Without looking these proofs up in Cloudesley's trailblazer, can you construct both of them? They require no knowledge of mathematics beyond a first course in high school algebra.

There are some mathematicians—rock-ribbed standpatters, obviously— who have professed an inability to follow Cloudesley's brilliant logic. What

arguments do these mathematicians usually advance in support of their out-
dated views?

These naive arguments have fatal weaknesses, elegantly disproved by
Cloudesley. Can you reproduce the decisive refutations?

Hints: Page 166.   Resolution: Page 191.

69   VEGETATION?

Speaking of Cloudesley, one of his early books, *The Identity of All Things*,
has been discomfiting botanists ever since its publication in 1921. In the book,
Cloudesley develops the thesis that all forms of vegetation are really the same,
it being possible to demonstrate that any plant is any other plant. Following
the Professor's logic, we have worked out proofs that:

> (1) A parsnip is really a horseradish;
> (2) A beet is really a turnip;
> (3) A melon is always a watermelon.

Can you duplicate our proofs with mathematical precision? In all fairness, we
must point out that the nature of these proofs is wholly unlike those involved
in the preceding problem.

Why is there a question mark after our title?

Hints: Page 149.   Resolution: Page 206.

70   A RETORT IN KIND

Imagine that you are a secretary, taking dictation from your boss. He is
discussing TO, TWO, and TOO, three English words the same in pronunciation.
He dictates this sentence:

> "There are three ——'s in English."

Baffled in regard to the correct spelling of the word omitted above, you ask the
boss for help. He suggests that you use one of the three spellings under consid-

eration, it matters not which one. You show him that this would be incorrect. In what way?

The boss thinks for a moment, and comes up with a second suggestion: that you create a symbol standing for the sound of all three words; a letter combination such as TU (rhyming with the Greek letters MU and NU), or TUE (rhyming with BLUE and RUE), or TEW (rhyming with FLEW and JEW). Warming to your negative stance, you prove to your boss that this would be even more incorrect, for each of three separate reasons. What are they?

Your boss is getting annoyed by now, but reflects on your arguments, admits you're right, and offers a third proposal: as an upright citizen of your community and a loyal patron of the English language, you have the prerogative of coining a word now and then. He suggests that you coin a word TUUH, assigning to it the desired pronunciation and the meaning "a word such as the English words TO, TWO, and TOO". Once again, you point out to your boss that there is a reason why his third solution is unacceptable. What is that reason?

Provoked to fury, your boss fires you, solving his problem and yours. While you are a lady of leisure (a euphemism for being unemployed), we want you to think of a way of writing that sentence which is beyond any possible criticism. We have found two distinct solutions to this problem, and are wondering if you're clever enough to discover them.

If you succeed, also figure out why the boss's statement is basically untrue. As a final gesture of your good will, tell us what our title has to do with all this, and what play on words it conceals.

Hints: Page 159.   Resolution: Page 222.

71 *YELLOW HAMMERS*

Long before the Cuban missile crisis erupted in October, 1962, certain Americans had found astonishing proof of intercourse between Moscow and Cuba.

Using only the information given here, can you duplicate that proof and expatiate upon it?

Hints: Page 144.   Resolution: Page 267.

72   REAL ENGLISH

The English language, with a few million words securely in its folds, offers its patrons a wealth of wordage not remotely approached by any other known tongue. Yet, most of us conduct our day-to-day activities with the aid of a paltry thousand words or so, and the works of our greatest writers seldom reflect a vocabulary of more than 20,000 or 25,000 words.

Take heart, friends! The Renaissance of Language is upon us, at last! Words are awakening from their long dormancy, springing to life, making themselves felt in home, school, and office. As part of the growing drive to rejuvenate our most important means of communication, to give words their full weight, we are going to train you to use language as it can and should be used, not as it is generally used by the slothful.

These thoughts came to us after we chanced upon the unfamiliar scientific term KOPHOBELEMNONIDAE and repaired to the *Funk & Wagnalls New Standard Dictionary of the English Language* in quest of its meaning. The definition we found in that dictionary:

> "A family of stelechotokean anthozoons, belonging to the alcyonarians,
> with a rachis longer than peduncle, cylindrical and with pararachides
> provided with retractile autozooids in indefinite rows."

This is the finest dictionary definition we have ever seen. It includes at least seven words (stelechotokean, anthozoons, alcyonarians, rachis, peduncle, pararachides, autozooids) unknown to most of us. Their skillful use within the definition keeps us from learning what the word KOPHOBELEMNONIDAE means. Before checking the dictionary, there was *one* word we didn't know; now there are *eight!*

Admittedly, only a scientist—a zoologist, in this case—could formulate a definition for a word such as KOPHOBELEMNONIDAE bursting with beauty. However, laymen can do their share by turning casual conversation and routine writing (letters to sweethearts, notes for the milkman, bookkeeping entries, etc.) into similar channels. A couple of elementary examples show how natural, how effortless the transformation is, once you acquire the knack and approach the task in the right frame of mind.

> (a) You wish to mention that, after the speaker finished his address, there was a
> question period. The elegant, graceful way of saying it is to state that "audience
> members were given an opportunity for spontaneous yet wholly personalized
> information seeking."

(b) You have put forward some proposals for consideration, but aren't yet sure in your own mind that they represent your final, best judgment. Comment upon them thus: "This preliminary position outline of primary proposals and objective strategy is not to be construed as a definitive program of recommended action, but rather as a tentative, unfinalized plan of implementation."

A little more practice, and you will be on a par with the author of a folder put out by the Navy League some time ago, describing Harvard University's new Carpenter Center for Visual Arts:

"It exemplifies conceptualistic innuendo pyramided upon spatial forbearance and altogether tokenish of tactile cosmological luminous volumentality."

Now, actually to train you in the art of topnotch speaking and writing, we are going to conjure up two situations, each of which demands a verbal response from you. Give them the best you've got; then compare your responses with ours, and absorb the consummate skill these display. Assimilate that skill into your own thinking and communicating processes, and you'll be on your way!

1. You are the president of a corporation, at lunch with a young executive who has submitted an idea to the Board of Directors, and who wants to know what the Board thinks of it. You have to tell him that the Board has not taken final action on the idea; that, at the moment, two directors are for it, two have doubts, and three haven't even read it yet; and that you will send him a written memo giving him all the details, as soon as the Board acts. What is the most forceful, most effective, and most inspired way of putting these thoughts across to your lunch partner?

2. You are a schoolteacher. Preparing Cadwallader's report card (your class doesn't happen to have a "Johnny" in it!), you have to add a note to the boy's parents, telling them that the dumb kid is lazy, probably doesn't give a hoot about his schoolwork, and can't be reasoned with. How can you relate these sad facts to the boy's parents in the most tactful and most elegant fashion?

Hints: Page 161.   Resolution: Page 271.

73 *THE HAWAIIAN WAR CHANT*

Everyone who is anyone "knows" that the Hawaiian alphabet, shortest of any existing language, has only twelve letters: the vowels A, E, I, O, U, and the consonants H, K, L, M, N, P, W.

Like a great deal of other widely accepted information, this is the purest tommyrot. The Hawaiian language has numerous words using other letters of the alphabet. Prove this by citing some examples, and explain why it is so.

Hints: Page 141.   Resolution: Page 240.

74 *KEOKUK, IOWA*

Several lists of adjectives are subjoined, for your perusal:

(1) Dark	(2) Woeful	(3) Bloody
Deadly	Weeping	Gloomy
Dismal	Wailing	Hideous
Doleful	Wonderful	Fearful
Desolate	Weird	Furious
Dreadful		Alarming
Desperate		Terrible
		Horrible
		Mournful
		Sorrowful
		Frightful
		Appalling

It is evident, even to the untrained eye, that all adjectives in Group (1) begin with the letter D, and all those in Group (2) with the letter W. What is the reason for this? With what letter should all of the words in Group (3) begin? Can you suggest a corrected list to replace this obviously defective one?

Quite aside from the matter of the initials in the third group, one or two of the words in our lists are out of step with the rest. Which ones? How would you replace them?

Getting down to brass tacks, of what are these words lists?

In what manner does our title relate to our problem? What appears to be wrong with the title? How can it be explained away satisfactorily? If you wanted to avoid the objection entirely, to sidestep the issue involved, with what would you replace the title?

Questions, questions, questions! How about some answers? Even what we have *just* said is a clue to the basic answer; in what way?

Hints: Page 148.   Resolution: Page 198.

75   MEGALOMANIA

Let us arbitrarily divide all English words into two categories, short words and long words. Let us define a short word as one using not more than 1000 alphabetic letters, and a long word as one with more than 1000 letters. Problems:

1. About how many short English words are there? About how many long ones?
2. Can you give us an example of a long word, as defined above? Name the word; define it; authenticate it; and evaluate it.
3. What is the ultimate criterion of your ability to spell the word correctly?

No proper names, hyphens, or other irregularities are permitted in the long word you choose.

Hints: Page 156.   Resolution: Page 226.

76   LET YOUR HAIR DOWN!

In this age of automation, electronic data processing equipment is intruding itself upon the domain of language, formerly safe from the predatory encroachments of mathematics. One of the discoveries for which we owe thanks (?) to modern technology concerns this sentence:

TIME FLIES LIKE AN ARROW.

A perfect sentence, at first glance; flawless grammar, no interior punctuation, and no proper names. Beyond this, however, the sentence exhibits a flexibility seldom encountered in language, for it lends itself to three interpretations, totally unrelated to one another:

(a) The temporal succession speeds onward in the same manner as does an arrow shot from a bow.
(b) Clock the speed of insects such as flies as you would measure the velocity of an arrow in flight.
(c) Insects of the hypothetical species known as "time flies" are fond of an arrow.

Reading these three interpretations into the one sentence exemplifies creativity and imaginativeness at its very best. Computers, whatever their merits may be, however, are not yet known for these qualities. It follows, accordingly, that the unassisted mind is able to excel the machine, and to devise simple English sentences subject to four or five mutually unconnected interpretations. The imperative selected as the title of this problem is a case in point. We have read four distinct meanings into our title. How many are *you* able to find?

Hints: Page 146.   Resolution: Page 278.

77   *SUGGESTIVE WORDS*

In ordinary English, there is no outward resemblance between the written or printed appearance of a word, and the object or idea for which it stands. This lack of connection makes it unduly difficult to learn how to spell words. How deplorable, when you consider that, with some imagination, words can be written in such a fashion as to connect them directly with the thoughts they express. To take three otherwise undistinguished terms, PUNCTURE, BOMB, and BOW TIE, the revised form of spelling shown below illustrates what we have in mind:

PUNCTURE

BOMB   BOW TIE

There are innumerable other words whose spelling may be modified so as to make it suggestive of the thoughts behind them. Listed next are fifteen such words which we have succeeded in modifying suggestively:

1. War	6. Step	11. Hit
2. Gallows	7. Nail	12. Kick
3. Hysterical	8. Soldier	13. Outhouse
4. Empty	9. Guillotine	14. Mommy
5. Fly	10. Blinds	15. Daddy

Your assignment is to see what you can do in the way of improving the written form of these words; then, compare your results with ours. Remember: this is an exercise aimed at testing the ability of your imagination to travel beyond the limits of conventional language.

Hints: Page 161.　　　　　　　　　　　　　　　　　　Resolution: Page 263.

78　DEMON OF THE ALPHABET

Those of us who enjoy exploring a subject from A to Z, minding our P's and Q's along the way, have long been enthralled by CHICAGO, a name that may be spelled in dozens of different ways, including some that use the letters A, P, Q, and Z as starters. So that you, too, may view *Chicago* with awe, we've done a little research on the subject. Our findings are reflected by these puzzlers:

1. How can CHICAGO be spelled so as to begin with A, or P, or Q, or Z?
2. How can CHICAGO be spelled using (a) an umlaut or double dot; (b) an acute accent; (c) an Arabic numeral?
3. How can CHICAGO be spelled starting with seven consonants in succession?
4. Chicago—the one in Illinois—is not alone! Identify three other communities in the United States also designated as "Chicago".
5. Our first two questions violated an assumption unconsciously made by you. Please explain.

Hints: Page 149.　　　　　　　　　　　　　　　　　　Resolution: Page 249.

79 ADVICE TO THE LOVELORN

In these progressive times, no newspaper is complete without a column of advice for the lovelorn and for others with problems. Since newspapers consist of words and we specialize in words, it follows with logic absolute that we must address ourselves to the problems of the lovelorn—yet another field of the many that lie beyond language, beckoning to the word-wise.

As we see it, the central problem of someone writing a letter to a newspaper column is to choose an appropriate alias as his or her signature. Many writers, obviously inexperienced, pick simple pseudonyms worn threadbare with overuse—old standbys like "Confused", "Desperate", or "Hurt". These people need help, and we want you to provide that help, by dreaming up a series of suitable noms de plume, as a match to our own efforts in that direction. More specifically, we are asking for three separate groups of apt anonyms, conforming to these standards:

(1) Adjectivally formed signatures revealing a "philosophical" bent of mind.

(2) Signatures, also in the adjectival mold, with particular appeal for the young, the lighthearted; those not so philosophically inclined.

(3) Substantive signatures, preferred by the minority with a nounal personality, as opposed to an adjectival character.

Keep in mind that this is a sincere attempt to assist those corresponding with advice columns. Do not brush the problem off lightly, for a time may come when you yourself will want to refer to a good list of pen names for guidance!

Hints: Page 167.   Resolution: Page 258.

80 A FACETIOUS PROBLEM

Old Jedediah Crumpworth had been teaching school in Jewelpoint, Nevada, for nigh unto 52 years. One of his favorite test questions in English consisted of writing on the blackboard this sequence of letters:

A   E   I   O   U   Y

and asking his students to point out the one letter that was out of place in the series, explaining why it did not belong there.

Today had started out like any other day, and Crumpworth posed his usual question, expecting little or nothing in the way of surprise answers from his largely mediocre class. There was something, however, with which the venerable schoolmaster had not reckoned: that today was that one day in every five hundred years when the King of Bedevilment leaves his cloud throne in the Land of the Elves, descends to Mother Earth, and infuses a spirit of fiendish glee into all he encounters. As chance would have it, the King had met several of Jedediah's students on their way to school this morning, and the result was evident in the test papers the pupils handed in.

Can you think of four of the answers submitted by Jedediah Crump-worth's class? Why is this problem facetious?

Hints: Page 152.   Resolution: Page 232.

81 *AN ODD PROBLEM*

For many years, mathematicians have suspected that any odd number whatever, multiplied by a factor of two, will yield an even number as a product. Since there is an infinite sequence of odd numbers, it is impossible to prove this theorem empirically, even with the aid of the most advanced electronic equipment.

We have discovered an elegant verbal proof for the proposition. Can you duplicate it?

Hints: Page 158.   Resolution: Page 266.

82 *HOW TO CURSE*

This book is intended to be all things to all men. It is sad but true that some men curse. Therefore, we must provide guidelines for the intelligent curser.

True, a whole book could be devoted to this complex subject, with its numerous ramifications. Space limitations compel us to be selective and to confine our analysis to one curse: "Go to the Devil!" There is something entirely too trite and too plebeian about this execration. Why go to the Devil, a creature of many names? You may as well be colorful and send the object of your scorn to Satan, or to Lucifer, or to Mephistopheles.

Your exercise in the Art of the Oath for today is to dig up 100 designations for Beelzebub, making your list of names a well-balanced one. In the course of your search, you will notice yourself becoming progressively more proficient in the techniques of Infernal Thinking, giving your mind the well-rounded, versatile appearance you want it to radiate to your associates. Speaking of the Devil, you'll become the man of distinction!

Hints: Page 156.   Resolution: Page 189.

83 *GOOD AT FIGURES?*

Series of numbers are a perpetual source of wonderment for the inquisitive. To satisfy the universal craving for things numerical, we present the most unbelievable number series ever concocted:

$$1 \quad 2 \quad 3 \quad 4 \quad 5 \quad 6 \quad 7 \quad 8 \quad 9 \quad 10 \quad 11 \quad 12$$

Warning! This series is not designed for children, and it is not designed for the dilettante. The series is subject to two entirely distinct interpretations, each of which is extremely difficult to find and to substantiate. Without doubt, this is the most difficult problem in the pages of *Beyond Language*. If you want our advice, skip it and go on to the next one. However, if you are stubborn, it's your privilege to apply your talents to answering four questions:

1. What are the two basic meanings in this number series?
2. Within the framework of each interpretation, three separate elements of "differentness" can be found (they were deliberately built in, of course). Can you detect these additional features?
3. By dropping these side features and sticking to the fundamentals, it is possible to extend both interpretations of this series down to zero. How?
4. Also by dropping the side features, one of the two series, but only one, may be extended upward, at least to 16. How?

Hints: Page 155.   Resolution: Page 245.

84   *REPETITIVE HOMONYMY*

Good friends, let us examine a rather obscure sentence:

"Is it true, for all that, that *that* THAT that *that* THAT represents, is not the THAT of which I am thinking?"

To clarify the sentence, we are paraphrasing it:

"Is it true, in spite of all that has happened, that the THAT which that particular THAT represents, is not the THAT of which I am thinking?"

The compelling reason for use of the first version is, of course, the fact that one particular word, "that", occurs 7 times in a row; a very good example of repetitive homonymy. A good example, but one on which we can improve, as use of the word "and" 13 successive times in the next sentence demonstrates:

"AND" and "AND", "AND" and "and", "and" and "AND", and "and" and "and" are phrases identical in meaning.

Even this display, however, can be bettered, if we interest ourselves in the peculiar plight of two typesetters, Boustrophedon Q. Jambalaya and Umquhile X. Hadd. So that you may gain the practice you need in repetitiousness, we are stopping here and asking you (a) to develop the story of these two men, and (b) to culminate that story with a sentence in which one word (or a perfect homonym of that word) occurs 16 consecutive times. As you will see in the "Resolutions" section, it can and has been done!

All of these sentences, regrettably, suffer from a glaring defect: they require the use of words extraneous to the homonymous sequence. Is it possible to write purely homonymic sentences?

Yes, though not easily. One classic example frequently quoted is drawn from the Chinese speech of Annam, a former protectorate of France, in Indochina. The sentence:

BA BA BA BA.

Properly pronounced, with each word accented differently, it is said to mean: "Three ladies gave a box on the ear to the favorite of the prince".

It seems possible, even likely, that some of you are a little rusty in your knowledge of Annamese Chinese. Accordingly, we turn to a language a little closer to home—Latin—for another such sentence:

MALO MALO MALO MALO.

This sentence may be translated as "I would rather be a bad man up an apple tree than a coward", or as "I would rather be in an apple tree than a bad man in misfortune".

There is always an irresistible temptation to match foreign accomplishments with English ones of like caliber. Not to gainsay you the satisfaction of such an achievement, we'll let you devise an English sentence of the same sort. After you have succeeded, you may wish to compare your prose with ours.

The advantage of homonymous communication is undisputed, for simplicity, in addition to being desirable for its own sake, also results in increased speed, permitting a larger volume of communication within a given length of time. It can safely be predicted, therefore, that in composing the homonymic sentence for which we have asked, you are helping to lay the groundwork for the Language of the Future. Yes, *you* can become the Man of Tomorrow, today!

Hints: Page 146.   Resolution: Page 290.

85 *A CAPITAL QUESTION*

What is the capital of DRUK-YUL? What and where is DRUK-YUL?

Naming the capital of some particular country is such a simple question that we are baffled by its inclusion here. How do you account for that fact?

How many interpretations can you read into the title selected for our problem?

Hints: Page 143.   Resolution: Page 184.

86 *IRRELEVANCE*

One of our justly famous (or is it notorious? ?) word lists is coming up again, so prepare yourself to feel puzzled:

1. ADDENDA	5. FLUMMOX	9. JOGGLED	13. STYPTIC
2. CHORDAL	6. GRAZING	10. KETCHUP	14. TWELFTH
3. DISTAFF	7. HUMBUZZ	11. LACKEYS	15. UPRIGHT
4. EMBASSY	8. IGNOBLE	12. OVIFORM	

All of the words are 7 letters long, and they are given in alphabetical order. HUMBUZZ has nothing to do with HUMBUG; it is an English name for the cockchafer (a kind of beetle).

What is it that makes these words a logical set? If you can figure it out, can you construct similar lists of 3-, 4-, 5-, and 6-letter words? Shorter words are easier to manipulate, so you should come up with somewhat longer lists.

What is the theoretical maximum length for any of these lists? Is it reasonable to assume that such maximum is attainable in practice?

If you must use some unusual words, please define them for us.

Despite itself, our title is highly relevant. Can you tell us why?

Hints: Page 151.   Resolution: Page 188.

87   *TRUMPETS AND FLOURISHES*

We live in a world teeming with symbols of every conceivable variety: numerical, linguistic, pictorial, and otherwise. To cope with our environment, we must learn to recognize the symbols that assail us from all quarters.

Reproduced below are some curious symbols. Examine them, please:

(a)   (b)   (c)   (d)

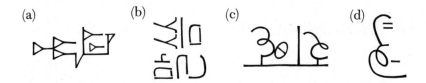

You *can* determine the significance of these symbols. *Will* you?

Hints: Page 153.   Resolution: Page 274.

88   *ISAIAH AND THE PRINCE OF MOROCCO*

Both Shakespeare and the Holy Bible speak of "the four corners of the earth".

Where are these four corners? When and how were they found?

Hints: Page 141.   Resolution: Page 251.

89   *ACES AND KINGS*

Note the word INKLING. A casual examination of that word gives not a hint of its innate beauty and poise. To uncover its true nature, we must replace the letters that form it with their numerical positions in the alphabet:

$$I \quad N \quad K \quad L \quad I \quad N \quad G$$
$$9 \quad 14 \quad 11 \quad 12 \quad 9 \quad 14 \quad 7$$

Next, we take the number sequence arrived at in this manner and compute the successive differences:

$$9 \quad 14 \quad 11 \quad 12 \quad 9 \quad 14 \quad 7$$
$$5 \quad 3 \quad 1 \quad 3 \quad 5 \quad 7$$

Taking this first set of differences, we compute a second set of differences:

$$5 \quad 3 \quad 1 \quad 3 \quad 5 \quad 7$$
$$2 \quad 2 \quad 2 \quad 2 \quad 2$$

Lo and behold! The second set of numerical differences is constant!

We can improve on the word INKLING by coining another word, PINKLING. If a "pink" is a person who holds somewhat radical economic or political views, then a "pinkling" is a minor or petty such individual, in analogy to a "princeling". Exactly the same constant difference results at the second level, but it is one digit longer, and the word to which it belongs is one letter longer.

INKLING is a 7-letter word, and the first difference level that is numerically constant contains 5 digits. Let us call INKLING a 7-5 word. By the same reasoning, PINKLING is an 8-6 word. Broadening our concept, any word that may be stabilized with a constant difference, which is a word of 7 or more letters, and where the second numeral, denoting the number of digits in the first constant difference level, is more than one-half of the first numeral, denoting the number of letters in the original word, is an Alphabetically Constant Entity, or an ACE word.

There are so few ACE words, and it is so difficult to locate them, that ACEs are, truly, the kings of the verbal world. We shall now devote ourselves to exploring our linguistic environment, in search of the kings. For practical reasons, we confine ourselves almost entirely to words in which the difference between the first and second descriptive numerals is 3—in other words, to 7-4, 8-5, and 9-6 words. The 7-letter words are comparatively easy to find, and we don't want to waste much time with them. A few 7-4 examples: AMERICA, HATCHET, and SENSION ("experience of sensation"). Another simple one is CHAFING (7-5).

In working with INKLING and PINKLING, the constant difference at which we arrived was 2, a small number. The constant differences with AMERICA and SENSION are even lower—1. By contrast, HATCHET produces an unusually high constant, 10. This raises two questions: (1) can you determine the highest theoretically possible constant? (2) can you exemplify it with a sequence of 8 letters that produces it? (These eight letters need not spell an actual word; it is utterly impossible for an existing word to exhibit so high a constant.)

Turning to 8-letter words, how would you systematically go about finding some? The chance of stumbling upon them by accident is very small, so that you *must* use a logical method for locating them, if you are to avoid extreme frustration. Since this question is preliminary to collecting ACE words, the answer to it is given in our "Hints".

The mathematical theory underlying ACE words tells us that about one half of all first-order reduplications—words and names such as HUSH-HUSH, BERI-BERI, and SING SING—are ACEs. Although this demeans ACE reduplications, it still makes them the easiest ones to find. We ask you, therefore, to supply several examples.

Because ACE reduplications are relatively easy to locate, and because there is a greater probability that adjacent letters in such words are far apart in the alphabet, it is not unreasonable to make a further request of you: that you find several producing a constant difference greater than 10.

It is logical to assume, and our assumption is confirmed empirically, that the next easiest word group in which to search for ACEs is that of second-order reduplications—words such as PING-PONG, WILDWIND, and LESSNESS. In fact, we accidentally come upon an 8-6 ACE word in this category, SLIPSLAP (a malapropism). Naturally, with this shining example before you, you will wish to find 8-5 ACEs of your own. We, however, are going to make the job more interesting for you by specifying that you ferret out at least one ACE word belonging to each of three classifications:

(a) genuine second-order reduplications, in which the reduplication is an intentional one—words such as PELL-MELL, or MISHMASH, or WINGDING.

(b) accidental reduplications that are divisible into two parts at their precise center: COOKBOOK, SHOESHOP, and WARTWORT, for instance.

(c) accidental reduplications divisible at their midpoint only by an act of force: RIVERINE, JINGLING, RETHRESH, etc.

To go one step further, there are third-order reduplications such as MOSSLESS, POSTPONE, and WOODWARD. Can you give us one which happens to be an ACE of a word?

We have exhausted whatever support tautonymy is capable of providing for ACE words, and must now turn to ordinary English words, not exhibiting any pattern, that are ACEs. If we could coin JOINTMEN (physicians who specialize in treating diseases of the joints), we could show you an 8-6 ACE word as a guide; this coinage, unfortunately, is a somewhat questionable one. Consequently, you are entirely on your own in trying to find several regular 8-5 ACEs.

The 8-letter ACE word does not represent the limit of human achievement. A number of 9-letter specimens are known. One is a 9-7 second-order reduplication, AREVAREVA (a severe skin disease observed in Tahiti). Your task is to round up several regular 9-6 ACE words.

So far, we have been considering ACEs linearly. What happens if we write these words circularly? No matter to what difference level we choose to carry our computations, the number of digits in that level will remain equal to the number of letters in the original word. Under this additional condition, some ACEs remain ACEs; the majority does not. Mathematicians who have examined the problem have concluded that only those words consisting of an even number of letters are capable of being circular ACE words. If the number of letters in a word is some power of two (4, 8, 16, 32, etc.), then the word necessarily becomes a circular ACE word at some difference level. If the number of letters in the word is even but not a power of two (6, 10, 12, 14, etc.), status as a circular ACE word can be attained, but only if it is attained quickly. The greater the number of "2" factors in the number representing the letter-length of the word, the greater the likelihood that ACE status can be achieved. Thus, a 12-letter word ($12 = 2 \times 2 \times 3$) is more likely to be a circular ACE than a word of 10 letters ($10 = 2 \times 5$) or one of 14 letters ($14 = 2 \times 7$).

Your final problem in the land of aces and kings is to pick out a number of ordinary ACE words which are also circular ACEs. From what we have just explained it follows mercilessly and relentlessly, as night follows day, that all of your discoveries will be in the 8-letter category.

Hints: Page 168.   Resolution: Page 223.

90   THE PREPOSITION PROPOSITION

An oft-repeated story is the one about the small boy sick in an upstairs bedroom, who hears his mother coming up the stairs with some reading material for him. He calls out to her, "Why are you bringing the book that I do not want to be read *to out of up for?*" This simple little question has taken on the purple robes of deathless prose, for it happens to end with five consecutive prepositions.

Well, let's not be too harsh on the lad; after all, he's so young. As he grows older, acquiring greater maturity and powers of judgment, he will surely learn to speak in sentences terminating with 8, 9, or even 10 successive prepositions.

You, dear reader, are an adult (we assume). Consequently, we are posing a logical problem for you: can you dream up a continuation or sequel to the tale begun above, one that will reflect your greater command of language, particularly insofar as its prepositional aspect is concerned? Are you game to try?

Hints: Page 147.   Resolution: Page 282.

91 *MYSTERIOUS Q*

It has always seemed to us that there is something different, something enigmatic, about the letter Q. Just how we came to feel that way must remain a matter of conjecture. Possibly, we were impressed by the fact that Q is a descendant of a vanished Greek letter, the letter *koppa;* by the use of Q as a symbol for the Second Source of the gospels Matthew and Luke, a hypothetical source also known as the "Redenquelle"; and by the "Q" Signals, a series of abbreviated radio questions and answers, such as the palindromic QUQ, standing for the inquiry, "Shall I train my searchlight nearly vertical on a cloud, occulting if possible and, if your aircraft is seen, deflect the beam up wind and on the water (or land) to facilitate your landing?" The "Q" Signals, innocent as they might appear to others, have struck us as cryptic communications from outer space, sent by a race of intelligent beings on a distant planet, in a probably vain attempt to establish contact with the comparatively primitive creatures here on Earth.

Whatever the genesis of our feelings about Q may be, we would like to impart to you a measure of the wonder and the mystery that we associate with that letter. Let us, therefore, explore another facet of Q, asking you to join us in our adventure along the periphery of language.

In defining the letter Q, the *Funk & Wagnalls New Standard Dictionary of the English Language* makes this statement:

> "It is always followed by *u* . . ."

In the realm of Language Proper, the statement is true. As so often happens, however, what is true in Language Proper is false in the wider and darker fields Beyond Language. As part of your initiation into the Higher Logic, into Advanced Thinking, we want you to descend into the deepest deeps of ocean gulfs, into the waste places where sands shift their yellow waves with a dry and bony sound, into the hidden horrors of the catacombs; we ask you to wander amid the virgin snows of Dhaulagiri, in the awful labyrinths of forests untrodden by man, in the wombs of dead volcanoes; we insist that you traverse surfaces of lakes and streams studded with the backs of hippopotami or enameled with the mail of crocodiles, the polar extremities of the world where spectral glaciers float over inky seas, strange parts where mountains are rent asunder by throes of primeval earthquake; acquire all the knowledge of all the centuries, all the craft and skill and cunning of man in all things, and return to us—return, with the answers to these questions about Q in the never-never land Beyond Language:

1. Name a word without a U in which there is a Q: (a) at the beginning; (b) at the end; (c) somewhere in the middle.
2. Name a word without a U but with a double Q: (a) at the beginning; (b) somewhere in the middle; (c) at the end.
3. Name a U-less word with two Q's: (a) one at the beginning, the other at the end; (b) one at the beginning, the other in the middle; (c) one in the middle, the other at the end; (d) both in the middle, but not consecutively.
4. Name three different words, each one containing three Q's, not a single one of which is followed by a U.
5. Name a U-less word containing two Q's which happens to be: (a) a palindrome, à la REFER; (b) a tautonym, à la BULBUL.

Your ability to pass this crucial test will be prima-facie evidence of your eligibility to enter the Temple of Words, of your qualifications to participate in the innermost councils of logology. *You dare not fail.*

Hints: Page 166.   Resolution: Page 172.

92 *THE EMPEROR OF AUSTRIA*

Time marches on. Relentlessly, implacably, mercilessly, it moves forward.

Men have always sought to escape from the tyranny of time. Some—Eastern mystics—have chosen the path that leads to samadhi or turiya, an ecstatic condition in which the human consciousness expands and merges with the Infinite, Timeless All. Others—Western scientists—have conceived the idea of escaping from Earth on a spaceship bound for Nowhere, a craft traveling outward at an ever-accelerating velocity. As the speed of the spaceship begins to approach that of light (approximately 186,282 miles per second, in an absolute vacuum), time slows down perceptibly. At the moment when the spacecraft actually attains the speed of light, time stops, and the fortunate occupants of the craft cease to age.

Possibly, neither of these alternatives appeals to you. If so, we'd like to interest you in the "Third Way", *our* way. It is a much more practical, down-to-earth approach to the problem, and is accessible to anyone with a yen to travel. We impose only one requirement: that you figure out yourself how to achieve a timeless existence here on earth; in other words, "Paradise Now"!

Incidentally, why are we involving the Emperor of Austria in our projected escapade? Why is it wrong to do so?

Hints: Page 154.   Resolution: Page 220.

93 BEYOND URANIUM

The advances of modern science have made most of us keenly aware of the names of the elements near the end of the periodic table: 91, BREVIUM; 92, EKAWOLFRAM; 93, AUSONIUM; 94, ESPERIUM; and so forth. Not too many of us, however, can come up with the name of Element 118, in a trice.

Can you?

Come to think of it, there is something mighty peculiar about the element names just cited. Whatever happened to PROTACTINIUM, URANIUM, NEPTUNIUM, and PLUTONIUM?

One of our four mystery names is different from the other three. Which one, and in what way?

Be sure to document all of these names properly.

Hints: Page 152.   Resolution: Page 259.

94 A FEAMYNG OF FERRETS

You are working a crossword puzzle. All but one section of it is solved. The stumbling block in the unfinished corner is a 7-letter word defined as "a company of ferrets". All you know about ferrets is that they are mammals of the weasel family used in hunting rodents. Since you are a dedicated puzzler, determined not to let the success of a complete solution elude you, you refer to *The Complete Crossword Reference Book* (Thorn System), by N. St. Barbe Sladen, F.R.S.L., Revised Edition, published by The Syndicate Publishing Company, London, 1949. That book gives a long list of "Group Terms" on Pages 135–137. Scanning the 7-letter terms, the object of your quest drops into your lap: a FEAMYNG of ferrets! Overjoyed, you insert that word into your puzzle and finish it off in no time flat.

The oddness of the word FEAMYNG bothers you, however, and you look it up in a good dictionary, only to suffer the disappointment of not finding it. Resolved to track the word down, you visit the library, and consult all the big, "unabridged", dictionaries, works with time-honored names such as Webster, Century, Funk & Wagnalls, Oxford, and Wright. You fail: there isn't any dictionary of any sort, large or small, British or American, old or new, general or special, that gives the word FEAMYNG.

At this point, inspiration comes your way, you try a new line of attack, and the seemingly impenetrable mystery dissolves in a blaze of light.

Give us the details of what you have discovered, won't you?

Hints: Page 146.   Resolution: Page 251.

95 *AUGMENTING THE ALPHABET*

What is the 27th letter of the English alphabet?

Quite curiously, there are four different solutions to this unusual question. It will be a test of your imaginativeness, of your ability to escape from conventional channels of thought, to see how many of the four solutions you find.

Hints: Page 147.   Resolution: Page 275.

96 *QUESTIONS FOR KAY?*

Those of us who would venture beyond language must first be thoroughly at home in the field of language itself. As a spot check of your qualifications for such ventures, we invite your attention to a series of questions about the "4-K" problem. How many of these questions can you answer correctly?

1. Phonetically, our alphabet contains four K's. Identify and exemplify them.
2. The shortest English word using four K's happens to be a palindrome (a

word such as ROTATOR, reading the same backward as it does forward).
Name it and define it.

3. Another "4-K" word happens to be a first-order reduplication (a word like
   HUSH-HUSH, consisting of two identical parts). What is that word?
4. A third "4-K" word is curious in that all four K's can be removed without
   altering the pronunciation of the remaining word in any way. What is
   this common word? It happens to be a second-order reduplication (a word
   such as HIGGLEDY-PIGGLEDY, in which the second half differs by one letter
   from the first half).
5. One of the "4-K" words is noteworthy for beginning with four consecutive
   K's. Name the word!
6. What is the longest word containing four K's, no more and no less? While
   we have a good candidate for this particular honor, our research on the
   subject has been far from exhaustive, and you may be able to top us. Try!
7. Who is Kay, anyway?

Hints: Page 164.   Resolution: Page 241.

97 *!!!PppppppP!!!*

Explain!

Hints: Page 165.   Resolution: Page 231.

98 *COFFEE, ANYONE?*

Our printer made a lamentable error. We gave him a list of unusual English words, arranged in the form of twelve pairs. The two members of each
pair present a striking contrast when considered in relation to each other,
and this contrast was to be our subject for the current hour. The situation
being what it is, however—and that's saying a mouthful, believe you us—the

printer rearranged the words into straight alphabetical order. Discombobulated, we beseech your help. Here is the printer's version of our list:

1. AH'S	9. ECKS	17. OUI
2. AI	10. EWE	18. OZ
3. AIX	11. EYE	19. PHI
4. AYE	12. FEE	20. PSI
5. CEE	13. I	21. QUAY
6. CHI	14. KEY	22. SI
7. CY	15. KI	23. WEE
8. EAU	16. OH	24. YOU

Can you, by some stroke of good fortune, put the list back into proper order, in the form of twelve matched but contrasting pairs?

If you can, then tell us what the underlying principle for the pairing is, and give us a similar example involving longer words. Also, explain our puzzling but highly pertinent title.

Hints: Page 151.   Resolution: Page 235.

99 EXCESS EXES

Those of us who celebrate Xmas, undergo X-ray treatments, and like xylophone music received a rude jolt in 1963. An excellent dictionary published that year by a division of Random House, Inc., in New York, asserts that the letter X "begins no word in the English language".

X-lovers of the world, arise! Your faith has been challenged! Now is the hour for you to vindicate the status of your beloved, and to assure it a position of honor in all future dictionaries! Should you falter, every last vestige of X will be eradicated from our language.

In the meantime, we have a number of questions for the less ambitious:

1. What dictionary is it that has dealt us so grievous a blow?
2. How do you explain this unbelievable statement?
3. Granting its truth, why is it nevertheless false?

Hints: Page 145.   Resolution: Page 280.

100   *IMMORTALITY*

Quoted below is a passage of five lines from a famous poem:

"Oft on autumnal eves, when without in the gathering darkness
  Bursting with light seemed the smithy, through every cranny and crevice,
  Warm by the forge within they watched the laboring bellows,
  And as its panting ceased, and the sparks expired in the ashes,
  Merrily laughed, and said they were nuns going into the chapel."

Can you identify the poem from which these lines are taken, and its author?

There is something astonishing about one of these lines. Which one, and what is it?

How could you have spotted that special line using purely aprioristic logic?

Our title hints at what is unusual about the line in question. Explain.

Hints: Page 154.   Resolution: Page 188.

101   *CAPSULE COMMENTS*

One of the very special uses to which language is applied is in the review of books, plays, and motion pictures. We call this use of language "special" because, particularly in the case of books, it represents an inward turning of language, a critical, introspective self-examination, a testing *of* language *by* language—in short, its supreme, soul-searching trial.

It has always gone without saying that the reviewer's comments should be appropriate to the material reviewed. Not as clearly understood or accepted has been the corollary principle that the review must also be appropriate to the reviewer, must be a faithful mirror of the one who writes it. A few examples will show what we have in mind.

Assume that the review is intended to be short, to the point, and highly favorable. How should a review appearing in a publication such as the *Journal of the American Medical Association* be worded? "Cuts to the very bone!" Or, visualize the *Pittsburgh Plate Glass Monthly* as passing on a new novel. "A Shattering Success!" Or, think of a newspaper, the *New York World-Telegram*.

"Electrifying!" The principle applies with equal force to individual reviewers. For instance, we can imagine Charles Darwin as saying, "Selectivity at work". Similarly, the comment, "Truly memorable!" would be an apt critique coming from Rip Van Winkle.

Instead of passively watching us do all the work, try to reap some of the glory yourself, by inventing your own capsule comments, comments unusually suited to the nature of the reviewer. After you are satisfied that your samples are in top shape, turn to the "Resolutions" section and compare them with a flock of ours.

Hints: Page 157.   Resolution: Page 238.

102 *FROM WORD TO NONWORD*

Some letter combinations are words, others are not. All of us know that RELAYED is a word, while PLDNCRA is meaningless; common sense is sufficient to make the distinction. Unfortunately, common sense has its limitations, and we are surprised to learn that ROYALED, which looks like a word, is no such thing, whereas TRKNMLI, which looks like gibberish, is a dictionary word (the name of an extinct language once spoken in Asia Minor, listed and defined in *A Dictionary of Linguistics* by Mario Pei and Frank Gaynor).

With common sense discredited, we turn to the dictionary for authoritative information, only to be frustrated. There are many, many dictionaries, each one containing words found in no other; unless you live in the Library of Congress and are free to devote your entire life to searching for words, you can never reach certainty as to whether or not some particular sequence of letters is a word. Furthermore, some entries in dictionaries are erroneous, and some words have never been recorded in any dictionary. In the case of valid dictionary entries, there are all sorts of inflectional forms on the border between language and nonlanguage, and it is the consultant who becomes the final judge as to whether a given combination is or is not a word.

The purpose of this section is to make you conscious of some of the peculiar problems that emerge to haunt the word searcher. We have selected 16 letter groupings that lay claim to being words. All of them have been drawn from the field of wordplay; some are common, others rare. Your problems:

1. Define or identify the unusual terms, giving the exact source of each.
2. Point out the features of these words that make them interesting in wordplay.
3. Pinpoint the various objections that can be raised in regard to these words.
4. Evaluate the situations intelligently.

Here is our word list, in alphabetical order:

1. Antenna array	9. Oeaei
2. Apollo, Pa.	10. Relatings
3. Delia's	11. San Diegos
4. Endolymphaticus	12. Superseptuaginarians
5. Eudaimony	13. Terror-stirring
6. Graciously's	14. Toot-toot
7. Hgrusa	15. Walpurgisnächte
8. Icc	16. Xsmwpdribvnwlxy

Hints: Page 150. Resolution: Page 174.

103 HALLOWEEN AND CHRISTMAS

In this vignette, we ask you to demonstrate, with mathematical rigorousness, that the two holidays named in our title are actually the same.

Let nothing deter you.

Hints: Page 156. Resolution: Page 217.

104 TWO WORDS = ONE BIRD!

Contemplate, if you will, the following sequence of alphabetic letters:

... M M O O T T F F S S E ...

Study these letters, penetrate their innermost being, come to know them more intimately than anything you have ever known. When success in this endeavor is yours, turn your attention to answering five questions:

1. What is the *obvious* next letter in this sequence, the letter immediately following the E?
2. What is the *true* next letter? Why?
3. What is the letter in this sequence that immediately precedes the first M? Why?
4. Shifting our viewpoint, the obvious sequel to E is also the true sequel. How is that possible?
5. Our title connects with our problem in two distinct ways. Explain them.

Hints: Page 147.   Resolution: Page 286.

105 *A "NON SEQUITUR"*

Merchandising firms and other concerns are habitually sponsoring limerick contests. The first four lines of the limerick are given, and contestants are asked to compose the final, fifth line, rhyming with the first two lines. Handsome prizes are awarded to the winners.

Not to be caught napping, we have decided to sponsor a limerick contest of our own. Here is the limerick which you are to complete by supplying with a fifth line:

> "The ancient Romans used centurions
> To keep close watch on their decurions;
> But did the former know
> That they were kept in tow
> .... "

Remember that the last line must rhyme with "centurions" and "decurions".

The prize for the best entry submitted? A round trip for two, all expenses paid, to NAIR AL ZAURAK!

Qualifying for the prize offered is a five-part proposition, as follows:

1. Complete the limerick by using the information presented here—*very specifically!*
2. Can you tell us the probable name of the hypothetical Roman emperor in whose reign the events described in the limerick took place, using the same method you used to complete the limerick?

3. Only because our title is *not* a "non sequitur" is it "non sequitur". Can you resolve this paradox?
4. If you win our prize, why are you certain to decline it?
5. Why is the limerick structurally unsound?

Hints: Page 152.   Resolution: Page 205.

106 *BELLES OF THE BALL??*

Three long-time friends, Jean Doe, Shirley Camp, and Vivian March, arrived at the class dance without dates. Although all three of them were extremely popular with their classmates, and the men at the dance happened to outnumber the girls by a goodly margin, not one received an invitation to dance from any of the men present. Enigmas:

1. How can we account for this highly implausible situation?
2. What is the hidden link between the surnames of the three friends?

Hints: Page 145.   Resolution: Page 242.

107 *WORDS*

Entirely too many of us are neglecting words. We shunt words aside in favor of pictures, actions, or even silence, that first and foremost of the Seven Deadly Sins. Something must be done!

The logical approach to our problem is to advertise. Let's dream up a series of dynamic, vibrant, stimulating slogans extolling the virtues of words, and place these slogans on billboards all over the country. People will read these slogans, become word-conscious, and start using words. There will be an upsurge in the national literacy rate, benefits to schools, libraries, and publishers will mount, and we shall find ourselves transforming America into a veritable Heaven on Earth.

All we need to start our project moving is to devise a large number of suitable slogans that carry a punch. We've already thought of twenty good ones (you'll find them listed in the "Resolutions" section), but we need the broadest possible spectrum of intelligent, imaginative, creative thinking to insure success. That is why your participation in the project is earnestly solicited. Give us the benefit of your most profound and original cerebrations!

Hints: Page 161.   Resolution: Page 298.

108 *THE INVISIBLE ALPHABET*

In handling telegrams by telephone, it is customary to spell unusual words or names, using an alphabet of the kind that starts out, "A as in Adams, B as in Boston, C as in Chicago, . . .". In an alphabet of this sort, even the most difficult letters are exemplified with common words and names: "J as in John . . . Q as in Queen . . . X as in X-ray . . . Z as in Zero."

The total absence of imagination displayed by such alphabets disturbs us profoundly. Why not replace the ordinary words with colorful ones, along the following lines:

A as in ABRACADABRA	N as in NEVER-NEVER LAND
B as in BUMBERSHOOT	O as in OVOVIVIPAROUSNESS
C as in CACOËTHES SCRIBENDI	P as in PIETERMARITZBURG
D as in DADDY-LONGLEGS	Q as in QUAI D'ORSAY
E as in EEK!	R as in RHODODENDRON
F as in FEE, FI, FO, FUM	S as in SIAMESE CAT
G as in GUNGA DIN	T as in TINTINNABULATION
H as in HOOTENANNY	U as in UUCHATHON
I as in ICHTHYOSAUR	V as in VARICOSE VEINS
J as in JEROBOAM	W as in WERELEOPARD
K as in KIDNEY STONE	X as in XANADU
L as in LICKSPITTLE	Y as in YELLOW-BELLIED
M as in MAJOR-DOMO	Z as in ZWITTERION

A signal improvement over the conventional communications alphabet, but nothing to tax your abilities as a language authority. We propose, therefore, a much more difficult problem, one that is specifically designed to measure your word capabilities. What we want you to prepare for us is an alphabet in which each of the 26 letters, in its turn, is represented by a word that contains the letter in its pronunciation though not in its spelling. For instance, you could include in your "invisible" alphabet entries such as "C as in SIEGE . . . O as in SEW . . . W as in CHIHUAHUA . . . Z as in LEAVES". You *could* include them, but you wouldn't, for that would amount to plagiarism.

You have no idea what harsh taskmasters we can be. Score yourself as follows: 26, good; 25, just barely passing; 24 or fewer, failing! If you have missed any—and that's a pretty big "if", we'll grant—you may turn to the "Resolutions" section to find out why you fell by the wayside.

Hints: Page 149.   Resolution: Page 250.

109 *SYNONYMS FOR SEX*

So far, we have been ignoring the facts of life. You can do that only for so long, and then something gives. Well, whatever it is has just given, and we propose to face the subject of sex squarely, mincing no words.

Secreted in a private world of their own, sex words have been breeding and multiplying, with synonyms as their offspring. We ask you to peek into that secluded world now, and to pluck from it anywhere from half a dozen to a dozen *exact* synonyms for each of the following terms, taking care to choose only the most literary, most scientific, and most socially acceptable terms: (1) coitus; (2) pregnancy; (3) nymphomania; (4) the membrum virile; (5) self-abuse. Remember: no slang, no vulgarity; nothing off-color or risqué!

Hints: Page 146.   Resolution: Page 240.

110 *APOCRYPHAL ANTITHESES*

As on many another occasion, we have assembled a list of words here, for your inspection. This list is one in which the words occur in pairs:

(1)	Best	Worst
(2)	Ravel	Unravel
(3)	Sharp	Blunt
(4)	Walk up	Walk down
(5)	Hot	Cool
(6)	Highly	Deeply
(7)	Chaste	Unchaste
(8)	High	Low

Even a neophyte at the whirl of words will immediately recognize that these are pairs opposite in meaning. Our title concedes that fact, though the word "apocryphal" in it suggests that something more is involved.

How true! Much, much more is involved. These words reveal a profound logical and philosophical principle to anyone who knows how to read them properly. Not to deprive you of the joys of discovery, we are letting you study the words undisturbed, setting you the problem of finding the Great Secret they conceal.

Hints: Page 160.   Resolution: Page 228.

111 *THE ELECTION OF 1948*

Not many of us are aware of the intimate connection between recent events in American politics, and European history hundreds of years ago.

Take the presidential election of 1948 as an example. That election was the only one in the past century in which each of four candidates received more than one million votes. The four candidates? Harry S Truman, the Democrat; Thomas E. Dewey, the Republican; J. Strom Thurmond, the Dixiecrat; and Henry A. Wallace, the Progressive. Strange as it may seem, there is a direct relationship between the 1948 election and the following events in European history:

(1) The occupation of Sardinia by Spanish forces in 1717;
(2) Peter the Great of Russia putting to death his son Alexis in 1718; and
(3) The accession to oligarchic rule in Sweden of Ulrica Eleanora and Fredrik I of Hesse, in 1719.

We *could* ask you to figure out the nature of the connection, but refrain from doing so on the grounds that the problem is too difficult. Magnanimously, we shall show you the connection, asking questions about it later.

Start by assigning numbers to the four presidential candidates in 1948:

(1) Harry S Truman
(2) Thomas E. Dewey
(3) J. Strom Thurmond
(4) Henry A. Wallace

Next, pick any one of these candidates according to his number, multiply that number by two, and add five. Take the result and multiply it by 50. Take the number at which you have now arrived and add the year to it of one of the historical European events we have cited. If you are working on this problem in 1967, add the year in which the Spaniards occupied Sardinia; if you are doing this in 1968, add the year in which Alexis died in prison; if it is 1969, add the year that saw the shift of government in Sweden. Finally, subtract the year of your birth.

The result, if you have been following our directions faithfully, is a three-digit number. The first digit is the number of the candidate selected by you; the second and third digits are your age on your birthday in the calendar year in which you are solving this problem.

For example, assume that you are reading this in 1967, and that you are 41 years old on your birthday in 1967. Assume further that you have selected candidate No. 3, J. Strom Thurmond. Multiply No. 3 by 2, giving you 6. Add 5, giving you 11. Multiply by 50, giving you 550. Add the Sardinian year 1717, for a total of 2267. Subtract the year of your birth, which must have been 1926, leaving a remainder of 341. The first digit of that remainder, 3, is the number of Candidate Thurmond; the second and third digits, 41, are your present age.

Now for the questions we promised you:

1. What is the algebraic equation or formula that shows why this method will invariably work?
2. What adjustment, if any, would you need to make in the procedure if you were more than 99 years old at present?
3. There were several other candidates for President in 1948: Norman Thomas of the Socialist Party, Claude A. Watson of the Prohibition Party, and Edward A. Teichert of the Socialist Labor Party, to name the most prominent ones. If we assigned the numbers 5, 6, and 7 to these candidates, what adjustment, if any, would you need to make in the procedure to obtain correct results?
4. Perhaps you are a slowpoke, and wait until 1970 before tackling this problem. What event from European history would you have to substitute for the ones suggested by us?

Hints: Page 162.   Resolution: Page 203.

112 *ETAOIN SHRDLU*

The queer title that graces this problem is a letter sequence of multiple significance and uses in English. Since it *is* a dictionary entry, we are taking the liberty of presenting it to you, asking you to mull over the following points connected with it:

1. What is the standard English definition of ETAOIN SHRDLU?
2. The phrase also belongs to that sector of English characterized by a special vividness or coloring, not generally used in formal speaking or writing, and popular only for a short time: to slang. What is its slang meaning?
3. The term has also come to be a kind of slang used in newspaper offices, as in the expression "knowing a field from ETAOIN to SHRDLU". What does this expression mean?
4. What is the special significance of ETAOIN SHRDLU for typesetters?
5. What is its special significance for cryptographers?
6. The first word, ETAOIN, is sometimes confused with another odd-looking word, EOTHEN. What is EOTHEN?
7. The 12 letters of ETAOIN SHRDLU seem to be rearrangeable into some 12-letter word or name. Why do they give this impression? Can you effect a suitable permutation?

Hints: Page 155.   Resolution: Page 173.

113 *THE KEY TO KNOWLEDGE*

We express ideas through the medium of language. Language consists of symbols: alphabetic letters, numerals, punctuation marks, diacritical marks, reference and proofreading marks, mathematical and logical symbols, and many miscellaneous signs used in various fields of science, technology, art, etc.

The number of symbols in use is large but very definitely finite. Excluding the many symbols that can easily be replaced by words having the precise meanings conveyed by the symbols, we are probably being generous in estimating that all human knowledge can be set down in writing without undue inconvenience, if we limit ourselves to using the 1000 most essential symbols.

A given number of symbols can be combined in a limited number of ways only, within a given space. Suppose that we want to write a text about life as it exists on our planet, making that description the last word on the subject: a description that will be comprehensive and authoritative, and that will stand the test of time; one that cannot and will not be invalidated or made incomplete by any future discoveries or advances, because it constitutes the ultimate truth. A *complete* description is not what we have in mind, since it would be possible to write a work 1000 times the size of the *Encyclopaedia Britannica*, devoted solely to the mating habits of the MAHOOHOO (the square-mouthed rhinoceros, *Rhinoceros simus*). What we are thinking of is in the nature of a reference work some 25 times the size of the *Encyclopaedia Britannica*, devoted to the subject of terrestrial life, past and future, covering all aspects of the subject comprehensively, devoting an amount of space to any individual topic proportionate to the importance of that topic in relation to the entire subject of life on earth. Viewed as a reference work of close to one billion words, this would give the average consultant more information on whatever topic interested him than he could want, need, or remember. The essential point is that the information given would be true in every particular; so true that a scientist of one billion years from now, reading this reference work from beginning to end, would not be capable of changing even one word in the entire text, or of making any significant addition to the text without violating the weighting considerations that went into its structure.

We have found a way of producing such a reference work now, without waiting for the accumulation of further knowledge on the subject in future millenia, in future eons, by races as far advanced beyond the men of today, as *Homo sapiens* is over the lowly paramecium. Yes, there is a way.

The number of ways in which our 1000 essential symbols can be combined to form a one-billion-word encyclopedia about terrestrial life (or about any other subject) is limited, is finite. Let us feed the 1000 symbols into the memory of the most advanced, high-speed electronic data processing equipment developed, and let the machine produce every possible combination of one billion words that is mathematically possible. One of those combinations will be the reference work we have proposed. Other combinations, incidentally, will be reference works of the same magnitude, dealing with every other subject known to man, and of the same absolute, ultimate degree of authority.

Do not object that the best computers of today are not up to the staggering job involved. Within a limited number of years—twenty or thirty years—it is eminently reasonable to assume that computers will be developed functioning at one million or one billion times the speed of today's computers. Let us wait until these more powerful instruments are available, let us build one million of them, and let us put all of them to work on this most important project in the entire history of the human race, and of life itself.

The vision of complete knowledge is the most alluring one dangled before mankind in its slow climb upward. Note that we now say *complete* knowledge. Our approach will produce one mammoth encyclopedia about life on earth; another about human life; a third about the specific subject of medicine; a fourth about yellow fever in particular; a fifth about the first description of that disease, given by Diego López de Cogolludo, relating to an epidemic of yellow fever that occurred in Yucatán, Mexico in 1648; a sixth about the breakfast that Diego López ate the morning he started writing his description; and so on. Whatever the subject, there will be some encyclopedia, one of a billion words, treating that subject in fantastic detail. The same will be true of all other realms of human thought and endeavor—true automatically and effortlessly, leapfrogging millions of years of continued effort on the part of humanity's greatest intellects.

The vision is alluring, indeed, but it is only a mirage. Our brainstorm is full of fallacies. How many of them can you detect? There are at least four distinct fallacies. One of them presents us with the strange paradox of two *identical* statements concerning objective phenomena, made at the same time and at the same place, one of them a truth, the other one not. Can you explain this paradox?

Hints: Page 153.   Resolution: Page 199.

114 *MATCH GAME*

The increasing complexity of our world calls for an expanding time consciousness on our part. Attainment of broader temporal vistas is possible in many ways: philosophically, scientifically, and even mystically. For ourselves, we have chosen the Way of the Word.

Listed below are the names of 20 periods of time, in alphabetical order. To the right of the name list is a list of the 20 time intervals, in order of increasing length. Your assignment is to match the two lists up properly:

1. BIMESTER	A. One billionth of a second
2. BISSEXTILE	B. One hundred millionth of a second
3. CHILIAD	C. 3 days
4. EMBOLISMIC YEAR	D. 5 days
5. HAAB	E. 7 days
6. HEBDOMAD	F. 20 days
7. INDICTION	G. 2 months
8. KALPA	H. 3 months
9. LIGHT-FOOT	I. One fourth of a year
10. LUSTRE	J. 360 days
11. MANVANTARA	K. 365 days
12. OLYMPIAD	L. 366 days
13. RAITH	M. 384 days
14. SHAKE	N. 4 years
15. TERJUBILEE	O. 5 years
16. TRIDUUM	P. 15 years
17. TRIMENON	Q. 150 years
18. TUN	R. 1000 years
19. UAYEB	S. 4,320,000 years
20. UINAL	T. 4,320,000,000 years

Most of these terms have been drawn from particular areas of human thought or activity. Can you place the terms where they belong?

Hints: Page 142.   Resolution: Page 209.

115   *WIDSHI ITÍKAPÁ*

It has been a long, hot day in your home on the outskirts of STOA PITK, and you decide to go for a drive in the evening, for some fresh air. Traversing the local roads, you pass SIKUL HIMALK, GU OIDAK, KOM VO, and other small communities. As you are about to turn homeward, a black limousine cuts across the road just ahead of you, bringing you to an abrupt halt. Two masked gunmen jump out of the limousine, force you out of your car into theirs, knock you unconscious, and drive off.

Hours—or days—later, you wake up and look around you. You appear to be in a luxurious but strange hotel room. A dull, throbbing pain in your head prompts you to get up from the bed and stagger over to the washroom for some cold water. You turn the faucet handle marked "C". A stream of hot water, scalding hot, greets you.

Where in the United States do you live? What is your probable racial origin? Where is the hotel in which you now find yourself? What bearing on this problem does our title have? How is the second faucet handle marked?

These are certainly legitimate questions. The answers are for *you* to establish.

Hints: Page 150.   Resolution: Page 202.

116 *DELVING INTO DIVINATION*

Let us shake off the shackles, not merely of language but also of science and of the present moment, moving boldly into the future, assisted by the many different forms of divination practiced largely in ancient and medieval times. Naturally, you know all about ASTROMANCY (astrology), or divination by the stars; CHIROMANCY (palmistry), or divination by inspecting the hands; and ONEIROMANCY, or divination by means of dreams. Consequently, we won't ask you about any of these. Instead, we shall briefly describe 25 other, more exotic, methods of divination, permitting you to provide the correct technical designation for each one. If you pass this test, you will qualify for the eagerly coveted insignia worn by members of the Occult Order of Osiris. For a membership card, send your scored test paper to the Order's headquarters in Heliopolis, Lower Egypt. That card, by the way, has an excellent picture of Mnevis, the black bull, engraved on it.

Divination by means of:

1. Figures produced by dropping melted wax into water.
2. The movements of mice.
3. Wheat flour mixed with barley meal or oatmeal.
4. Inspecting water in a basin into which plates of gold and silver were put, with jewels.
5. The sound of, or signs upon, the belly.
6. A cock encircled by grains of corn placed on the letters of the alphabet.
7. Observation of a shoulder blade as blotched or cracked from the fire.
8. Someone walking in or around a circle until he fell from dizziness.

9. A hatchet and a jet-stone laid together upon a fire of hot embers.
10. Observing the soles of the feet.
11. Throwing black and white beans, or little bones.
12. The entrails of men, women, and children, a particularly delightful form of divination practiced by the Roman emperor Heliogabalus (Varius Avitus Bassianus).
13. Burning straws on red-hot iron.
14. Barley flour and honey loaves.
15. The heads or entrails of fishes.
16. Smoke in sacrifices.
17. Observing the mode in which air bubbles rise in springs or fountains.
18. Noting motions and figures in molten lead.
19. The turning of a sieve held on a pair of shears.
20. The letters of a name, as the number of vowels in the name, or the sum of the numerical values of the letters.
21. Cake dough offered in sacrifices and the meal strewn over the victims.
22. Boiling the head of an ass on burning coals.
23. Observing substances burned in a lamp or with a candle.
24. A young boy acting as a medium and reporting on images visible to him in water.
25. The figure assumed by a handful of earth thrown down on some surface.

Hints: Page 160.   Resolution: Page 196.

117 *INDUCTION*

From time to time, we ask that you exercise and sharpen your powers of logical, inductive reasoning. This is such a moment—brace yourself! Listed below are four seemingly unrelated words:

EXPEDIENCY   EMPTY

AISLE   KNICKKNACK

These four words possess a most unusual characteristic, one shared by very few other words. While the general characteristic is the same, it breaks down into several different varieties in its actual application to the four words. Can you recognize the subgroups as well as the fundamental group?

Hints: Page 148.   Resolution: Page 172.

118 THE END IS NEAR!
(Are You Ready?)

Yes, the jig is up—unless you can unravel the mystery we are about to show you. Focus your attention on the following word list:

Betwixt	Huh	Polyonym
Caoutchouc	Huzza	Pontacq
Countertug	Hydropolyp	Protomartyr
Electrolyze	Intermezzo	Snarleyyow
Evelyn	Kikuyu	Squawk
Fuzz	Leitmotiv	Stub
Fuzzy	Lloyd	Styx
Guys	Nazi	Underturf
Hadj	Oxybenzyl	

The problem this word list poses for you is of a characteristically multiple nature. To descend from the general to the particular, you need to cope with these questions:

1. The words listed form a group. Define the group, giving both its primary and its secondary attributes.
2. The secondary attribute of the group has deliberately been modified. How and why?
3. In three instances, the modification has not been applied. What are the three exceptions, and why were these exceptions made?
4. Assuming that you wanted an entirely unmodified group, what revisions would you make in the word list?
5. The sensation-seeking title of our problem relates to it in four mutually distinct ways. Name them.

Hints: Page 165.   Resolution: Page 186.

119 THE LIVING END

In 1937—the year that the constitutionality of a Louisiana tax on chain stores was upheld by the United States Supreme Court—a prisoner in a New Orleans court gave his name as: MAILLILIAGEYEAYAEGYAYE EDENCEYEARYILO

ANILILYLLAYIO. Using *only* the information we have just given you, can you tell us:

1. What was the nationality of the prisoner?
2. In what three different ways is our title connected with this problem?
3. What is the pertinence of the Louisiana tax on chain stores in the given context?

If you have learned the lessons of *Beyond Language* well, these questions will seem too easy for you.

Hints: Page 154.   Resolution: Page 308.

BAFFLERS

So FAR, for each problem served up to you, we have also offered a neat, complete solution. This wonderfully tidy arrangement is an unrealistic one, for in real life, some problems have no solutions, and this is just as true of our adventures in word and thought as it is of other human activities.

This unit of *Beyond Language* addresses itself to "insolutes"—problems to which no solution is known, or only an incomplete one, either because the problem is so recent in origin that there has not been enough time to find a solution, or because it is so difficult that no one has yet demonstrated the ingenuity to conquer it.

Each of our "Bafflers" will be presented to you fairly and squarely, with such elements of the ultimate resolution as may already be known, or with the nearest thing to a true solution now available. You are invited to take up the challenge, to pursue those of the problems to which you feel attracted, and to succeed where we have failed.

The unresolved problems with which we propose to have you wrestle add a new dimension to the concept of *Beyond Language*. While they are much more directly word problems than many of those in the body of our text, they are clearly beyond the present territories of language, for no one has been able to penetrate them yet!

120 *DOUBLETAILS*

What is it that unites MILWAUKEE, TREADMILL, and PEACOCKISHNESS? The fact that each is a word ending with a doubled letter—EE, or LL, or SS. A word or name of this sort is known as a "doubletail" to the Epoptae of Logology (initiates into the highest grade of the ancient Logological Mysteries).

For quite some time, a struggle has been in progress between the initiates and the language presumed to be their willing tool, to determine whether all 26 letters of the alphabet can be employed in the service of doubletails. The heroics of the epoptae have conquered 23 of the 26 letters, as demonstrated by the word list that follows. The less common terms are briefly defined.

AA — MUSHAA, undivided common property in Mohammedan law.
BB — STUBB, a fogdog or luminous spot sometimes seen in fog near the horizon.
CC — ???
DD — MISADD
EE — SEMIJUBILEE
FF — QUARTERSTAFF
GG — GOLLIWOGG, a kind of grotesque black doll.
HH — SAHH, a Moroccan measure equal to 1.59 bushels.
II — HAWAII
JJ — HAJJ, the pilgrimage of a Moslem to Mecca.
KK — RIKK, a small Egyptian tambourine.
LL — THUNDERSQUALL
MM — MUMM, to play in a dumb show, mask, or disguise.
NN — AIDENN, the celestial paradise of Edgar Allan Poe.
OO — COCKATOO
PP — STUPP, a black deposit obtained in distilling mercury ores.
QQ — RIQQ, a modern tambourine without snares, about 10 inches in diameter.
RR — SUSURR, to whisper.
SS — CONTEMPORANEOUSNESS
TT — MICROWATT

UU — MAKAPUU, a point on the southeast corner of Oahu Island.
VV — ???
WW — ???
XX — FOXX (James Emory Foxx), prominent American League baseball player
     from 1928 to 1941.
YY — YABLONOVYY, a mountain range in the Soviet Union, east of Lake Baikal.
ZZ — RAZZMATAZZ

Examine the foregoing list casually, and you find that three terminal combinations, CC, VV, and WW, are unrepresented. There is certainly a job cut out for someone here—you, perhaps?

121 THE SHIFTING SANDS OF TIME

Astronomers have long been puzzled by the red shift, a displacement of characteristic spectrum lines in the light of distant stellar galaxies toward the red, caused by an increase in the light wavelengths of the galaxies, believed to indicate that they are receding from us at incredible speeds.

Logologists have been puzzling over a different sort of shift, the calendar shift. For totally unknown reasons, the name of one month in Language "A" is sometimes the name of the next month in Language "B". Some examples follow:

> APRIL in Polish (Kwiecień) =
> MAY in Czech (Květen)

> JUNE in Croatian (Lipanj) =
> JULY in Polish (Lipiec)

> JULY in Croatian (Srpanj) =
> AUGUST in Polish (Sierpień)

> SEPTEMBER in Croatian (Rujan) =
> OCTOBER in Czech (Říjen)

> OCTOBER in Croatian (Listopad) =
> NOVEMBER in Czech (Listopad)

While the form of the word usually differs from one language to the other, both forms are invariably from the same etymological root.

This situation creates two problems urgently in need of resolution: (1) is it possible to find a logical reason for the calendar shift phenomenon? (2) is it possible to find additional examples of the calendar shift, so as to construct a complete set of twelve consecutive shifts, circling the calendar, with each month properly related to the months both preceding and following it? These problems are being worked on in linguistic laboratories all over the nation!

122 *FINITE PROJECTIVE GEOMETRIES*

Some purely mathematical problems have verbal analogues that can be understood and solved on a purely linguistic basis. One such problem has its root in the field of finite projective geometries. The reader interested in the mathematical aspects of the problem is referred to the article "Soup, Fish, and Finite Geometries", by Ronald C. Read, in the February, 1963 issue of *Recreational Mathematics Magazine,* published by Mr. Joseph S. Madachy of Kent, Ohio, and to a further note on the subject in the January–February, 1964 issue of the same magazine (Page 46). We shall confine ourselves to exploring the language side of the problem.

Fundamentally, the problem is to assemble a set of words, all of some given number of letters, using some specified group of alphabetic letters, and conforming to two essential conditions:

(1) Any two letters of those being used are to be found simultaneously in only one word;
(2) Any two words of those being used are to have only one letter in common.

In the mathematical version of the problem, an infinite number of distinct versions of the problem exists, but only three of these cases can be expressed verbally in a language limited to a 26-letter alphabet.

Case No. 1

The first and simplest version of our problem asks us to make up a group of seven 3-letter words, using any 7 alphabetic letters of our choice, each one exactly three times, so that: (a) any two of the seven letters being used, chosen at random, will happen to be found in one and only one of the seven words; (b) any two of the seven words being used, chosen at random, will happen to have one and only one letter in common. Mathematical investigation of the problem reveals a further condition that is inescapable: if we designate the six letters A, E, I, O, U, and Y as vowels, and all other letters of the alphabet as consonants, then, no matter which seven letters we decide to use, we cannot form the specified word group unless one of the seven words comprising it consists either entirely of vowels or entirely of consonants. This condition is quite independent of the particular six letters that we happen to call vowels. If we were sufficiently unconventional to label J, K, Q, V, X, and Z as our vowels, and the remaining 20 letters as consonants, the condition would hold unchanged.

Case No. 1 is really an easy problem, one to which numerous solutions exist. An example of a word group including one all-vowel word is ADO, BAR, BED, BOY, DRY, ORE, YEA. An example of a word group including one all-consonant word is ACT, AIM, AWE, CWM, ICE, MET, WIT. That all-consonant word, CWM, is given in *Webster's Seventh New Collegiate Dictionary* (1963), and is defined as a deep, steep-walled basin on a mountain, shaped like half a bowl.

Since the problem is comparatively elementary, it is permissible to impose additional conditions of logological interest. For instance, one may stipulate that the seven letters selected for use be transposable so as to spell an English word of 7 letters. Thus, if we decide to build our word group out of the letters E, N, O, R, T, U, and Y, we first arrange them to spell the word TOURNEY, and then develop the word group NOR, NUT, RUE, TOE, TRY, YEN, YOU. As a further condition, one may propose that the seven words constituting one's group be arrangeable in the form of a meaningful sentence.

For the latter stipulation, no thoroughly satisfactory solution has yet been discovered. A variant of the "tourney" solution arranges the seven three-letter words so as to read:

> "You rue, yen not, nor try toe."

This may be interpreted as an admonition to someone who regretted visiting a swimming pool in chilly weather. Of course, the English is rather strained, and the problem cannot yet be classified as fully solved.

Case No. 2

The second version of our problem, intermediate in difficulty, calls on us to constitute a group of 13 four-letter words, using any 13 alphabetic letters of our choice, each one exactly four times, so that: (a) any two of the thirteen letters being used, chosen at random, will happen to be found in one and only one of the thirteen words; (b) any two of the thirteen words being used, chosen at random, will happen to have one and only one letter in common. Mathematical investigation of the problem reveals that any solution to it must conform to one of two possible patterns:

(a) Dividing the alphabet into 20 consonants and 6 vowels, the 13 words in the group must consist of 4 words containing 3 vowels each, 3 words containing 2 vowels each, and 6 words containing 1 vowel each, with each of the 6 vowels appearing in one of these 6 words. Accordingly, one word must feature Y as the only vowel—a word such as CYST, HYMN, GYPS, SPRY, STYX, or BYRD.

(b) Alternatively, the 13 words in the group must consist of 1 word with four vowels, 1 word with three vowels, 6 words with two vowels, and 5 words with one vowel, selected from any four using *twice* that vowel which appears in both the 3-vowel and the 4-vowel words. For the 4-vowel word, one may pick a word like OUIE (in music, a soundhole), or EIAO (one of the Marquesas Islands in the Pacific), or OUEI (an Egyptian lady, sister of the scribe Thoth who was an overseer of the bulls of Amen-Ra).

Case No. 2 is appreciably more difficult than Case No. 1. The best solution to this problem given in *Recreational Mathematics Magazine* is as follows: AIRY, AUTO, DIEU, LION, OYES, PALE, PITS, PROD, PUNY, RENT, SAND, SLUR, TYLD. The first 12 words are excellent in quality, even if one needs to look OYES up in a dictionary (it means "Hear! Hear ye!"), but the final word, TYLD, is far off the mark, used in the 15th and 16th centuries to designate each of the four cuts or portions into which a quarter of beef may be divided.

If we do some letter juggling of a very high order, we come up with an improved solution that looks like this: AIRY, AUTO, DIEU, KINO, OYES, PANE, PITS, PROD, PUKY, RUNS, SKAD, TREK, TYND. Uncommon but quite acceptable in the revised list are PUKY (inclined to nausea), KINO (short for "kinematograph"), and SKAD (a large number or quantity). That brings us to the final word, TYND, a variant form of "tine" (a prong). This word is one currently in use, but in a very limited section of the English-speaking world—northern England and Scotland. From a selective point of view, this is still not a satisfactory solution, and you are welcome to plunge into Case No. 2 with the anticipation of delivering the needed coup de grâce.

Case No. 3

The third and final version of our problem is the real challenge, and one that has never been investigated. This time, we are required to create a group of 21 five-letter words, using any 21 alphabetic letters of our choice, each one exactly five times, so that: (a) any two of the 21 letters being used, chosen at random, will happen to be found in one and only one of the 21 words; (b) any two of the 21 words being used, chosen at random, will happen to have one and only one letter in common.

We have no solution to offer you, good, bad, or indifferent, nor a more detailed statement of conditions applicable to the problem in practice. This is virgin territory, yours for the taking. . . .

123 *"X" MEANS "UNKNOWN"!*

Coincidence—a remarkable concurrence of events or ideas, apparently by mere chance—has a peculiar effect on the minds of most of us. It sets us to wondering whether the coincidence is really the result of chance, or whether there is an unseen, possibly occult, agency at work intentionally producing it.

Let's start with a very simple coincidence, one that has never been mentioned in print. Go to the map of Washington state and draw a circle in the southwest corner of Snohomish County (an area a little north of Seattle). Place the center of the circle at Merwin, Washington, and give it a radius of ten miles. You will discover that, scattered along or extremely close to the circumference of your circle, are another seven communities, all beginning with the same letter M with which Merwin begins. Reading clockwise around the circumference, we have Monroe, Maltby, Mountlake Terrace, Meadowdale, Mosher, Mukilteo, and Machias.

Is this purely a coincidence, or did some driving, tempestuous logological power, engaged in a love affair with the letter M, willfully bestow "M" names on these eight localities in a corner of Snohomish County? This is the sort of question that excites some logologists, but the research needed to get at the facts in the matter is still waiting to be performed. Interested?

We go on to a coincidence with more mysterious overtones: the case of the disappearing Ambroses.

Ambrose Gwinnett Bierce, American journalist and author—one of his books happens to be included in our "Bibliography"—was born in 1842. On or about November 6, 1913, at the age of 71, he disappeared across the Mexican border at Laredo. He was never seen again. His purpose, not clear from messages he left behind, was either to join Pancho Villa, the Mexican revolutionary leader, or to continue on to South America. It was later alleged, but not proven, by various informants, that Bierce: (a) was killed by Mexican revolutionaries; or (b) was seen in the wilds of South America; or (c) joined the staff of Kitchener's army in war-torn France. Most reference books give Bierce's date of death as "1914(?)".

On December 2, 1919—just six years later—Ambrose Small, owner of the Toronto Opera House, was in his office. Although he was surrounded by assistants, no one saw him leave. That evening, he vanished and was never seen again. His secretary then disappeared, with $105,000 of Small's securities. The secretary was found, tried, and convicted of theft. The evidence to convict him of kidnapping Small was insufficient.

In *Strange Mysteries of Time and Space*, Harold T. Wilkins attributes mystery to the disappearance of Kitchener. In *Wild Talents,* Charles Fort asks, "Was someone collecting Ambroses?" It happens that Ambrose Bierce himself had written short stories about similar disappearances.

The crux of our problem here is this: two prominent men, both named "Ambrose", disappeared in relatively close succession—in 1913 and 1919. Did any other Ambroses also vanish in the decade 1910–1920? If so, was their disappearance a mere coincidence, or was something more sinister involved? For instance, were spaceships from another world on the prowl in the vicinity of Mother Earth, with instructions to snatch men named Ambrose for examination and study on a planet in an alien stellar galaxy? Again, there is a great deal of investigation in store for the right person.

We turn to a third, more recent coincidence. On the leadership level, the two great protagonists of World War II were Franklin D. Roosevelt and Adolf Hitler. Roosevelt assumed office on March 4, 1933 and died on April 12, 1945. Hitler assumed office on January 30, 1933 and died on April 30, 1945. The discrepancy in '33 was 33 days; in '45, it was 18 days.

The third case seems different from the first two. One feels that it would amount to sacrilege to look for a third leader who came to power in 1933 and who died in 1945. Roosevelt and Hitler, symbolizing the Allies and the Axis, were in a class by themselves. It appears that the pinnacles of the forces of good and evil emerged on the world scene at the same moment of time, and vanished at the same moment of time. It appears so, but was it really so? To answer that question authoritatively and finally, one must journey beyond language, into the realms of extrasensory perception, divination, and mysticism. Will you be the possibly solitary traveler on the murky, peril-ridden road into the unknown?

124 *PROXIMITY*

Words display an affinity for each other; they are close to one another. The question up for debate before the house just now is this: how near can words come to each other without actually colliding?

In the "Problems" section of *Beyond Language,* we saw words in collision, as in the case of TANGIER the city and TANGIER the comparative adjective, or POLISH the nationality and POLISH the verb. We shall now attempt a far more difficult maneuver, that of bringing words so close to each other that they almost touch—almost, but not quite.

Let us first lay down some rules of procedure. One basic requirement is that the words being compared do not have a common origin; they must be etymologically unrelated. A second equally important condition is that words may be compared only if they are equal in letter-length.

The rules just enunciated can be illustrated with some short words. BARE and BARK are both four-letter words, unrelated in origin or meaning, making it permissible to compare them. Their first three letters are identical, establishing a certain degree of kinship; their fourth and final letters, E and K, are 6 spaces apart in the alphabet, providing an exact numerical measure of their distance from each other. Closer to BARE than BARK is another unrelated word, BARD. Again, the first three letters are identical, but this time, the fourth letters are only one alphabetic space apart, which is another way of saying that they are in adjacent positions.

Can we locate seven-letter words with the first six letters identical and only the final letters different? Yes, we can. First, there is a trio of words, SHALLOP (an open boat), SHALLOT (a small onion), and SHALLOW. All three words have the same first six letters. On the final, seventh letter, SHALLOP and SHALLOT are 4 spaces apart, while SHALLOT and SHALLOW are only 3 spaces apart.

Surpassing these words in proximity are three other 7-letter word pairs, each characterized by adjacency: COLLIER-COLLIES, STEPPER-STEPPES, and HIDEOUS-HIDEOUT. The latter pair is particularly attractive for the sharp pronunciation change that it offers the viewer.

As in the case of many other forms of wordplay—the construction of word squares, for instance—the 7-letter words constitute a base or plateau from which to fan out in the quest for longer and finer examples of verbal art. Unfortunately, "proximate" words of greater length resist conquest. The only first-rate longer pair that has turned up so far is ASPIRING-ASPIRINS, with the final, eighth letters 12 spaces apart. Two still longer specimens leave much to be desired. One is the case of CORROBORATE and CORROBOREES, two 11-letter words identical through the first 8 letters and four spaces apart on the ninth letter. Corroborees are tribal dances held at night by the Australian aborigines, which is nice for anthropologists to know, but remote from the normal concerns of the rest of us. The other case is that of TANANA RIVER (in eastern Alaska) and TANANARIVES (cities such as Tananarive, capital of the Malagasy Republic on Madagascar). Mathematically, these proximate words are ideal: 11-letter words identical through the first 10 letters and only one space apart on the final letter. In all other respects, however, *everything* is wrong: both terms are proper names, capitalized; one is a two-word term; the other is a pluralized name, using the singular form in a figurative sense; and both names come to us from "native" languages in distant parts of the world, languages beyond the perimeter of the Indo-European language family in which we feel at home.

The example just cited is one in which considerations entirely beyond the field of language—considerations from the realm of esthetics—effectively veto routine logological findings. It is a demonstration of how we are compelled to go outside language, beyond language, for permission to use language!

The longer, more desirable, proximate word pairs and trios are still in the matrix of logology, waiting for someone to extract them. They are waiting . . . for you to bring them out into the sunlight. They, too, are entitled to their day. Can you be so heartless as to ignore their piteous plea for freedom?

125 *THE FATAL FORMULA*

Letters of the alphabet serve us in life . . . and in death.

In France, morticians use a state-determined formula with which to price funerals. Here it is:

$$\frac{P}{PO} = R + B\left(\frac{S}{SO}\right) + C\left(\frac{M}{NO}\right) + B\left(\frac{V}{VA}\right) + A\left(\frac{N}{NA}\right)$$

Some research has established that, in this formula, the term M/NO represents the variation in the price of fodder for the horses that draw the hearse. The exact significance of the remaining terms is an unresolved mystery, which we commend to your tender care.

It has wisely been observed that death is something with which one learns to live. Oh, well!

126 *BROTHERS AND SISTERS*

Brothers and sisters under the skin, we have a problem, a serious one.

Take a German-English dictionary—any one at all will do—and look up the word GESCHWISTER. You will see that it is translated into English as "brothers and sisters". Think of it! English, the richest language ever seen on earth, seems to own no word capable, by itself, of translating the simple, everyday German word GESCHWISTER. To accept the verdict of the dictionaries would humiliate our language beyond words, in a manner of speaking. That is why we have not accepted the verdict, and are fighting back, desperately seeking a word that means "brothers and sisters".

Our first recourse is to a highly esteemed anthropological term, SIBLINGS. Superficially, siblings give the impression of being brothers and sisters, but do not translate the German word adequately, for GESCHWISTER are brothers and sisters considered in relation to each other, while SIBLINGS are considered in relation to the parents they have in common, being children of the same parents though not necessarily of the same birth. Put another way, if I have GESCHWISTER, they are mine; SIBLINGS cannot be mine.

Our second recourse is to GERMANS, of all things. A GERMAN is one's own brother or sister, so that GERMANS are brothers and sisters. Regrettably, the term is faulted on two separate counts: (1) it is obsolete, thus excluded from the speech of today; (2) a GERMAN may also be a first cousin, making the word ambiguous in meaning, whereas no ambiguity whatever attaches to its rival GESCHWISTER.

Our third recourse? We haven't found one yet. This is where you come in. Jump into the breach and save the day! Find a word, a reputable English word, that means "brothers and sisters". Uphold the honor of English!

127 *THE AUTOLOGICAL PHENOMENON*

Some words describe themselves. This is particularly true of adjectives, whose function is to describe or to qualify. Thus, ENGLISH is an English word, making it a self-describing one, and BEVOWELLED is a word containing four vowels, so that it, too, is self-describing. Other elementary examples of self-describing words: ADJECTIVAL, SHORT, POLYSYLLABIC, UNHYPHENATED, MAJUSCULAR. The technical term for self-describing words is "autological words".

It is only a minority of words that are autological. Most words are non-self-describing, or "heterological". For instance, LONG is a short word, and does not describe itself, making it a heterological word. The same is true of MONOSYLLABIC, UNCAPITALIZED, PREPOSITIONAL, TRILITERAL, HYPHENATED, and scores of other words.

Autological and heterological words create a series of problems to which no satisfactory solutions have yet been found, partly because the problems are difficult, partly because no one has investigated them thoroughly as yet. Let's examine some of these problems.

The first problem is one to which some attention has already been devoted, and which is known as "Grelling's paradox". Presumably, all adjectives are either AUTOLOGICAL or HETEROLOGICAL. If we concede the truth of this assumption, then a question immediately arises: is the adjective HETEROLOGICAL an autological or a heterological word? If HETEROLOGICAL is autological, then it is self-descriptive, which contradicts its meaning of not being self-descriptive. If HETEROLOGICAL is heterological, then it is not self-descriptive, which is what the word means, making it autological, or in contradiction to its real meaning.

One way of trying to escape from this paradox is to introduce the rule that words designating a class of words cannot be discussed as members of that class without wreaking havoc with the laws of logic. This is the "metalanguage" approach, explained more fully in connection with Baffler No. 132. However, HETEROLOGICAL is an adjective, and if we are classifying adjectives into two all-embracing groups, the two groups are not a valid division unless the word HETEROLOGICAL can be placed in one of them. We must, therefore, reject such a restriction summarily.

Another means of escape is to assume that there are three kinds of adjectives: autological, heterological, and those to which the first two categories do not apply. Thus, it could be argued that the adjective CREAMY is neither autological nor heterological, for it designates a quality to which the classifications of "autological" and "heterological" don't apply. There are two things wrong with this solution. First, you can exercise your imagination and think of someone writing on a blackboard with cream instead of with chalk. If CREAMY is written with cream, it is autological; if it is written with anything else, it is heterological. No matter what the adjective might be, it is possible to dream up situations in which the distinction between "autological" and "heterological" becomes a meaningful, pertinent one. Second, this solution violates a basic logical principle: if a certain quality is specified, all things either do or do not possess that quality, and no third category is admissible.

We are forced to the conclusion that Grelling's Paradox remains unresolved, at least to the satisfaction of the logologist, whose standards are unusually exacting.

A second aspect of autological and heterological words is that they have heretofore been limited to adjectives. This seems arbitrary and pointless. The word NOUN is a noun; the verb TERMINATE obviously does terminate; the pronoun "it" is the one applicable to the word IT whenever *it* is being discussed, as in this sentence; the adverb POLYSYLLABICALLY must be thought of polysyllabically; and so on. Why limit the distinction between autological and heterological words to adjectives? There is no need for us so to cripple ourselves. Most English words are nouns; since nouns can easily be classified as being or not being self-descriptive, their inclusion widens the scope of autology enormously.

A third aspect of the autological phenomenon, directly concerned with wordplay, is its application to words denoting forms of wordplay. Certainly, a skilled logologist should be able to demonstrate that many of the terms used in wordplay are autological. Here are some illustrations of what can be achieved by the dedicated word expert: ANAGRAM is an anagram of the phrase "a ragman"; TRANSPOSITION is a transposition of "antipositrons", an advanced synonym for "electrons"; CHARADE is just that, divisible into "char" + "ade"; CURTAILMENT is, indeed, a curtailment—of the word "curtailments"; etc. There are scores and scores of such terms, and each must be studied to determine how best it can be made autological.

There is another autological problem, if you'd like to go off into the wild blue yonder. It is possible to construct closed chains of autological words. Thus, ENGLISH is a transposable word (being rearrangeable into "shingle"); TRANSPOSABLE is a long word; LONG is a short word; SHORT is a monosyllabic word; MONOSYLLABIC is a polysyllabic word; POLYSYLLABIC is a Greek-derived word; GREEK-DERIVED is a hyphenated word; and HYPHENATED is an English word. In eight consecutive steps, we have made the circuit from English, through all sorts of other categories, back to English.

Imagine that you place the eight categories at equal distances along the circumference of a circle, and that this circle is entirely on the surface of a sphere: a circle similar to the meridians girdling the globe through the two poles, or to the lines along the outside of a gooseberry. Next, suppose that you construct additional chains of autological words, of the same length, also closed. Design them so that they, too, start and end with ENGLISH, with MONO-SYLLABIC as the link in fifth position. Going back to the globe analogy, you now have a collection of closed autological chains, each of which may be fitted around the globe along meridian lines, with ENGLISH at the North Pole and MONOSYLLABIC at the South Pole. A question arises: how can you space the autological circles so that they will be equidistant from one another at the equator? More fundamentally, what criteria are you going to invoke in order to determine what distance apart at the equator any two given autological circles ought to be?

We have no idea what the answers to these questions are.

128 *THE PENTAGON*

If you are expecting an essay on America's military posture at this point, then you haven't quite caught on to the spirit of *Beyond Language* yet. No; the object here is to study perfection and uniqueness in words.

For the genesis of the "pentagon", we go into elementary mathematics. A perfect number is defined as one the sum of whose divisors, including 1 but excluding itself, is equal to itself. The smallest perfect number is 6, being the sum of 1, 2, and 3. The next larger perfect number is 28, since $28 = 1 + 2 + 4 + 7 + 14$. The third and fourth perfect numbers are 496 and 8128. Beyond that, the size of the perfect numbers increases very rapidly; thus, the ninth perfect number is one of 37 digits.

Two numbers may exhibit the quality of perfection not individually but in relation to each other. A pair of such numbers is known as amicable, or friendly, or sociable. The smallest pair of amicable numbers is 220 and 284.

The divisors of 220 are 1, 2, 4, 5, 10, 11, 20, 22, 44, 55, and 110. The sum of these seven divisors is 284. Conversely or reciprocally, the divisors of 284 are 1, 2, 4, 71, and 142. The sum of these five divisors is 220. Hundreds of pairs of amicable numbers have been discovered; other examples include 1184 and 1210, 2620 and 2924, and 5020 and 5564.

Mr. Howard W. Bergerson, poet-mathematician of the Land of Red Apples°, has been investigating the possibility of finding verbal analogues to amicable numbers. In the course of his researches, he has made a discovery which may prove to be the most remarkable, the most historic, revelation about words in the entire evolution of human thought. We expatiate upon his discovery, as well as on subsequent research on the matter by Rudolph W. Castown of New York and by J. A. Lindon of Addlestone, a community in Surrey, England.

The numerical equivalent of a word is the sum of the positional values of the letters comprising it. The numerical value of IOWA is 48, since I = 9, O = 15, W = 23, and A = 1. For many years, this was a very apt value, Iowa being one of 48 states. Since Hawaii and Alaska were granted statehood, the balance has been disturbed, and a ready solution is not in sight yet.

Are there any perfect number names—numbers whose names have a numerical value equal to the number itself? If we employ the ordinary nomenclature, in which a number such as 459 is designated FOUR HUNDRED FIFTY-NINE, then no perfect number name exists in English. If we adopt an alternate nomenclature, in which 459 is called FOUR HUNDRED AND FIFTY-NINE, two perfect number names appear: those for 251 and 259. If we adopt an altogether different style for naming numbers, one in which 459 is referred to as FOUR-FIVE-NINE, then we find just one perfect number name, the one for 146.

Are there any amicable number names in the ordinary nomenclature? There are no amicable pairs, trios, or foursomes. There is, however, an amicable group of five, an amicable pentagon. The five number names comprising this pentagon are mutually or sequentially amicable:

Number Name	Value
TWO HUNDRED FORTY	216
TWO HUNDRED SIXTEEN	228
TWO HUNDRED TWENTY-EIGHT	288
TWO HUNDRED EIGHTY-EIGHT	255
TWO HUNDRED FIFTY-FIVE	240

° Oregon.

In this sequence, each number name has a numerical value exactly equal to the next number name, and the last number name has a numerical value equal to the first number name, so that a complete, closed set is formed.

Note that the smallest number in the group of five, 216, is exactly 4 less than the lower member of the smallest amicable number pair (220), and that the largest number in the group of five, 288, is exactly 4 greater than the upper member of the smallest amicable number pair (284). A fascinating coincidence!

In the ordinary nomenclature, our pentagon is unique: neither is there any other amicable pentagon, nor is there any other group of mutually amicable number names, whether larger or smaller. It follows that all number names, small or large, without any exception, lead to one of the five names, one of the five "portals", in the pentagon. Let us show you what we mean.

The number name ONE has a numerical value of 34. The name THIRTY-FOUR has a value of 160. The name ONE HUNDRED SIXTY has a value of 205. And so on. If we continue this process, the following number sequence results:

1, 34, 160, 205, 174, 278, 291, 253, 254, 258, 247, 281, 240

The thirteenth number in the series is 240. The chain beginning with ONE has arrived at one of the portals to our pentagon, and will make the circuit of its perimeter for all eternity to come from this point on—over and over and over.

Astonishing as the existence of this pentagon may seem, we do not appreciate its truly extraordinary nature until we realize that not only do all number names lead to it, but so do all English words and names, none excepted. Thus, the words STOMP, FOSTER, and ELISION all have numerical values of 83, leading to the portal 216 (via 130, 208, and 181); the words TROUTY and POTTERY have values of 119 each, leading to the portal 255 (via 194); the words TRUTH, NOTION, and ROLLING all have values of 87, eventually leading to the portal 240; and so forth. Accordingly, the magic pentagon epitomizes the entire English language!

What happens if we number the letters of the alphabet in reverse, from Z = 1 to A = 26? Instead of a unique pentagon, we discover an even more remarkable entity, a unique hexagon, consisting of the numbers 273, 296, 242, 212, 213, 255.

What happens if we seek analogues to our pentagon in foreign languages? In Italian, with its 21-letter, alphabet, a unique heptagon is discovered: 171, 184, 232, 177, 204, 179, 191. There appears to be no unique polygon of amicable number names in French, Spanish, or German, but much larger polygons are observed. Thus, German and Spanish both exhibit 18-sided polygons, and

French a 20-sided polygon, coexisting with smaller polygons and with some perfect number names. As in English, more than one system of naming numbers is possible, leading to various results.

Returning to English, what happens if we replace the conventional number names in each of the name chains that we construct with the names of the numbers into which each named number can be factored? It appears, but has not yet been proved, that a 14-sided polygon, or tessarescaedecagon, of unique status results: 232, 323, 195, 197, 260, 257, 263, 285, 184, 337, 295, 150, 212, 238.

It should be obvious by now that the realm of perfect and amicable number names is an enormous one, and that it has barely been scratched. What is the largest amicable polygon of unique status that can be found in any language, using any of the systems with which we have experimented in English? Is there any language with a unique, perfect number name? What other systems can be devised? What happens if we involve Roman numerals and the names of the numbers they represent? These and other problems are unsolved, some of them even undefined.

You are cordially invited to help explore the unknown.

129 *CALLING ALL OCULISTS!*

We have evidence of the fact that millions of persons are color-blind. The only difficulty is that we're not sure who they are, or why. The evidence? Judge for yourself:

GOLDEN in Spanish (rubio) =
RED in Latin (rubeus)

YELLOW in Slovene (rumen) =
RED in Czech (ruměný)

PURPLE in Portuguese (roxo) =
RED in Spanish (rojo)

RED in Latvian (sarkans) =
YELLOW in Hungarian (sárga)

YELLOW in Albanian (verdhë) =
GREEN in French (vert)

GREEN in Albanian (gjelbër) =
YELLOW in German (gelb)

YELLOW in Low Latin (calthinus) =
BLUE in Albanian (kaltërt)

BLUE in Calabrian (bru) =
BROWN in Catalan (bru)

BLUE in Romanian (albastru) =
WHITISH in Low Latin (albaster)

BLUE in Lithuanian (mēlynas) =
YELLOW in Welsh (melyn) =
BLACK in Greek (mélas)

By some perverse quirk of fate, the single instance in which the two (or three) words in other languages are identical in form (the Calabrian "bru" and the Catalan "bru") is one in which the two words come from different roots. In all other cases, where the word forms differ somewhat, they are traceable to the same ultimate source.

Why do different peoples assign the same name to different colors? Is there a difference in the nature of their color perceptions? Do the names hark back to a time when man's awareness of colors was not as acutely developed as it is today, so that what looked red to people in one region, looked yellow to those in another? Or is there no rational explanation at all for these contradictions?

So far as we know, this problem has never been investigated. It ought to be.

130 *GEOGRAPHIC MNEMONICS*

Over the years, American geography has been getting increasingly burdensome for schoolchildren to master. Take a simple example: states and their capitals. We started out with a mere 13 states, and have gradually built up to 50 states. Memorizing a list of 50 cities matching a list of 50 states, in corresponding order, is quite a strain. Obviously, something must be done.

Professor Cloudesley, in the course of his untiring logological efforts on behalf of a mostly unappreciative humanity, has found a unique mnemonic device for making it easy and enjoyable to commit lists of states and state capitals to memory. The trick is to devise sentences in which the names are buried, properly matched. Take this sentence, for instance:

I mighT EXASperate my beAU, STINGy as I am.

Intelligently read, the sentence informs you that the capital of TEXAS is AUSTIN, which it is.

By no means is this a freak case. Many other such pronouncements have been made. Observe:

The MAIN EVil of the AUGUSTAn age was imperialism.
COLOR A DOll, hoyDEN, VERy neatly and quietly.
WASHING TONs of laundry requires OLYMPIAn powers.
A VIRGIN, I Allure the RICH MONDays and all other days.
"He's ILL!", I NOIse about each SPRING, FIELDing comebacks deftly.
MISSIS, SIP PINk lemonade slowly, but eat flapJACKS ON the double!

Often, it is necessary to introduce personal names into the conversation to achieve the desired effect. Thus:

CaN EVA DAnce outside, with CARS ON CITY streets?
KEN, TUCK Your shirt in and be FRANK, FORThright, and courageous!
DEL, AWARE he is watched, must DO VERy well.
Did MARY LAND as ANNA POLIshed apples?
Go NORTH, CAROL, IN A car owned by FLORA LEIGH.
Still moRE GONgs, AL, EMbarrass us all.
GuM ON TAN Apparel irritates RacHEL, ENAbling her to rant.
Lewis CONS INdians into believing that a noMAD IS ON duty.
AL, ASK Anne and JUNE A Useful question!
LOUIS, IAN, And Eric BAT ON ROUGE-colored playing fields.

Occasionally, it is possible to place the state and its capital directly adjacent to each other:

Are you afraID A HOBO IS Entering your house?

In rapid succession, we have listed for you Professor Cloudesley's 18 creations. Unfortunately, Cloudesley was sidetracked to a more important project, that of writing a creed for The Logological Institute of America, before finishing his humanitarian task, and we find ourselves stuck. Accordingly, we are passing the buck to you, asking readers to draft the corresponding mnemonic sentences for the remaining 32 states. For those who decide to respond to our appeal, the ground rules are to construct sentences of the same general type as the fine specimens provided by Cloudesley. In particular, you must stay within the same "lucky" limitations imposed by the Professor—a minimum of seven words, a maximum of eleven. In other words, seven come eleven!

Cloudesley's Creed? Truly, one designed to inspire AWE:

1. <u>A</u>sk and you shall receive.
2. <u>W</u>ishing will make it so.
3. <u>E</u>verything comes to him who waits.

This Creed, formally adopted by the LIA, has since become the cornerstone of the logological way of life. May it spread to other areas of activity!

131 *THE ANTIFREQUENCY CRUSADE*

It is generally conceded that the four least commonly used letters in the English language are J, Q, X, and Z. The challenge that this fact poses for the true word lover is almost self-evident: find a word that contains all four of these letters!

Much ingenuity has been invested in the search for such a word, with little in the way of tangible results. So as to give you some idea of the problems involved, we list and explain some of our nonsuccesses:

1. Assume that the first woman Senator in the United States had been the Honorable *Jezebel Quixote*. How thrilling it would have been to discover the four desired letters in this most implausible name! Unfortunately, there seems never to have been a Senator, or any other prominent person, known as Jezebel Quixote. O *exquisite Jezebel*, you were not meant to be!

2. Maltese, the Semitic language of the Maltese people, an ancient dialect of Arabic with Italian elements, now written in Latin characters, is full of weird and promising words such as MXAQQAQ ("cracked"), MŻEWWAQ ("speckled"), and QŻEJQEŻ ("piglet"). But does it feature the word we are seeking? Apparently not; the closest approach is the Maltese term for the plant called a "bladder campion" in English: HAXIXA QASQAJŻA. The four letters are there, but distributed among two separate words.

3. There ought to be a term in chemistry something on the order of *oxyazojequiritol*, or of *diazadidesoxyjonquillin*. There ought to be, but doesn't seem to be. The best we've been able to locate up to now is a horribly compound term, *4-oxazolo [ij] quinolinium*, which hardly corresponds to our idea of a "word".

4. An extremely entertaining book about word games recently published, John G. Fuller's *Games for Insomniacs* (Doubleday & Company, Inc., Garden City, New York, 1966), quotes a large number of pangrammatic sentences, one of which uses the coined word *Zedfkjhgrbqctswvxypmln*. Not only does this word include the "fatal four", but it has all 20 consonants of our alphabet, with 15 of them occurring in successive positions. Sad to relate, it is impossible to determine from the context just what this word means or to what language it is to be attributed. All we are told is that it is something that can be owed us by one of the emerging nations.

5. A little book of double word square puzzles published in England some years ago, by an author using the pseudonym "Jax", is entitled "Story of 'The Jax Square' and 100 Jax Square Puzzles". The little poems inserted into the text of this publication invariably spell the name of the puzzle as "Jaxsquare". The plural of that name is, of course, *"Jaxsquares"*. The final S in the plural is pronounced like a Z. Phonetically, we have achieved our goal, within the context of a coined word. A good deal remains to be desired.

6. Years ago, one W. E. Beard authored a pamphlet on military codes, using as a title the words "military ciphers" as enciphered in a special U. S. Naval Code: YIYKAEJR GZQSYWX. Once again, our quadruplets are present, but split between two words.

7. In the summer of 1958, certain facts came to light regarding the big-money television quiz shows then on the air. As a result of these disclosures, all of the shows were cancelled within a few months. The revelations may aptly be described as having been of a *quiz-jinxing* nature. We have another candidate for the supreme honor, but must reject it on the grounds that it is both a coined word and a hyphenated one.

   The true logologist is never daunted. The search for a bona fide J-Q-X-Z word goes on, day and night.

132   *TOPPED!*

Let us consider all numbers to which names have been assigned—large and small, positive and negative, rational and irrational, real and imaginary, finite and transfinite. Let us select all of those numbers possessing names that

can be represented in writing with the use of not more than fifty characters—
letters, numerals, punctuation marks, and mathematical symbols. Let us consider that one of the selected numbers which is larger than any other selected
number. Let us refer to it as the largest number written with fifty characters.

Let us now add the number one to this largest number. The increased
number may therefore be designated by means of the following expression:

The largest number written with fifty characters, plus one

A careful count shows that the number of characters used in designating the
increased number is exactly fifty. Consequently, the first number that we
described as being the largest number written with fifty characters wasn't the
largest such number at all; it is our second number that must be so described.

Obviously, we may choose to add the number one to our new largest
number, going through the same procedure, and we may repeat the process
ad infinitum: each number, as soon as it is designated largest, can be proved
not to be largest.

There is a problem here, the solution to which is not clear at all. Since
the problem purports to concern numbers, it has been studied by a good many
mathematicians, and has come to be known as the Richard Paradox or as the
Skolem Paradox, after two of these mathematicians.

Have mathematicians been able to resolve this paradox? They have tried,
but without success. One so-called solution of the paradox is to decree that all
the numbers considered as candidates for the honor of being the largest one
constitute a set, and that a number which must be defined in terms of the set,
by reference to the set, is a different type of number which it is not permissible to consider. All of the numbers originally considered were definable without referring to the set they comprise; the larger numbers are not. The principle
invoked here states that numbers can belong to different hierarchies, and if we
mix numbers of different hierarchies, paradoxes will result.

Elegant phraseology has been invented to keep the two categories of number names apart. The first set of names belongs to an "object language" that is
being talked about. The second set of names belongs to a different language,
the "metalanguage", which is used to talk about, or to investigate, words in the
object language.

What has actually been done here? We don't want to accept the larger
numbers, because they create a seemingly insoluble problem; so, we exile
them. Unfortunately, banishing what we don't like does not cause it to cease

existing. The ostracized numbers remain to taunt us, by their mere existence.

No satisfactory solution to the paradox has yet been found. The real problem is not a mathematical one; rather, it is central to pure thought.

Think!

133 *THE UNCERTAINTY PRINCIPLE*

It is easy enough to solve some word problems. The difficulty or impossibility lies in proving that the solution obtained is correct. To illustrate our thesis, let's study a question we posed a few years ago: what are the alphabetically first and last place names in the United States?

After quite a bit of investigation, we came up with AA JUNCTION and with ZYLONITE as answers. AA JUNCTION is at the southern border of Johnson County, Arkansas, south-southwest of Clarksville, the county seat. ZYLONITE is in Berkshire County, Massachusetts. It is in the northern part of the county, and is officially part of the town of Adams.

How did we know that there was no name in the country preceding AA JUNCTION or following ZYLONITE? We didn't know because there was no way of knowing with absolute certainty; a complete list of all American place names, past and present, does not exist. All atlases, gazetteers, and other geographic reference works ever compiled are *partial* listings.

It was not too long before our complacency about the solution to this problem evaporated under a barrage of discoveries. First, we ran across ZYPHO, West Virginia, alleged to have been somewhere in Harrison County. Next, our attention was drawn to ZYRZA, Georgia, in Putnam County, near Eatonton. Then, we lit upon a name remarkable enough to make one's head swim: ZZYZX SPRINGS, California. A map published by the Automobile Club of Southern California, covering San Bernardino County, shows and indexes the community as being about 8½ miles south of Baker, on the western edge of Soda Dry Lake. It is off the abandoned right-of-way of the old Tonopah and Tidewater Railroad, and is both a hydrologic feature and a privately owned spa catering to the senior citizen.

Things were not too peaceful at the other end of the alphabet, either. In Massachusetts, on the western shore of Buzzards Bay, east-northeast of

Mattapoisett, there is a cove given as AACOOT COVE in an 1893 Rand McNally atlas. More recent atlases, however, show the name as the more prosaic AUCOOT COVE. While we were puzzling over this discrepancy, an even better location came to hand—AABYE, Minnesota, in the southwestern part of Norman County, near Perley.

There the matter rests—for the moment. Who is to say that AABYE and ZZYZX SPRINGS are the real first and last names in America? Consider the AABYE situation, for instance. How many names are there which could theoretically precede AABYE?

That depends on the number of letters in the name. There could be 1 one-letter name, 1 two-letter name, and 2 three-letter names (A, AA, AAA, and AAB). Beyond this point, the number of possibilities increases very rapidly. There are 51 possible four-letter names preceding AABYE, ranging from AAAA to AABY, and 1304 such five-letter names (from AAAAA to AABYD). Now, the number increases by a straight factor of 26: there are 33,904 possible six-letter names preceding AABYE, 881,504 seven-letter names, etc. Since some geographic names in the United States are spelled with as many as 45 letters, the total number of possibilities staggers the imagination.

The same situation prevails at the other end of the alphabet, with a fantastic number of names that could lie beyond ZZYZX SPRINGS, just as improbable, or possibly more so, than the name ZZYZX SPRINGS itself.

There is virtually no limit to the number of maps and name indexes that could be consulted in the search for record-breaking names. Certainly, one lifetime would not suffice, and no matter what marvels were uncovered, uncertainty would *always* remain—further searching might reveal still greater extremes.

This is the challenge of words.

134 *THE SUN IS OUR UNDOING!*

For an Oriental problem, we turn to Uruguay. (An *Oriental* problem? Yes—the full name of our South American neighbor is "República *Oriental* del Uruguay". Locally, the country is sometimes called the "Banda *Oriental*".)

The flags of the various nations have an attraction for young and old alike, probably because of their colorfulness and historical and patriotic associations. The flag of Uruguay is no exception. The present flag of that nation, adopted in July, 1830, features nine horizontal stripes, five white and four blue, the colors alternating. In the upper left corner of the flag is a small white area, a "canton", containing a yellow or golden rising sun insignia—a sun badge known as the "Sun of May", the symbol of Uruguayan independence. Streaming out in every direction from this sun are sun rays.

The flag of Uruguay, and especially the sun badge on it, have been our undoing. We have studied pictures of Uruguay's flag in 20 different reference sources (dictionaries, encyclopedias, atlases, etc.). *No two* of these pictures are alike!

Let's begin with the four blue stripes. Six pictures show pale blue stripes; two show a medium blue; ten show a very dark blue; one makes the stripes bluish-red; one makes them bluish-gray. Of these five colors, which is the true color?

How many rays does the "Sun of May" have? Two of our pictures show twenty rays. Ten pictures show sixteen rays. Eight pictures show eight principal rays, with several times that many shorter rays filling in the spaces between the long rays. How many should there be?

In the center of the rising sun insignia there is a sun face. On thirteen of the flags, the eyes in that face seem to be looking straight ahead. On four of the flags, those eyes are definitely looking toward the left, while on three flags, they are clearly glancing toward the right. Are they living eyes, shifting their gaze from time to time?

Each flag has a nose on the sun face. No two flags draw the bottom line of that nose in the same way. Here are some of the outlines we observed in our study:

What *should* the bottom outline of that nose look like?

There are other differences. On most flags, the sun is a relatively pale yellow or gold. One flag, however, makes it a very dark gold, and three have it speckled with tiny red dots. The shapes of the sun rays differ: on some flags, they tend to be shaped like isosceles triangles, on others they are needle-shaped. The exact size and shape of the white canton differ from one flag to another, as do the relative dimensions of the entire flag. Etc., etc., ad infinitum.

What is the truth behind this medley of false appearances? What does the real flag of Uruguay look like? Up to now it has been so well concealed from the public that absolutely no one has been able to reproduce it! Is there a real flag? Perhaps Uruguay has no flag; this would be the simplest way of explaining why no two books seem ever to have published the same picture of that flag.

If a solution to this problem exists, wouldn't it be interesting to try and find that solution?

Those shifting eyes haunt us. Alone at night, we can feel them watching us, following our every movement, ready to strike if we drop our guard even for a moment. HELP!!! THE EYES OF URUGUAY ARE AFTER US!!!

135 *INTERSECTION POINTS*

Somewhere out there, intersection points exist—points at which different areas of human thought converge and collide. Let us explore one of these intersections, the meeting place of logology, art, and mysticism.

Think of Rembrandt, the 17th-century Dutch painter and etcher; Rembrandt Harmenszoon van Rijn, to quote his full name. Think of an etching by Rembrandt, believed to be dated 1652, and variously titled *The Magician, Doctor Faustus*, or *Faust in His Study, Watching a Magic Disc;* or, more prosaically, as "Hind Catalog No. 260".

The etching shows Faust standing in his laboratory—he has evidently just gotten up from his chair—watching an effulgent magic disc or circle that has suddenly appeared in the lower center of a casement window to his right. A shadowy hand is pointing to a reflection of the radiant disc in a mirror held by another hand below. On the disc itself are three concentric, anagrammatic letter circles. The outermost circle reads ALGASTNA ✠ AMRTET ✠ ALGAR; the middle circle, DAGERAM ✠ ADAM ✠ TE; and the innermost circle, I N R I.

The letters I N R I are obviously an abbreviation for the Latin title IESUS NAZARENUS, REX IUDAEORUM ("Jesus of Nazareth, King of the Jews"). Of what, however, are the letter combinations in the other two circles anagrams? It has been very difficult to explain this etching, and only a relatively short time ago was it discovered that Rembrandt had taken this cabalistic anagram from an amulet to which magic power was attributed. Moreover, in the practice of magic, the mirror at which Faust is looking signifies the hidden side of the world. This mirror is pointed out to Faust by an apparition emanating from but concealed by the luminous disc. It is possible that Rembrandt had learned the secret of the anagram from a neighbor, Samuel Menasseh ben Israel, who was deeply interested in the occult. Whether or not Rembrandt knew its meaning, he used the magic formula to suggest unknown powers, thereby pointing to the errors of Faust. The First Epistle to the Corinthians (13:12) states, in part: "For now we see through a glass, darkly; but then face to face . . .". It seems as though Rembrandt, pondering this line, wished to make clear that Faust did not share in the divine revelation.

These speculations, absorbing as they are, do not answer the specific question as to what has been anagrammed on the disc at which Faust is gazing. Original prints of the etching may be inspected both at the Metropolitan Museum of Art and at the Pierpont Morgan Library, in New York City.

It is surely irrelevant, yet noteworthy, that all of the letters in AMSTERDAM, the name of the city in which Rembrandt resided from the age of 25 on, can be taken out of the letters in the two outer circles, as can all of the letters in the name REMBRANDT itself, with the exception of the B. If we remove all these letters, those that remain do not lend themselves to any meaningful arrangement. Some of the individual letter groupings can be transposed into Latin words, but most unconnectedly. Thus, TE is a reversal of ET ("and"); ADAM is a cyclic transposal of DAMA ("fallow-deer"); ALGAR is an ordinary transposition of LARGA ("abundant, plentiful"); and so on.

The anagram, after 315 years or so, remains a cabalistic conundrum. Does it inspire you to try your own hand at it?

136 *THEORY AND PRACTICE*

Science and mathematics are replete with subjects originally developed for their theoretical interest only, but which subsequently proved to have important practical applications. Thus, much astronomical information considered of no practical use until very recently, has suddenly become crucially important in connection with space travel.

We want to believe that this is the situation in which major aspects of wordplay such as palindromes, anagrams, and word squares find themselves. Up to now, no one has turned these pastimes to practical use. The time is at hand to do so. Riding the wave of the future, can you contribute to the progress and welfare of mankind by adding palindromes, anagrams, and word squares to the portfolio of what might be termed applied linguistics? Posterity will be grateful to you, if you can.

It might be possible to give wordplay commercial standing by creating games based on it, but that is not exactly what we have in mind. Its use in aptitude tests or in government ciphers would be more to the point; surely, all sorts of other applications can be found.

To refresh your mind, a palindrome is a word or sentence which reads the same backward as it does forward, viewed literatim. The phrase SO MANY DYNAMOS is a palindrome, as is the following poem, *Edna Waterfall*, by Mr. Howard Bergerson of Sweet Home, Oregon. You may read this 1034-letter poem from the end just as well as from the beginning:

> Deliver no evil, avid diva I saw die.
> Render an unsung aria for erotogenic id.
> O never egg Alec Naif, fairer Edna Waterfall,
> A nonassimilative, volatile reef-dweller—apparelless brag!
> Natasha I saw die, render an unsung aria.
> For Edna Waterfall—a liar—familiar feuds live:
> Dastard Ogre and Edna!
> Pupils, one tacit song or poem—or didos deft.
> Celestial lives (Ida rapt as Naomi)
> Laud smegma, alas—keep never a frondlet on.
> So did no solo snoop malign
> Irised sad eyen. Oh dewed yen—
> Oh tressed May noon, hello! Tacit songs rev!
> Love's barge of assent carts base tarts,
> A cerise deb abed, unreined flesh.
> Sin—a viand—Edna sees and Edna has,
> Or bust fossettes, or redder rosettes.
> Soft sub-rosa hand Edna sees,
> And, Edna, I vanish—self-denier!
> Nude babe, desire castrates abstractness.
> A foe grab's Evolver's Gnostic Atoll, eh? No!
> On, yam, (dessert-honeydewed), honeyed as desiring!
> I lampoon solos on didos. Not eld nor far
> (Even peek! "Salaam, gems dual", I moan)
> Sat Paradise Villa, its elect fed.

So did Romeo prognosticate no slipup,
And Edna, ergo, drats a devil's due:
"Frail! I'm a frail all a-fret, a-wander!
"O fair Agnus nun, a red Nereid was I.
"Ah Satan, garb's seller,
"Apparel (lewd fee) relit a love vital I miss anon.
"All a-fret, a wanderer I affiance—
"Lagger even odic—in ego 'torero'.
"Fair Agnus nun, a red Nereid was I.
"Avid diva, live on reviled."

The proper interpretation of this poem might well afford the basis for an advanced course in English Literature.

An anagram, the second subject brought forward for your deepest thought, is the rearrangement of the letters in a word, name, or phrase into an appropriate description of, or comment upon, itself. For instance, THE UNITED STATES OF AMERICA may be anagrammed into the description, A SITE FOR EACH DESTITUTE MAN; the slogan, TURN THE RASCALS OUT! may be synonymized anagrammatically as OUST THE TARNAL CURS!; and ETERNAL DEVOTION elicits the comment, I NOTE ARDENT LOVE.

Certainly, anagrams have already made themselves felt in history. To cite just a few instances, a Florentine poet, AGOSTINO COLTELINI, 1613–1693, anagrammed his name into an apt pseudonym, OSTILIO CONTALEGNI; a Frenchman, ANDRE PUJON, upon discovering that he could anagram his name into PENDU A RION ("hanged at Rion"), went out and committed murder so that he might be hanged at Rion, the seat of criminal justice in Auvergne; and Thomas Billon acquired such skill as a maker of anagrams that Louis XIV of France gave him a pension and appointed him "Anagrammatist to the King". With *your* imaginative assistance, the future of anagrams looks bright, indeed.

```
A M E N D S              R A S C A L
M I N I O N              A C T I V E
E N A B L E              S T A G E S
N I B B L E              C I G A R S
D O L L A R              A V E R S E
S N E E R S              L E S S E N
```

Word squares, the third area of wordplay advanced for mature consideration on your part, are letter arrays such as those depicted here, forming a set of words that may be read both horizontally and vertically. They may be constructed in any desired size from 2 x 2 to 10 x 10; those shown are each 6 x 6. The construction of a word square, especially one of larger size, requiring the use of less common words, an "art formative", is a mental exercise that not only embraces the victory of conquest but adds the decided advantage of enriching the mind with a varied and pleasing assemblage of facts, words, and knowledge that no other course of reasoning or study, in the same time, can possibly produce. The wide grasp of English involved, the necessary development of analytical tendencies and close reasoning, the exhaustion of obscure references in search of needed words, satisfaction only with completeness, cultivation of rapid reading and thinking habits—these and other facets of word square construction provide an education without match, training the mind to correct and logical modes of thinking, the practical application of which, in everyday affairs, proves a valuable asset.

We have made somewhat random suggestions. It is for you to follow them out, or to use them as inspirations for new and superior ideas of your own. In any event, there is an enormous potential inherent in wordplay, waiting to be harnessed for the benefit of humanity.

137 *ZERO REDUNDANCY!*

The advent of modern computer technology has created an intense interest in communication and information theory, and a not inconsiderable amount of material on this subject has been published in recent years. An excellent treatment of the subject is to be found in *The Mathematical Theory of Communication* by Claude E. Shannon and Warren Weaver (University of Illinois Press, Urbana, 1964).

Communication theory has interesting offshoots, one of which deals with crossword puzzles. The obligation devolves upon us to acquaint ourselves with the findings of the technological experts, and to evaluate those findings against a logological background.

In English text, letters do not follow one another in purely random order. For example, the letter Q is almost always followed by a U, almost never by other letters. Likewise, the letter B, except at the end of one unit of a multiunit word, is usually followed by A, E, I, L, O, R, U, or Y; very rarely by D, H, J, or W; and virtually never by other letters. Many other instances of nonrandomness could be adduced—as a reader of English, you are familiar with them.

Statistically, the existing situation may be described by using the terms "redundancy" and "relative entropy". To the extent to which letters exhibit nonrandom, consistently recurring patterns, they are said to be characterized by redundancy. In complementary fashion, to the extent to which letters occur randomly, they are characterized by relative entropy. A choice of letters in the process of writing words that proves to conform to observed statistical patterns is redundant; a choice of letters that is truly random, that is a free choice in actuality as well as in appearance, comes under the heading of relative entropy.

Languages differ in degree of redundancy. One language, on the average, may be 25% redundant, another 60% redundant. If the degree of redundancy is 25%, the degree of relative entropy will be 75%; if the degree of redundancy is 60%, the degree of relative entropy will be 40%. The sum of the two percentages must always be unity, by definition.

Shannon has applied several tests to English, and established that it is approximately 50% redundant, possibly a trifle more. This means that about one half of the letters we write are statistically predetermined by the letters immediately preceding them, while the balance—just barely one half—may be regarded as freely chosen by us, untrammeled by a compulsion to conform to statistical laws.

There are exceptions, of course. Thus, text written in Basic English is more redundant than ordinary English, and the text of *Finnegans Wake*, by James Joyce, is less so.

Shannon has applied his theory to the construction of crossword puzzles, and has formulated these conclusions:

(1) In a language with 50% redundancy, it is just possible to construct crossword puzzles in sufficient number and size to make them a popular pastime.

(2) In a language 80% redundant, the construction of crossword puzzles would be so difficult that not enough of them could be produced to turn them into a national hobby.

(3) In a language only 33% redundant, it would be possible to construct, not merely the conventional two-dimensional crossword puzzles, but also three-dimensional puzzles.

(4) In a language with zero redundancy, *all* arrays of letters would be potential crossword puzzles.

The tendency of life runs counter to that of the physical universe. In the universe, which apparently conforms to the second law of thermodynamics, energy is diffused and dissipated with the passage of time. In life, the course of time sees the evolution of ever higher forms, representing successively more concentrated energy foci.

As in life, so in language. The statistically observed 50% redundancy of English is a challenge to the logologist to demonstrate that it is possible to reduce that redundancy to zero. For our final "Baffler", we have set down a record of our attempt to achieve zero redundancy. The attempt qualifies as a "Baffler" because it has not been entirely successful. However, we have come so far along the road to our goal as to know that success is possible, and will eventually be achieved. It is only a matter of time. You may wish to take up the cause where we have left off.

The first letter of a word may be any one of 26. This is equally true of the second letter. Consequently, a word may begin with any one of 676 two-letter combinations—in theory. Our task today is to transform theory into actuality, if we only can.

Let us examine *Webster's Third New International Dictionary of the English Language* (1961), and see how many of the 676 combinations are represented there. In going through Webster's Third Edition, we must exclude some of the entries we run across: abbreviations and symbols; two-word phrases such as G SUIT, where the first word consists of one letter; hyphenated words such as N-TUPLE, where the hyphen separates the first two letters; terms in which the first several letters are obviously initials, as is true in the case of BCG VACCINE, where the first three letters stand for "bacillus Calmette-Guérin"; and a number of miscellaneous letter collocations which sober reflection recognizes as not being representative of English letter sequences.

Subject to the restrictions enumerated, we have compiled a list of valid letter combinations represented in Webster's Third Edition, showing one example for each, taken from that dictionary. Our tabulation, comprehending 384 of the possible 676 combinations, follows, labeled "Exhibit A". The single entry open to debate is the one beginning with xx ("xx-disease"). We chose to include it because of its extreme rarity. If you feel that it violates either the letter or the spirit of our restrictions, strike it out. The other 383 entries in Exhibit A are, like Caesar's wife, above suspicion.

Exhibit A

AA — aardvark	AH — ahead	AO — aorta
AB — about	AI — airplane	AP — apple
AC — across	AJ — ajar	AQ — aquarium
AD — address	AK — akimbo	AR — artist
AE — aerial	AL — alone	AS — assert
AF — after	AM — among	AT — attic
AG — again	AN — angry	AU — author

AV — avenue	EB — ebony	GU — gullible
AW — awaken	EC — echo	GW — gwyniad
AX — axiom	ED — edge	GY — gypsy
AY — ayes	EE — eerie	HA — harpoon
AZ — azalea	EF — effect	HE — health
BA — baboon	EG — eggplant	HH — hheth
BD — bdellium	EH — ehretia	HI — hijack
BE — because	EI — eight	HJ — hjelmite
BH — Bhutan	EJ — ejection	HO — hour
BI — binder	EK — eking	HS — hsin
BL — black	EL — elbow	HU — hungry
BO — bonnet	EM — empty	HW — hwan
BR — break	EN — enough	HY — hyacinth
BU — bubble	EO — eonism	IA — iambic
BW — bwana	EP — epidemic	IB — ibis
BY — bygone	EQ — equal	IC — icicle
CA — candy	ER — erase	ID — ideal
CE — ceiling	ES — escape	IE — ieie
CH — chair	ET — ether	IF — iffy
CI — civil	EU — euphony	IG — ignore
CL — clock	EV — every	IH — ihleite
CN — cnidaria	EW — ewer	II — iiwi
CO — coast	EX — extra	IJ — ijolite
CR — credit	EY — eyebrow	IK — ikon
CS — csardas	FA — factor	IL — illegal
CT — ctenoid	FE — feeling	IM — immoral
CU — curious	FI — field	IN — innocent
CW — cwm	FJ — fjord	IO — iodine
CY — cyclone	FL — flag	IP — ipecac
CZ — czarist	FO — forgive	IQ — Iquito
DA — daisy	FR — fresh	IR — iron
DE — dealt	FU — furious	IS — island
DG — dghaisa	FY — fylfot	IT — itself
DH — dhole	GA — gazelle	IU — Iulus
DI — divide	GB — Gbari	IV — ivory
DJ — djebel	GD — Gdansk	IW — iwan
DN — Dnepropetrovsk	GE — geology	IX — ixodid
DO — dozen	GH — ghostly	IY — iynx
DR — dreamy	GI — girl	IZ — izard
DU — duality	GJ — gjetost	JA — jacket
DV — dvandva	GL — glass	JE — jelly
DW — dwarf	GM — gmelinite	JH — jharal
DY — dynamo	GN — gnash	JI — jingle
DZ — dzeren	GO — goodness	JN — jnana
EA — eager	GR — green	JO — joint

JU — juice
JY — jyngine
KA — kangaroo
KE — keeper
KH — khaki
KI — kiss
KJ — Kjeldahl
KL — kleenex
KM — Kmer
KN — knife
KO — kodak
KP — Kpelle
KR — kraal
KS — Kshatriya
KT — kthibh
KU — kudos
KV — kvass
KW — Kwangtung
KY — kyphosis
LA — laziness
LE — league
LH — Lhasa
LI — light
LJ — Ljubljana
LL — llama
LO — location
LU — luckless
LV — Lvov
LW — Lwena
LY — lyric
MA — maiden
MB — mbori
MC — McKay
MD — Mdewakanton
ME — meadow
MH — mhometer
MI — milky
ML — mlechchha
MN — mnemonic
MO — money
MP — Mpondo
MR — Mrus
MS — msasa
MU — murder
MW — mwami

MY — mystery
MZ — Mzabite
NA — nameless
ND — Ndebele
NE — negative
NG — ngege
NH — Nhang
NI — ninety
NJ — njave
NK — Nkole
NO — nominal
NR — nritya
NS — nsambya
NT — nth
NU — number
NY — nylon
OA — oatmeal
OB — obey
OC — ocean
OD — oddity
OE — Oedipus
OF — offer
OG — ogre
OH — Ohio
OI — oilman
OJ — Ojibwa
OK — okapi
OL — olive
OM — ominous
ON — onward
OO — oozing
OP — operation
OQ — oquassa
OR — oracle
OS — ostrich
OT — otherwise
OU — outrage
OV — overtake
OW — owlish
OX — oxblood
OY — oyster
OZ — ozone
PA — package
PE — peaceful
PF — pfennig

PH — phlox
PI — piccolo
PL — Platonic
PN — pneumonia
PO — pocket
PR — precious
PS — psyche
PT — Ptolemy
PU — pulpit
PW — Pwos
PY — pygmy
QA — qasida
QE — qeri
QI — qibla
QO — qoph
QR — qre
QU — queer
QY — Qyrghyz
RA — rabbit
RE — reality
RH — rheumatic
RI — rigid
RO — roach
RS — rsi
RT — rta
RU — rubbery
RW — Rwala
RY — rye
SA — salty
SB — Sbrinz
SC — scholar
SD — sdrucciola
SE — selfless
SF — sferics
SG — sgabello
SH — shadowy
SI — silence
SJ — sjogrenite
SK — skeleton
SL — slender
SM — smirk
SN — snooze
SO — soapy
SP — speaker
SQ — squelch

SR — sravaka	UI — uinal	XE — xebec
ST — stadium	UJ — uji	XH — Xhosa
SU — sumac	UK — ukulele	XI — xiphoid
SV — svelte	UL — ulcer	XM — Xmas
SW — swinish	UM — umbrella	XO — xoanon
SY — system	UN — universe	XR — Xray
SZ — szmikite	UP — uplift	XT — Xtra
TA — talent	UR — urchin	XU — xurel
TC — tchaviche	US — useful	XX — xx-disease
TE — teaspoon	UT — utopia	XY — xylophone
TF — tfillin	UV — uveal	YA — yawn
TH — theme	UW — uwarowite	YC — yclept
TI — timeless	UX — uxorial	YE — yellow
TJ — tjaele	UZ — uzarin	YF — yfere
TL — tlaco	VA — vaccine	YI — yield
TM — tmesis	VE — velvet	YL — ylang-ylang
TN — tnoyim	VI — vicar	YN — ynambu
TO — topmost	VL — vlei	YO — yodel
TR — treason	VO — vocal	YP — yperite
TS — tsantsa	VR — vrille	YT — ytterbium
TU — tulip	VU — vulture	YU — yucca
TW — twinge	VY — vying	ZA — zany
TY — typist	WA — warlike	ZD — Zdarsky tent
TZ — tzigane	WE — weapon	ZE — zealous
UA — uakari	WH — wheel	ZH — Zhdanov
UB — ubiquity	WI — wizard	ZI — zigzag
UC — ucuuba	WO — wormy	ZL — zloty
UD — udder	WR — wrathful	ZO — zodiac
UF — ufer	WU — wulfenite	ZU — zucchini
UG — ugliness	WY — Wyoming	ZW — zwieback
UH — uhlan	XA — xanthic	ZY — zygote

Exhibit A reflects one further restriction, arbitrarily imposed for esthetic reasons: two-letter words such as EH and BS were excluded. The number of combinations omitted from the Exhibit as a result of this restriction is very small.

Using just one dictionary, we have conquered 384 of the 676 combinations theoretically possible, leaving 292 open. This is a redundancy of only 43.2%, better than Shannon's 50% figure. It stands to reason that, by examining other reference works, our redundancy percentage can be reduced materially. Let us cull what we can from three other dictionaries published in recent years:

(1) *The New Century Cyclopedia of Names*, 3 volumes, Appleton-Century-Crofts, Inc., New York, 1954.

(2) *Musical Instruments: A Comprehensive Dictionary*, by Sibyl Marcuse; Doubleday & Company, Inc., Garden City, New York, 1964.

(3) *Handbook of American Indians North of Mexico*, 2 volumes, by Frederick Webb Hodge; Rowman and Littlefield, Inc., New York, 1965.

A study of these three sources provides us with words and names for 127 of the 292 open combinations. Our findings are tabulated in Exhibit B. Accordingly, only 165 unsolved combinations remain, reducing our redundancy to 24.4%, well below the level at which three-dimensional crossword puzzles become possible.

Exhibit B

BJ — Bjerknes	HR — Hrvatska	NN — Nni-ottiné
BS — bsura	HV — Hvar	NP — Npuitcin
BZ — bzura	JJ — jjembe	NQ — Nquabe
CC — Ccapac Yupanqui	JL — Jlaacs	NV — nvatt
CG — Cgwálikc	JS — Jsleta	NW — Nwanati
CK — Ckūtc	KC — Kcäl tana	NX — nxonxoro
CP — Cpuzum	KF — Kfwetragottine	NZ — Nzima
CQ — Cqague	KG — Kgatla	PK — Pkíwi-léni
CV — Cvijić	KK — Kkhaltel	QC — Qȼāsi úɳȼiⁿ
DB — dbang-dung	KQ — Kqlĭm-kwaic	QD — Qdhasi ukdhiⁿ
DC — Dȼe-tú	KX — Kxalxadi	QL — Qltlâsen
DL — Długosz	LC — Lctāmēctîx	QM — Qmuskīem
DM — Dmitri	LD — lda-man	QN — Qnicapous
DS — Dschagga	LG — Lgulaq	QQ — Qqichua
DT — 'Dtinnè	LK — Lkamtcin	QS — Qsâloqul
EZ — Ezra	LQ — Łqoayedî	QT — Qtlumi
FF — Ffestiniog	LR — Lrak	QV — Qvivira
FH — Fhear Monach	LT — Ltaoten	QW — Qwathi
FT — Fthiotis	LX — Lxor	RB — rbairbe
FW — Fwaha	MF — Mfumbiro	RC — Rchūch-ēdi
GC — Gcaleka	MJ — Mjöllnir	RG — Rgwe
GF — Gfeller	MK — mkinda	RJ — Rjukanfoss
GP — Gpaughettes	MM — mmanga	RK — rkan-gling
GQ — Gqunukhwebe	MT —Mtsensk	RN — rnga-ch'un
HL — Hlavi	MV — Mvele	RR — Rrayados
HM — Hmĭsĭs	NB — nbogoi	RX — Rxö-yinĕs tûnnĕ
HN — hne	NC — Nchumburu	RZ — Rzhev
HP — hpa si	NL — nlambula	SS — Ssángha-kŏn

sx — Sxqómic   vn — Vnnagoungos   ym — Ymir
tb — Tbilisi   vp — Vpelois   yq — Yquitos
td — Tda-bo   vs — Vsetín   yr — Yriarte
tg — Tguas   vt — Vtiangue   ys — Ysleta
tk — Tkuayaum   wd — Wd*o*w*o*   yv — Yvetot
tp — Tpelois   wl — Wladislaw I   yx — Yxcaguayo
tq — Tquayum   wn — Wnoghquetookoke   yz — Yzeure
tt — ttinya   ws — Wschowa   zg — Zgierz
tv — Tvashtri   xp — Xptianos Manssos   zj — Zjen Kuttchin
tx — Txĕixtskunē   xw — Xwãxõts   zn — Znojmo
ue — Uechtland   yb — Ybbs   zr — Zrinyi
uo — Uon-a-gan   yg — Yggdrasil   zs — Zsigmondy
uq — Uqair   yh — yheku   zt — Ztolam
uu — Uusimaa   yj — Yjar   zv — Zvolen
uy — Uyáda

What do all the words in Exhibit B mean? They are names of musical instruments; of American Indian tribes and villages; and of persons, places, and tribes the world over.

Further progress toward our goal of zero redundancy is more difficult, because there seems not to be any one reference work with a substantial number of the missing combinations. What becomes necessary is to consult every conceivable dictionary, encyclopedia, atlas, gazetteer, and other available source, extracting from each one the comparatively few items it is capable of contributing to our list. The process is one of gradual attrition rather than of sweeping victories.

Exhibits A and B included 511 of the 676 possible combinations. We have been making the sort of tedious, time-consuming search for the remaining combinations that is required to succeed, and have found words fitting 118 of the 165 left. To reproduce the entire list, defining and locating each one, would take up too much space here. Accordingly, we have selected three dozen of our discoveries, from 36 different sources, and present them in Exhibit C below. These 36 selections are fully representative of the entire group of 118.

Exhibit C

bg — Bgug-Panir—an Armenian cheese made of skimmed ewe's milk. (Hugh Weideman, *The Rapid Fact Finder*, 1958).

bk — bKah-hgyur—the Tibetan translation of the Mahayana Buddhist scriptures, used in Lamaism. (*Encyclopaedia Britannica*, 1956.)

BN — Bninski—Alexander Bninski, Polish count and tactician, 1788–1831. (Albert M. Hyamson, *A Dictionary of Universal Biography*, 1951.)

BP — Bpirtsimas—a surname listed in the 1966 Brooklyn, New York telephone directory.

BT — Btfsplk—Joe Btfsplk, the world's worst jinx, a recurring character in Al Capp's comic strip, *Li'l Abner*.

BV — Bvekenya—an alias used by one Stephanus Cecil Rutgert Bernard in 1886; mentioned in *The Ivory Trail* by T. V. Bulpin (Cape Town, 1954).

BX — bxg—a spelling of "bog" used by Edgar Allan Poe in his short story, *X-ing a Paragrab*.

CB — Cboski—a surname listed in the 1966 Nassau County, New York telephone directory.

DK — Dkelpnishte—a populated place in Albania. (*Gazetteer No. 5, U. S. Board of Geographic Names, Standard Names Approved By.*)

FG — Fgura—a Roman Catholic Parish in Malta. (*The Malta Yearbook, 1966.*)

FN — fnese—to breathe heavily, or to sneeze; a 14th-century word. (Webster's Second Edition, 1955.)

FQ — fqdhr—the spelling of "father" used in *Fwnetik Orthqgrafi* by Frederick S. Wingfield of Chicago; quoted in H. L. Mencken's *The American Language*, 1957.

FS — Fsadni—a surname listed in the 1966 Chicago, Illinois telephone directory.

GG — Gg—pseudonym of the translator into French of a Russian work on history; the translator is known only by another pseudonym, "Nicolas-on". (New York Public Library card catalog, 1966.)

GV — Gvosdev—Michael Gvosdev, a Russian geodesist who sailed to Alaska in 1730 with some Siberian Cossacks. (*The Encyclopedia Americana*, 1955.)

GZ — Gzhatsk—a town in the Soviet Union, 90 miles west of Moscow. (*Webster's Geographical Dictionary*, 1963.)

HT — htone na—a peripheral neuritis of malarial origin occurring in Burma. (W. A. Newman Dorland, *The American Illustrated Medical Dictionary*, 1951.)

JB — Jbayl—a village on the coast of Lebanon, north of Beirut. (*The Times Atlas of the World*, Mid-Century Edition, 1959.)

KD — Kdyně—a town in Bohemia, in Czechoslovakia, southwest of Plzeň. (*Hammond's Ambassador World Atlas*, 1961.)

LB — Lbarber—a surname listed in the 1966 Queens, New York telephone directory.

LN — Lnianno—a community in West Prussia, Germany, northwest of Kulm, now in Poland. (*The Century Atlas of the World*, 1902.)

MG — Mglin—a town in the North Chernigof government of European Russia. (*Funk & Wagnalls New Standard Dictionary of the English Language*, 1945.)

PP — Pparle—a surname listed in the 1966 Manhattan, New York telephone directory.

PV — Pvill—Edward A. Pvill, a chemist whose name has appeared in *Chemical Abstracts,* without biographical data.

RP — Rpdrpd—a word in James Joyce's *Finnegans Wake* (The Viking Press, 1958, Page 234), apparently intended to mean "very rapidly".

WG — Wgah'nagl—part of a ritual chant in a special language in *The Cult of Cthulhu,* a science-fiction story by H. P. Lovecraft. The word occurs in a phrase meaning "dead wait, dreaming".

WJ — Wjatka—a commercial city in European Russia, also known as "Viatka". (*A Standard Dictionary of the English Language,* 1898.)

WV — Wv-ro-hae—title of a collection of Ioway Indian language hymns, by William Hamilton. (Available at the New York Public Library.)

WW — Wwhimsey—title of a short-lived poetry magazine published 1955–56 in St. Louis, Missouri.

XB — Xbonil—a village in Campeche state, Mexico. (*Rand McNally New Cosmopolitan World Atlas,* 1965.)

XG — xguthe—a Hottentot stringed instrument. (Percival R. Kirby, *The Musical Instruments of the Native Races of South Africa,* London, 1934.)

XL — Xletra—a railroad stop in Yucatán state, Mexico. (*The Official Guide of the Railways and Steam Navigation Lines,* August, 1965.)

XQ — Xquiq—in Mayan mythology, the maiden wife of the spittle of Hunhun-Ahpu. (Frank Chapin Bray, *Bray's University Dictionary of Mythology,* New York, 1964.)

YY — yye—a 15th- and 16th-century spelling of "eye". (Webster's First Edition, 1909.)

ZF — zfoot—an abbreviated form of "God's foot", used as a minced oath in the 17th century. (*The Oxford English Dictionary,* 1933.)

ZZ — zzxjoanw—a Maori drum, also a fife. (Rupert Hughes, *Music Lovers' Encyclopedia,* 1954.)

Including the 118 words from which Exhibit C was selected, 629 of the original 676 combinations have fallen. The 47 still remaining are listed in Exhibit D. These are the proud, defiant survivors of a once-rampant, invincible horde, but they cannot stem the tide of history. Their days, too, are numbered, and total victory for us lies just around the next bend.

Exhibit D

BQ	FD	HD	JT	PG	QX	VQ	XK
CD	FM	HF	JZ	QB	QZ	VW	XV
DF	FP	HQ	LF	QF	RF	WB	ZP
DQ	FV	JC	NF	QG	RM	WF	ZQ
FB	FZ	JP	PB	QJ	RQ	WQ	ZX
FC	HB	JQ	PD	QK	VF	XJ	

The remaining 47 combinations reflect a redundancy of less than 7%. We have reached a relative entropy of more than 93%, a figure quite undreamt of in Shannon's technologically oriented philosophy. Yet, we are not satisfied, we cannot be satisfied, until the very last combinations lie vanquished at our feet.

The end is gloriously close. Would you like to be in on the kill, so to speak? All you need to do to share in the honors is to knock off a few of the hardy survivors on whom we have put the finger in Exhibit D. They are marked for death—are you the trigger man of fate?

HINTS

D O OUR problems perplex you? Are you thoroughly bewildered, hopelessly lost? Are you weighing the possibility of ending it all?

Despair not! We have provided assistance for you in the following pages, help that is yours for the asking. For each problem, there are one or more hints, calculated to put you on the road to resolving it. In some instances, our clues are quite straightforward and make the original problems almost embarrassingly easy to clear up. In many more cases, happily, the hints are just as devious as the problems to which they relate, increasing the overall complexity of the situation confronting you. In a few of these, new channels of thought pertinent to the problem unfold before your unbelieving eyes, and they acquire added dimensions, giving you an ever deeper insight into the world around you.

In isolated instances, the problem under discussion is of a character that does not respond to clue treatment, or which has proved itself superior to our imaginative powers in devising suitable hints. In these unfortunate cases, we have openly and honestly paltered and pussyfooted!

The order in which the clues are presented is jumbled in comparison with the orders of the problems and of the resolutions, to minimize the possibility of your consciously or subconsciously noticing the hint for the next problem before you've had a chance to work on it unassisted. (The extent of our fairness to you is sometimes too much for words!)

You may be so intrigued by our clues as to forget where you came from or where you are going. To eliminate any distress, the page number of the problem is shown in parentheses immediately after the title, and the page number of the resolution just below the clue text.

88 *Isaiah and the Prince of Morocco* *(page 73)*

Deimos, Demeter, and Dione . . . Baltimore, Maryland.
Resolution: Page 251.

73 *The Hawaiian War Chant* *(page 63)*

Hawaiian was a primitive language, unable to satisfy the needs of a modern world . . .
Resolution: Page 240.

61 *Three-Dimensional Thinking* *(page 53)*

Must each path in a word cube of the sixth order be occupied by one six-letter word? Why not use two short words along some paths, which have a total of six letters? No matter how unrelated the words may seem at first encounter, it is always possible to write a plausible sentence in which they appear in the desired order, consecutively. This gives us the justification needed to use them in developing our unprecedented word cube. If we can do it, so can you!
Resolution: Page 230.

114 *Match Game* (*page 94*)

Fields you should investigate in quest of our time units include the Mayan calendar, recent scientific and technological literature, Hindu cosmogony, medical terminology, and the language of Greek and Roman antiquity. Do not, however, limit yourself to these areas if you wish to identify all 20 terms. Our suggestions are but a starter!

Resolution: Page 209.

46 *Memory Hooks* (*page 43*)

It seems unlikely that you would want to pursue precisely the same lines of thought followed by us. In such an improbable eventuality, however, we would have to recommend to you the "Cradle of American Industry"; an extremely high reading on a thalassometer; a wide-ranging ardilla; and tmesis.

Resolution: Page 202.

15 *"The"* (*page 15*)

Rule, Britannia! (Identify our clue, please.)

Resolution: Page 234.

40 *Jockeys and Yankees* (*page 39*)

An Englishman, Ivor Brown, has written quite a number of books about English: *Say the Word, I Break My Word, Chosen Words, No Idle Words, A Word in Edgeways,* and others. He must think it great sport!

Resolution: Page 228.

62   *Italian Genius*   (*page 54*)

Since the various elements of our verbal problem have dual aspects, our clue is also a two-part affair, half pictorial and half numerical:

$$
\begin{array}{r}
1564 \\
+\quad 78 \\
\hline
1642
\end{array}
$$

Resolution: Page 212.

54   *Decussate Deliberations*   (*page 48*)

It would appear to be a matter of timing, eh?
Resolution: Page 239.

85   *A Capital Question*   (*page 71*)

The capital of Spain is San Sebastián. A former polestar, Thuban, is in the constellation Draco, *The Dragon*.

The easiest way of answering our question is to make a trip to DRUK-YUL. We, at least, know of no easier way.

Resolution: Page 184.

20   *Group Theory*   (*page 18*)

A brace of dogs, a cast of hawks, and a gemini of baboons—what a multitude!

Resolution: Page 282.

6 *Jays That Aren't* (*page 8*)

A palindrome for an oilman: "Sad I, Noel, saw I was Leonidas." If that clue is not crystal-clear, then consider the practical angle: we wouldn't dare write about two of the three men!

Resolution: Page 306.

17 *The Scacchic Scoop* (*page 17*)

As a clue to what is wrong, we quote the definition of *countergambit* given in the *Funk & Wagnalls New Standard Dictionary of the English Language*, first published in 1913:

> "*Chess* A gambit played in reply by the second player; as, the Calabrese *countergambit.*"

While this definition provides the lead to solving the mystery, we must warn you that it, too, is defective, in being ambiguous. A gambit played in reply to what? To a gambit offered by the first player, or to any opening employed by the first player?

Resolution: Page 297.

59 *Ministerial Meditations* (*page 51*)

A double-edged clue: Missouri played a role in Churchill's life.
Resolution: Page 273.

71 *Yellow Hammers* (*page 60*)

Is this where the Civil War started? Hardly!
Resolution: Page 267.

99 *Excess Exes* (page 82)

"Backward, turn backward, O Time, in your flight,"—Elizabeth Akers Allen, *Rock Me to Sleep*, Stanza 1.

Resolution: Page 280.

106 *Belles of the Ball??* (page 87)

1. Do we observe sex intruding itself here?
2. A cosmopolitan orientation includes languages other than English.
   Resolution: Page 242.

7 *The Great Pretender* (page 9)

For an outrageous clue, we ask you to ponder about the Duke in Shakespeare's *Two Gentlemen of Verona*. More reasonably, we pose a question: who is the ultimate authority as to your own name?

Resolution: Page 288.

42 *Bamboozling the "Bambino"* (page 40)

What makes you think that George Herman Ruth was a Sunni Moslem, or a Yusafzai Pathan? Hmmmm?

Resolution: Page 244.

23 *Sequels to Aleph* (page 20)

Be honest with yourself: is there any place for a purely numerical problem in a book devoted to the ramifications of language? . . . Transcend the finite!

Resolution: Page 247.

94 *A Feamyng of Ferrets* *(page 79)*

Errors piled upon errors . . . fantastique! (Now, that's a French word—why?)

Resolution: Page 251.

76 *Let Your Hair Down!* *(page 64)*

Leases and disillusionment seem to fall all about us!

Resolution: Page 278.

109 *Synonyms for Sex* *(page 89)*

The best sources for the refined terms you are seeking in answer to our question are the medical dictionaries. Some terms, of course, can also be found in the largest "unabridged" general dictionaries.

Resolution: Page 240.

84 *Repetitive Homonymy* *(page 70)*

Buffalo had enough. Enough of what? Of itself.

Resolution: Page 290.

2 *Beyond the Law* *(page 5)*

Word lists hold the key to resolution of your problem. If the job seems too tough, become a poet!

Resolution: Page 295.

60 *A Study in Frustration* (page 52)

Keats takes Kate's steak! Just a minute, bub!
Resolution: Page 299.

104 *Two Words = One Bird!* (page 85)

A French morpheme . . . a Chinese gong . . . an English count . . .
Resolution: Page 286.

95 *Augmenting the Alphabet* (page 80)

What are the ingredients of our witches' brew? An orchard, a circle, a hornbook, and a llama!
Resolution: Page 275.

90 *The Preposition Proposition* (page 76)

Australia . . . Land of the Kangaroo . . . Land of the Cornstalk . . . Bananaland . . . Diggerland . . .?
Resolution: Page 282.

22 *Shakespeare and Cervantes* (page 20)

(1) Who was Aloysius Lilius? (2) Death has its equiliteral correlative, you know! (5) The number 46 tells all!
Resolution: Page 291.

117   *Induction*   *(page 97)*

It sounds to us as if these words have great capacity for being compressed.
Resolution: Page 172.

58   *Sight and Sound*   *(page 51)*

Born of repeated failure and heartbreak, this advice goes out to you: try
the sound of N for your first sentence, and the letter P for your second one.
Nothing else has similar potential.
Resolution: Page 204.

74   *Keokuk, Iowa*   *(page 63)*

How shall we translate "moonlight" into Latin? As LUNA LUX? That's
twisting things quite a bit, you know!
Resolution: Page 198.

45   *The New Chemistry*   *(page 43)*

Can there be any DIFFERENCE of opinion about the proper procedure?
Certainly, the notion of combining the letters I, C, and E is pretty old-fashioned,
as is that of stringing H, O, and H together. This is the dawn of a new era—live
creatively!
Resolution: Page 221.

11   *Shadchonim Wanted!*   *(page 12)*

In its own way, this problem is a perfect illustration of our theme:
BEYOND LANGUAGE. Waxing expansive, we suggest that you devote yourself to a
study of the sublanguages *within* that all-embracing medium known as English.
Resolution: Page 214.

69 *Vegetation?* *(page 59)*

Look for proofs on foreign soil, proofs developed in stages. Europe and geometric reasoning will turn the trick—we vouch for it!

Resolution: Page 206.

56 *Asphalt, Cliff, and Raven* *(page 50)*

High French and Low!

Resolution: Page 274.

19 *One Ida: An Oneida?* *(page 18)*

Muliebrity superimposed? How tragic!

Resolution: Page 289.

78 *Demon of the Alphabet* *(page 66)*

How was the name CHICAGO spelled in bygone days? To what was the name CHICAGO applied in days of yore?

Resolution: Page 249.

108 *The Invisible Alphabet* *(page 88)*

A. A covey of pheasants rising from the center of a beat. B. The capital of CHUNG-HUA JEN-MIN KUNG-HO KUO. C. A small piece of clay on wh—oh, come on, now, you can't expect us to give you a complete set of definitional clues! Choose your own words!

Resolution: Page 250.

47   *Bowdlerized English?*   *(page 44)*

A dictionary can be elephantic!
Resolution: Page 210.

38   *Antipodal Identities*   *(page 37)*

Have you looked into the possibility of increasing the definitions from 17
to some larger, *even* number?

As we see it, the *smallest* number is zero, first, last, and always.
Resolution: Page 224.

115   *Widshi Itíkapá*   *(page 95)*

Who is the husband of Mama Goose? What well-known song by Jimmy
Kennedy and Michael Carr was popularized by Gene Autry?
Resolution: Page 202.

102   *From Word to Nonword*   *(page 84)*

Think straight and think hard, and come to the right conclusions before
we do. That's about all the advice we can give you, other than mentioning
that the logological interest in our 16 words revolves around things like palindromes, reversals, tautonyms, nonpattern words, consonantal concentrations,
vowel concentrations, and miscellaneous letter groupings. This is incidental to
the main problem, of course, which is to teach you how to think about words.

Incidentally, our title characterizes our problem with singular aptness.
What do we have in mind?
Resolution: Page 174.

86   *Irrelevance*   (page 71)

True relevance must, naturally, be sought in irrelevance. Comprehend this principle, and you have unmasked us.

Resolution: Page 188.

98   *Coffee, Anyone?*   (page 81)

"Hear ye! Hear ye! The underlying principle concerns the . . ." (REST OF MESSAGE CENSORED!)

Resolution: Page 235.

10   *The Shell-and-Kernel Game*   (page 10)

Look at the words in our list under a magnifying glass. Do you notice how the words are coming apart at the seams (the ones between 3rd and 4th letter, and between 9th and 10th letter)? Well, they are!

Resolution: Page 210.

27   *Stately Sobriquets*   (page 23)

Are you familiar with the Law of Diminishing Returns? An inverse principle, the Law of Accelerating Returns, applies in solving this quiz. Your problem, essentially, is to match up our list of nicknames with a list of the 50 state names. As you correctly identify some of the sobriquets, you remove the identified nicknames from one list and the corresponding state names from the other list. The unsolved remainders of the two lists become progressively shorter. As they do so, the possibility of making intelligent guesses as to what nicknames might belong to what state names, in the shrinking balance, becomes greater, resulting in more and more rapid progress toward your goal of a perfect score. The closer you come to perfection, the more swiftly you move toward it. Our method has only one drawback: it is the *first* step that seems hopeless. We are still experimenting with a view to ironing out the kinks in this wonderful scheme!

Resolution: Page 266.

105   A *"Non Sequitur"*   (*page 86*)

What doesn't follow is a little mixed up, isn't it? If you need still more help, look to the stars!

Resolution: Page 205.

80   A *Facetious Problem*   (*page 67*)

You must understand that Mt. Everest, the common housefly, and the French poet Arthur Rimbaud are all involved in your attempt to solve this truly facetious problem.

Resolution: Page 232.

93   *Beyond Uranium*   (*page 79*)

You have heard of synonyms, we presume? Go back into history!
Resolution: Page 259.

16   A *Peri's Sad Lot*   (*page 16*)

Slavkov u Brna: what more is there to say?
Resolution: Page 207.

32   *Socrates and Serendipity*   (*page 33*)

What was Napoleon's last name? Are there other names for Ceylon? What are we to infer from the seemingly irrelevant title of the problem?

Resolution: Page 241.

87   *Trumpets and Flourishes*   (*page 72*)

We'll make it short and sweet: what is this book about?

Resolution: Page 274.

41   *Kipling Revised*   (*page 40*)

If you are looking toward Maine or toward Florida, an immediate volte-face is indicated. "Westward, turn westward, O Mime, in your sight!" *

Resolution: Page 237.

113   *The Key to Knowledge*   (*page 92*)

Are the symbols in use today adequate for the expression of knowledge that will be acquired a million years hence? As our knowledge of some particular subject becomes ever more detailed, will a text of some particular length remain as adequate as it was originally for describing that subject? As regards knowledge we have not yet acquired, if a statement is put forth, how will we know whether it is true or false? Do we have the means at hand even to recognize everything that comes under the heading of future knowledge?

Resolution: Page 199.

* Ravenscroft J. Cloudesley, *Sotadic Visions*, Stanza 11.

100 *Immortality* *(page 83)*

This is the forest primeval.
Resolution: Page 188.

13 *Homonymic Humdingers* *(page 13)*

Are we going too far in surrounding this problem with an air of mystery?
We've said enough!
Resolution: Page 181.

92 *The Emperor of Austria* *(page 78)*

To govern a nation for 68 years is quite an achievement for a monarch.
Of course, Louis XIV of France reigned for 72 years, and Pepi II, of the Sixth
Dynasty in ancient Egypt, presumably a peppy individual, held the throne for
94 years, to make his reign the longest one in recorded history.
Faraway places, with strange-sounding names . . . Again??
Resolution: Page 220.

44 *The Collective Farm* *(page 42)*

Strange things are happening . . . to words. They are corrupted, they are
misspelled, they fall victim to typographical errors. We are overcome by it all!
Resolution: Page 212.

119 *The Living End* *(page 98)*

This is an "educational" clue. Some words can be replaced by other
words, called "synonyms", possessed of the same meaning. For instance, "begin-

ning" can be replaced by "start", and "middle" by "center". That's your lesson for the day!

Resolution: Page 308.

63 *A Singular Plural* (page 54)

One-syllable words are a fertile source for word pairs of the CARES-CARESS type. To find those of the PIRATES-PIRATESS stripe, consider the various suffixes ending with a double S (-LESS, -NESS, etc.).

The half of a word both in SINGULAR and in PLURAL could be UL, LU, LA, AL, AR, or RA. So much to choose from, so little time in which to choose!

Resolution: Page 219.

83 *Good at Figures?* (page 69)

In its own way, the clue we are about to give you is a masterpiece of ambiguity. Why?

"Far away places, with strange-sounding names . . . Count 'em!"

Resolution: Page 245.

51 *Thoughts for Today* (page 47)

Our thoughts? EYE and NEIGH!

Resolution: Page 182.

112 *Etaoin Shrdlu* (page 92)

Think about Thackeray, substitution ciphers, fount-schemes, confusion, and operating a linotype machine.

Resolution: Page 173.

75   *Megalomania*   *(page 64)*

The longest English words are chemical terms. We recommend, therefore, that you check through the indexes of publications such as *Chemical Abstracts*. The experience will be an eye opener!

Resolution: Page 226.

103   *Halloween and Christmas*   *(page 85)*

Although we use the denary or decimal number system in everyday life, we are aware of competing number systems, such as the binary, the octal, and the vigesimal systems. Interested?

Resolution: Page 217.

14   *Scrabble!*   *(page 14)*

You may find this difficult to believe at first, but Mrs. Byrne has achieved a score of 2448 in one game, and a score of 1175 on one single move of that game. If you can, do better. Try hard!

Resolution: Page 217.

82   *How to Curse*   *(page 68)*

The best sources in which to search for alternate names for the Devil seem to be the Bible, Bible dictionaries and handbooks, and comprehensive thesauruses.

Resolution: Page 189.

39 *Beauty in Ugliness* (*page 38*)

We are making this problem unduly, unconscionably easy for you by noting that the first positive quality in the string stretching from UGLY to BEAUTIFUL is PROUD. Take it from there!

Resolution: Page 191.

3 *Symbol of the Sun* (*page 6*)

(a) (b) (c)

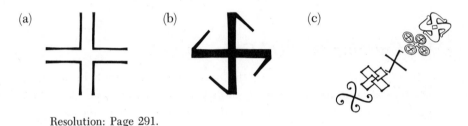

Resolution: Page 291.

67 *The Other One* (*page 58*)

Mirabile dictu, the amphora, the oenochoë, and the loutrophoros all bear on this problem. If any dare dissent . . . off with their heads!

Resolution: Page 242.

101 *Capsule Comments* (*page 83*)

The natural interrelationships observable among English words and names will enable you to create capsule comments apposite in regard to the reviewers who make them, without further assistance from us.

Resolution: Page 238.

25 *Desperation* (page 22)

Our first clue is a dead giveaway:

2   3   4   5   6   7   11   8   9   1   10

Our second clue is less obvious, perhaps: Since the title of this book is *Beyond Language,* we have a problem here that certainly goes beyond language. Remember that, in order to approach language, it may be necessary to recede from language.

Resolution: Page 208.

31 *Cracking the "Q" Code* (page 29)

It is not easy for us to believe that you genuinely desire help in solving the mystery of Q, in probing behind and beyond that letter to get at its well-springs. However, if such be the case, then we suggest that you focus your efforts on the following three subjects: (a) the CHOGAK, an East Indian tree whose pods are infested with insects; (b) the doom of Mesopotamia; (c) the Mohammedan scriptures.

Resolution: Page 260.

81 *An Odd Problem* (page 68)

America is a nation of 50 states. How would you go about proving this statement? By replacing each letter in the name AMERICA with its numerical position in our alphabet:

A   M   E   R   I   C   A
1   13   5   18   9   3   1

Add the seven numerical values. Their sum is 50.

Resolution: Page 266.

70 *A Retort in Kind* (page 59)

To be very frank with you—and you wouldn't want it any other way, we know—it was our fond hope that you would refrain from seeking our "Hints" in this problem. Now that our daydream has been rudely shattered, we must pose some questions for you to ponder: (1) How many TOO's, exactly, are there in English? (2) Are TU, TEW, and TUE new words, or do they already exist? (3) What about numerals? (4) How about rewording the original sentence?

Resolution: Page 222.

4 *Charming Spelling* (page 6)

Good luck will solve this problem for you.

Resolution: Page 283.

24 *A Ponderous Postal Problem* (page 21)

Don't you think something ought to be done about the flimsy stamps now in use?

Resolution: Page 285.

48 *Know Your Colors!* (page 44)

This is, quite obviously, a case of exclusiveness versus jointness. Need we say more?

Resolution: Page 262.

53 *Of Rulers and Subjects* *(page 48)*

Analyzing and synthesizing words should do the trick, we believe.
Resolution: Page 281.

35 *Etymological Eccentricities* *(page 35)*

Wend your way—if you are wending!—first to the city of Plymouth, in Devonshire, in southwest England. Once you are comfortably settled there, turn your attention to the British names for short musical notes.
Resolution: Page 204.

110 *Apocryphal Antitheses* *(page 89)*

To unravel this problem, you must begin by raveling it. Finally, however, you will have to sound off!
Resolution: Page 228.

116 *Delving into Divination* *(page 96)*

For extensive divination lists, you could consult a noted 17th-century work, *The Mag-astro-mancer,* by John Gaule; or, either of two 19th-century texts, *Primitive Culture* by Edward B. Tylor, and *The Occult Sciences* by Edward Smedley and others. Since you are not likely, however, to find any of these books on the shelves of your home library, we have an alternate suggestion: examine a comparably revealing list given by Rabelais in *Gargantua and Pantagruel* (Third Book, Chapter XXV). One final word: DUKKERIPEN!
Resolution: Page 196.

77 *Suggestive Words* *(page 65)*

This is one of those isolated instances where we don't believe that you ought to get a hint from us. There isn't necessarily any one correct solution to each of the problems posed here. By giving you clues to our own train of thought, we would be trammeling *your* imagination, which is exactly the opposite of what we'd like to achieve. Let your creativity bloom unfettered!

Resolution: Page 263.

55 *Permutational Language* *(page 49)*

Noun, verb, adjective . . . similibus or equivonym!

Resolution: Page 255.

72 *Real English* *(page 61)*

Never use a 5-letter word if an 18-letter synonym is handy. Never settle for one, simple word if you can fabricate an eight-word circumlocutory periphrasis. Use language with gusto and with zest!

Resolution: Page 271.

43 *The Game of Cross-Reference* *(page 41)*

Nothing personal intended, of course, but even an idiot could figure this one out!

Resolution: Page 278.

107 *Words* *(page 87)*

It should be possible to adapt some of the advertising already in use for other products, to the service of words.

Resolution: Page 298.

5   *Eminent American Palindromist?*   *(page 7)*

Poe's poems prove profound palindromic proclivities.
Resolution: Page 269.

49   *Minorca Didn't Quite Make It!*   *(page 45)*

Why don't you analyze these words letter by letter? What are you afraid of?

Resolution: Page 287.

36   *The Witching Hour*   *(page 36)*

Could it be, do you suppose, that all three of the countries mentioned are really one and the same *land?* If so, what land?

Resolution: Page 229.

111   *The Election of 1948*   *(page 90)*

Without meaning to be too helpful, we do wish to point out that our method also applies to the 1965 French presidential election with its six candidates: Marcel Barbu, Charles de Gaulle, Jean Lecanuet, Pierre Marcilhacy, François Mitterrand, and Jean-Louis Tixier-Vignancourt.

Frenchmen doing this stunt in 1965 used the death of Louis XIV of France in 1715 as their historical mainstay.

De Gaulle won.

Resolution: Page 203.

57   *Apple and Arrow*   *(page 51)*

Fourteenth-century Switzerland, we have news for you, is not the proper locale.

Resolution: Page 197.

66   *The Mathematical Minimum*   *(page 57)*

Definiteness as opposed to indefiniteness: why, Premier?

Resolution: Page 236.

1   *A Jug of Wine, a Loaf of Bread—and Thou* *(page 5)*

"In the beginning was the Word . . . "—from the Gospel according to St. John, Chapter 1, Verse 1, as given in the Authorized King James Version of the Holy Bible.

Resolution: Page 171.

28   *Discovered by Herschel!*   *(page 25)*

Miranda, Ariel, Umbriel, ..., Oberon. There is something missing here!

Resolution: Page 279.

18   *The Witches' Prayer*   *(page 17)*

Look to Latin for light!

Resolution: Page 269.

52 *Synonym Sets* *(page 47)*

If you feel outfoxed by our problem, we are rushing to your rescue with this helpful hint: the title of the problem is so conspicuously ambiguous that more than mere chance must be at work. Think about it!

Resolution: Page 276.

96 *Questions for Kay?* *(page 80)*

Take a gander at these clues—dead giveaways! (1) An ex-quack?? (2) A bird wading in the Pacific! (3) Yellow legs. (4) A gewgaw or a gimcrack. (5) Geoffrey O'Hara, 1915. (6) Repositories and collections. (7) Homonymy.

Resolution: Page 241.

65 *Un-French French* *(page 57)*

You could, of course, use an English-French dictionary, but that would be cheating! Use your own knowledge!

Resolution: Page 230.

34 *The Black Island* *(page 34)*

Do you like Cinerama? How do you feel about cherry trees?

Resolution: Page 171.

8 *E Pluribus Unum* *(page 9)*

Even if you're in Washington, you'll be in Dutch if you don't figure this out. You may then acquire a split personality and wander off to the East. How much more obvious can we make it?

Resolution: Page 264.

30   *Frontier Days*   (*page 28*)

The most effective technique is to take already existing words that convey some portion of the desired meaning and to alter some elements in them so as to incorporate the additional meaning desired. Blend words, composition, and onomatopoeia all enter the picture.

If you have better methods at your disposal, why are you reading this clue?

Resolution: Page 243.

118   *The End is Near!*   (*page 98*)

The most forward approach to this problem is a backward approach, of course. Try and succeed!

Resolution: Page 186.

21   *The Sinister Seven*   (*page 19*)

What does this diagram mean to you, viewed against the backdrop of the problem transmitted to you here?

Resolution: Page 195.

97   *!!!PpppppppP!!!*   (*page 81*)

What clue do we have to this, the shortest problem in *Beyond Language?* Observe:

Was Elizabeth Barrett Browning the author of *Sonnets from the Portuguese?* Yes, indeed!

Resolution: Page 231.

91   *Mysterious Q*   *(page 77)*

So that you may concentrate your search in the most fruitful areas of language, we mention several facts: (1) some French words end in a Q not followed by a U; there are numerous English words of Hebrew or Arabic origin, containing one or more Q's without a U; (c) NAMES ARE A CATEGORY OF WORDS —an admissible category, provided they are listed in English-language reference works.

Resolution: Page 172.

68   *True and False*   *(page 58)*

In a spirit of almost fantastic magnanimity, we are giving you the two conclusions at which you need to arrive:

$$(1) \quad (a \neq b) = (a = b)$$
$$(2) \qquad 1 = -1$$

All that remains for you to do is to provide the simple and conclusive operations that produce these results, and then to justify them verbally, holding the ramparts against all comers.

Resolution: Page 191.

9   *Supercalifragilisticexpialidocious!*   *(page 10)*

A steadily increasing percentage of English words is derived from Latin or/and Greek roots.

Resolution: Page 272.

50   *The Silent Host*   *(page 46)*

Finding silent letters incarnate is not infrequently a matter of chance or of serendipity. However, you can find some of the words you want by reading the paragraphs under the names of the 26 letters in the largest, "unabridged", dictionaries.

Resolution: Page 219.

79   *Advice to the Lovelorn*   *(page 67)*

Since this is an exercise in creativity, you shouldn't be peeking into the "Hints" section. However, we are not your moral guardians. If you really want or need help, why not look at actual advice columns and pick out the more novel, imaginative, inspired signatures you see there? We shall surely not know the difference!

Resolution: Page 258.

29   *Balance and Beauty*   *(page 25)*

To be frank with you (and that's quite difficult for people not named "Frank"), there aren't any hints we can give you. So far, there is no known method of locating ABC's other than the obvious and tedious one of taking lists of words and methodically and mechanically computing their value totals. Since most words are not ABC's, this is a very slow process, and there is virtually no way of directing one's efforts toward isolating ABC's of some particular variety or classification. If the backbreaking chore of searching for ABC's is not quite your cup of tea, relax; turn directly to the "Resolutions" section, and gaze at the marvels assembled there for your enjoyment.

Resolution: Page 257.

33   *Doppelgänger!* (*page 34*)

Monos: Translate the following thought into Romanian: "Do I forget sounds in a country that's without roads, dirty, and without rest rooms? I don't know."

Una: My translation: "UIT SUNETE LA O ȚARĂ FĂRĂ DRUM, MURDARĂ, FĂRĂ TOALETE? NU ȘTIU."

Resolution: Page 293.

12   *Mabel A. Funk (1739–1937)* (*page 13*)

To begin with, we want to make it clear that our heroine, Mabel A. Funk, is not a member of the famous family of dictionary makers. Beyond that, we can only advise you to *permute* and to *commute*. If this tires you out, relax by giving a bit of thought to centenarians and to Professor R. L. Gregory of the Psychology Department at Cambridge University, in England.

Resolution: Page 201.

89   *Aces and Kings* (*page 73*)

The best thing we can do for you is to suggest a method for locating ACE words. Take common prefixes of four letters (ANTI-, MONO-, OVER-, SEMI-, etc.) and establish their final, one-digit difference at the third level. Do the same with common suffixes (-ABLE, -LESS, -MENT, -SHIP, etc.). Then, determine which *two* letters immediately following the prefix or immediately preceding the suffix will duplicate that one-digit difference at the third difference level. You now have five-letter combinations with which to work, for most of which words exist, and for each word you find, the numerical consequences of the three remaining letters only need to be examined, which is a considerable economy. Use regular word lists for the prefixes and reverse-alphabetical lists for the suffixes. If these are not readily available to you, use the dictionary itself for the prefixes and special word lists given under the suffixes in the dictionary.

If all this seems like too much work, just turn to the "Resolutions" section and savor the tidbits presented there.

Resolution: Page 223.

26   *A Magic Circle*   (*page 23*)

There are ways and ways of arranging letters, both in groups and in subgroups. You had better start thinking about some of those ways, if you want to avoid crushing defeat hereabouts!

Resolution: Page 215.

37   *H O N*   (*page 37*)

Think of a low shoe laced at the instep. Recall William III, king of England from 1694 to 1702. Realize that BEGORRY is one of the longest words in our language in which the letters happen to be arranged in proper alphabetical order. Clues enough!

Resolution: Page 233.

64   *A Syllabub of Syllables*   (*page 55*)

Try looking for the unusual meanings of words. Check the Funk & Wagnalls unabridged, for a starter.

Resolution: Page 181.

RESOLUTIONS

THE "Moment of Truth" has arrived. The profoundest secrets of logology, the science of words, are about to be unveiled to you. Nothing is to be kept back; the very soul of human word and thought shall be stripped bare before you. Every last veil is being torn aside, so that you may see all and know all.

Why have we elected "resolutions" as an apt name for our stunning revelations? Because that is what they are. *Webster's Third New International Dictionary of the English Language,* 1961, defines the word RESOLUTION as "the act of solving; something separated into its component parts or reduced to a simpler form; a clarifying statement".

You are in for all sorts of surprises, possibly even shocks. Accept them with open mind and open heart. Let your life be enriched by insights that many, less fortunate than you, are destined not to gain in an entire lifetime. Now you belong to the Chosen Few; you belong to the ages!

For your convenience in referring to the original problem, its page number is given in parentheses following the title. The order of the resolutions as compared to problem and hint orders has been scrambled, lest you inadvertently glimpse the resolution of our next problem before you've had an opportunity to work on it independently.

Eminently fair? Indeed!

1 A JUG OF WINE, A LOAF OF BREAD —AND THOU

(*Page 5*)

Our question is also our answer. WHAT is the essence, substance, or distinctive quality of the passage quoted.

The verse is an accidental acrostic. The initial letters of the four lines constituting the rubai (tetrastich), read in succession, spell the word WHAT. That word, used as a noun, means, "the essence, substance, or distinctive quality of something".

Our "hint" was equally meaningful. The word WHAT is formed vertically along the beginning of the stanza, and the problem built around it is placed at the beginning of our adventures into the mysterious realm beyond language.

34 THE BLACK ISLAND

(*Page 34*)

The State of Illinois replaced English with American as its official language in 1923 (see *Acts of the Legislature of Illinois*, Chapter 127, Section 178, 1923 edition).

George Washington, sometimes referred to as the *Atlas of America,* is said to have called the Illinois country "Black Island" because he thought the French spelled its name *Île Noire.*

Our "Hints"? CINERAMA is a transposal of AMERICAN. George Washington is associated with cutting down a cherry tree ("I can't tell a lie, Pa . . .").

91 *MYSTERIOUS Q*

(*Page 77*)

1. (a) QABBALA, an occult system of theosophy; (b) CINQ, the number five in dice or cards; (c) MIQRA, the Hebrew text of the Bible.

2. (a) QQICHUA, any of various Incan tribes in the central Andes; (b) HOOQQA, a kind of Turkish tobacco pipe; (c) RIQQ, a small tambourine used in Egypt.

3. (a) QALĀLTQ, the Hellelt, a Salishan Indian tribe on the Chimenes River, southwest of Vancouver Island—a name used by the anthropologist Franz Boas; (b) QARAQORUM, the capital of Genghis Khan in Mongolia; (c) ABQAIQ, an important oil field in Saudi Arabia; (d) AQEIQA, the name of a wadi or watercourse in Jordan.

4. QARAQALPAQ, a Turkic people living near Lake Aral in Central Asia; QEQER-TARSSUAQ, native name of Godhavn, Danish capital of North Greenland; EL AQQAQIR, a village in northern Egypt near El Alamein, scene of an important tank battle in World War II.

5. (a) QAZAQ, any central Asian Turkic language, particularly that of the eastern group; (b) QARQAR, an unidentified place in the western part of ancient Syria, perhaps Apamea on the Orontes river.

Three of the fifteen "Q" words just listed do contain a U, but in no case does that U immediately precede or immediately follow a Q, so that there is no connection between the two. Did you outperform us?

117 *INDUCTION*

(*Page 97*)

Our "Hints" spoke of *sound* and of *compression*, informing you that the four words under consideration could be compressed or shortened without changing their sound or pronunciation. This we now propose to do:

KNICKKNACK — KKKK = NICNAC   EMPTY — EPY = MT
EXPEDIENCY — EEIEY = XPDNC   AISLE — ASE = IL

Altogether, the four words have 30 letters. We have removed 15, leaving 15, without altering the pronunciation in the slightest. This is a saving, an economy, of exactly 50% in the space required to write, type, or print the words. You might say that we have the beginnings of a new kind of shorthand or "speed-writing" here.

In general, we have removed about one half of the letters in each word. Just how we have done it differs from one word to the next, however. In the case of KNICKKNACK, we have removed the only four like letters—the four K's. It is interesting to note that Webster's Third Edition gives NICNAC as a variant spelling of KNICKKNACK. It also lists the intermediate form NICKNACK, but omits the equally plausible alternative, KNICKNAC.

With EXPEDIENCY—and we do feel that we have acted expediently!—the letters removed are the 5 vowels, the letters retained are the 5 consonants. In the case of the two five-letter words, we have removed all letters occupying odd-numbered positions: the first, third, and fifth letters in each word, without regard to the distinction between consonants and vowels. The remainder MT is to be pronounced one letter at a time, to duplicate the sound of EMPTY; the remainder IL is to be fused in sound, resembling the contraction I'LL, but shorn of the apostrophe and of one L.

Those of you who would reform English spelling are counseled to give the most serious consideration to our style of economical writing.

112 *ETAOIN SHRDLU*

(*Page 92*)

Fundamentally, ETAOIN SHRDLU is a combination of letters set by running a finger down the first and then the second left-hand vertical banks of six keys of a linotype to produce a temporary marking slug not intended to appear in the final printing. If the linotype machine jams, the entire slug may drop, so that the letter sequence may accidentally appear in print.

From this origin, the term has come to indicate a jumbled line of type or meaningless expression that sometimes occurs in newspapers. As someone has said, it is descriptive of the linotype gone temperamental. From newspaper cant, the expression has entered general slang with the meaning of "confusion, mistakes" (". . . 98% accurate and 2% etaoin shrdlu.")

The expression "from etaoin to shrdlu", a sort of slang term used in newspaper offices, means "thoroughly, from A to Z".

From the standpoint of the typesetter, the letters in ETAOIN SHRDLU represent the relative frequency with which the various letters of the alphabet appear, although the letters H and R, about equally common, are often switched, as in the following complete frequency-alphabet:

E T A O I N S R H D L U C M F W Y P G B V K J Q X FI FF FL Z FFI FFL

There are other font-schemes, of course, in which the relative positions of the letters differ slightly from the order shown above.

From the cryptographer's viewpoint, the order of the letters indicates the relative frequency with which they appear in ordinary English text, making such a frequency alphabet useful in decoding substitution ciphers.

A most curious confusion has been that of ETAOIN with EOTHEN. The latter word is the title of a book of travels in the Levant, by the English historian Alexander W. Kinglake, published in 1844. It is also the title of a chapter in Thackeray's *Vanity Fair* describing Major Dobbin's return to England from India (from the East). The name is derived from a Greek adverb meaning "from morn" or "at dawn", from Eos, Greek goddess of the dawn.

Because the 12 letters comprising ETAOIN SHRDLU are the most commonly used ones in English, and because the proportion of vowels to all the letters is similar to that observed in average English, the belief persists that the letters can be transposed to form some English word or name. No one has truly succeeded in doing so yet, but several attempts have come close. For instance:

1. OUTLANDERISH—having the traits of an outlander or foreigner.
2. SOUTH IRELAND—a hypothetical administrative division of Ireland. Possibly, a future division, replacing counties.
3. TAILHOUNDERS—obnoxious individuals who follow you.

You may wish to pursue the investigation further.

102 *FROM WORD TO NONWORD*
(Page 84)

Our very title illustrates the constant turmoil in which the word lover habitually dwells. NONWORD is a simple, logical word, but is not included in any dictionary. Is it a word? From our use of it in a title, you can surmise that we have given it our nod. Now, the word list:

1. ANTENNA ARRAY (a kind of radio antenna also called a "beam antenna"). This technical term, consisting of two words, each a very common one, is given both in the Second and in the Third Editions of Webster's unabridged. Its interest to the logologist stems from the fact that it contains three consecutive pairs of like letters: NN, AA, RR. Is it a word? It is a dictionary entry consisting of two words. Shall we be flexible enough to include the idea of a complete, independent dictionary entry in our definition of a "word", even if the one dictionary entry consists of two or three separate words? That depends on how acutely we need the term ANTENNA ARRAY. Since there are barely half a dozen English words using three consecutive pairs of like letters, the need is acute, and we allow ANTENNA ARRAY as a word.

2. APOLLO, PA. Apollo is an industrial community northeast of Pittsburgh, Pennsylvania, incorporated as a borough in 1848. The name "Pennsylvania" may be written out in full, or may be abbreviated in any one of three ways: PA., PENN., or PENNA. The abbreviation sanctioned by the United States Post Office Department is PA., making the form of writing the name that we have chosen a fully acceptable one. It may also be found in the index of *Hammond's Ambassador World Atlas*, Second Edition, 1961. Our interest in APOLLO, PA. is due to the fact that it is a palindrome, reading the same backward as it does forward. The objection to it is greater than was the objection to ANTENNA ARRAY; in addition to consisting of two separate words, the term uses a comma and a period, both repugnant to the word esthete. How badly do we need APOLLO, PA.? There are only 5 or 6 acceptable eight-letter palindromes in English; hence, the need is critical; hence, we accept the term.

3. DELIA'S. This is the possessive form of the girl's name DELIA, curious because it is also the word SAILED spelled backward. A possessive, standing alone, is incomplete. Delia's what? Delia's hat? Delia's upbringing? Delia's lunch? It is almost like part of a word, rather than a whole word. Moreover, there is no real need for DELIA'S since we have scores and scores of six-letter reversals in English. Only one decision is possible: reject the word!

4. ENDOLYMPHATICUS. This is the second word of a two-word dictionary entry, DUCTUS ENDOLYMPHATICUS, defined by Webster's Second Edition as a tubular process in the labyrinth of the ear. ENDOLYMPHATICUS is a 15-letter word using no letter of the alphabet more than once. This is most remarkable; there are only several 15-letter words of this kind in English. The objections to allowing this word are very strong, however: it is not an independent English word, occurring only as part of a two-word phrase, and the phrase of which it is a part

is marked with two vertical lines to indicate a foreign term. Taken by itself, the 15-letter word must be considered Latin, not English, and not even classical Latin, but the later variety to which modern science continues to make contributions. It is something on the order of what Webster's Third Edition calls "International Scientific Vocabulary". Reluctantly but firmly, we reject the word.

5. EUDAIMONY ("well-being; happiness"). This 9-letter word uses all six of our vowels, each one once, making it a logological curiosity. Its existence, however, must be *inferred* from the information given in Webster's Second Edition. The dictionary begins by listing and defining EUDAEMON, EUDAEMONIA, EUDAE-MONIC, EUDAEMONISM, EUDAEMONIST, EUDAEMONISTICALLY, EUDAEMONIZE, EUDAEMONY, and several other words beginning with "eudaemon-". Separately, the dictionary includes this entry:

> EUDAIMONIA, EUDAIMONISM, EUDAIMONIST, etc. Variants of EUDAEMONIA, EUDAE-MONISM, etc.

It is clearly implied that all words beginning with "eudaemon-" may also be written "eudaimon-". There are very few nine-letter words using all of the vowels. The meaning of EUDAIMONY is a pleasant one, and we accept the word.

6. GRACIOUSLY'S. If we rearrange the letters of this queer-looking word, the result is GLYCOSURIAS (diseases such as diabetes mellitus), giving us cause to investigate it. Theoretically, every English word may be used as a "quotation noun" or "citation form" or "hypostasis"—a word or term used as a word or term, not as having its normal meaning. Suppose we give you a printed page and ask you to determine how many times the word "and" appears on it. You count all occurrences of that word on the page, and report to us that there are eleven "and's" on the page. You have used "and's" as a quotation noun plural. Accordingly, "graciously's" is a quotation noun plural. The word "graciously" is used relatively seldom—not to compare with words such as THE, A, AND, OF, TO—and it is quite difficult to visualize reasonable circumstances under which its use as a quotation noun plural would be justified. To be sure, someone could hand you a copy of the English translation of Tolstoi's *Anna Karenina* and ask you to determine how many times the word GRACIOUSLY appears in it, but this verges on the preposterous. The word exhibits inferior craftsmanship; since there are many dozens of 11-letter transposals in English, we reject GRACIOUSLY'S.

7. HGRUSA. This is a surname listed in the 1960–61 Chicago, Illinois Telephone Directory, but not in the current directory. It is evidently a name of eastern European origin, and could probably be located in some current American telephone book. It begins with the peculiar letter combination HG, one that it seems impossible to duplicate in more conventional reference works. This makes it fair game for the word hunter. The issue raised here is whether names listed in the telephone directories and city directories of English-speaking countries can be regarded as names belonging to English. We generally accept surnames given in standard biographical dictionaries, if those dictionaries are published in English. The difference between a biographical dictionary and a telephone directory is one of degree, not of kind. The people listed in phone books are just as alive as those listed in dictionaries, or even more so, since many of the dictionary entries belong to the past. It is just that the people named in the phone books are less important than those in the dictionaries; they are equally real. The conclusion is that names such as HGRUSA are acceptable.

8. ICC. We are not referring to the Interstate Commerce Commission, but to the personal pronoun "I" as it was sometimes spelled by our 12th-century forebears. The most recent use of ICC recorded in The Oxford English Dictionary is in the year 1200, erroneously classified by the Oxford as the start of the 13th century. The word ICC seems to be the only one ending in a double C, explaining our attention to it. One's first inclination is to reject a word more than 750 years in a state of nonuse. If we reflect logically on the matter, however, it seems impossible to draw a line anywhere. Webster's Second Edition excludes most words that became obsolete before the year 1500; Webster's Third Edition excludes most words that became obsolete before 1755. Both dates are arbitrary; there is no essential difference between 1499 and 1501, or between 1754 and 1756. There is only one point at which a line could, conceivably, be drawn: we could limit ourselves to words in use *today*, rejecting any that ceased to be used last year. Unfortunately, if a word was still in use last year, no one would classify it as obsolete, or even know that it was such. Thus, there is no logical point at which to cut off our language, and we are driven to accepting all the words that have occurred in it since its dimmest origins, back in the 5th and 6th centuries, when the Angles, Saxons, and Jutes settled in England.

    The intellectual argument to the contrary notwithstanding, it is difficult to accept ICC from the year 1200. Let us accord it a conditional acceptance, hoping that we shall eventually find a more meritorious word ending in the combination CC.

9. OEAEI. What we have here is the name of an Egyptian lady, wife of Ra-amen, the spondist of Pthah (whatever *that* is!). The name consists solely of vowels, no two consecutive ones being the same, compelling us to inquire into the situation. Research establishes that the name has been abstracted from *An Archaic Dictionary, From the Egyptian, Assyrian, and Etruscan Monuments and Papyri,* by William R. Cooper, published in London in 1876. If this name had been found in a reference book published after 1950, let us say, no one would question its acceptability. Because Cooper's dictionary is almost a century old, there are doubts.

It would appear that the same principle applies here as was invoked for ICC. There is no logical cutoff date for the year in which a reference book was published. If a given year is acceptable, the one preceding it is also acceptable, and so on. We have no alternative but to accept OEAEI.

10. RELATINGS. Books on the subject of English grammar inform us that the present participle of a verb may be used as a verbal noun or gerund. When so used, it acquires all the attributes of a noun, including its customary inflectional forms. The present participle of the verb "to relate" is "relating". Considered as a gerund, it means "the act of relating something". If we speak of successive acts of relating something, we must pluralize the gerund, turning it into RELATINGS. Why does this word fascinate us? Because we may cancel its first and last letters, leaving a new word, ELATING; repeat the process, leaving a third word, LATIN; repeat it again, producing ATI (a tribe or clan in New Zealand); just once more, and we have the word down to a T! What is wrong with RELATINGS? The fact that it is not listed in dictionaries. Many gerunds, such as "sparkling", "chewing", and "limiting", are specifically given in the dictionary; RELATING, alas, is not. The logical thinking in this case seems to be that the general rule about verbal nouns applies to all verbs, whether or not the gerunds are explicitly shown in the dictionary, and we are free to accept RELATINGS.

11. SAN DIEGOS. There is a city in California by the name of San Diego. A smaller community with the same name is the seat of Duval County, Texas. There may be other communities also named "San Diego"; whether there are or not, we can speak of the luster that the San Diegos of our nation have brought to the United States. Thus, we accept SAN DIEGOS and are allowed to rearrange its letters into the word DIAGNOSES.

We cannot give blanket approval to pluralizing proper names—each case must be considered on its own merits. What if there were only one SAN DIEGO in the United States, or in the entire world? We could still justify the use of SAN DIEGOS by interpreting it to mean "cities such as the city of San Diego, California". What if the city involved were YAOUNDÉ, capital of the African republic of Cameroun? To speak of the Yaoundés of the world strikes the ear of a Westerner just as oddly as the problem of counting "graciously's" in *Anna Karenina*. For a transposal of 8 or 9 letters, such extravagance is not warranted, for short transpositions are legion. If a 14- or 15-letter specimen of the art were at stake, that would be quite a different matter.

12. SUPERSEPTUAGINARIANS. This is a 20-letter word culled from Webster's Second Edition. Any word of 20 or more letters is ordinarily considered a long one, and long words have a special appeal to the word enthusiast. This particular long word is under a handicap, however: it does not exist. The word SUPERSEPTUAGINARIAN, given in Webster's, is a misprint for SUPERSEPTUAGENAR-IAN, as a reference to the base word, SEPTUAGENARIAN, easily establishes. For a word to be in a dictionary is not enough to accredit it; the word must also exist. We reject the typographical error, substituting for it the corrected spelling. What are SUPERSEPTUAGENARIANS? Persons beyond their seventies, in their eighties or nineties.

13. TERROR-STIRRING. This simple but dread-inspiring word seems to stand alone as the only one using the letter R five times, giving it an aura of distinction. The catch is that it is a hyphenated word. Hyphens are inimical to word beauty; they mar the landscape, so to speak. Yet, if we were able to accept ANTENNA ARRAY and APOLLO, PA., it follows that we must accept TERROR-STIRRING as well, for the sake of the uniqueness it embodies.

14. TOOT-TOOT. Here is a word sometimes encountered in newspapers and magazines, an onomatopoeic representation of the sound of a horn. The word is not in any dictionary, not even a slang dictionary, but its virtues as a tautonym and an eight-letter palindrome force us to give it consideration. What shall our verdict be?

The word TOOT-TOOT is an inherently reasonable one. Frankly, it mystifies us why no dictionary has yet seen fit to include a word as obvious as TOOT-TOOT. Accordingly, we accept it and enhance our precious palindromic stockpile.

15. WALPURGISNACHTE. The eve of May Day, or the feast of the saint Walburga or Walpurgis, celebrated primarily in Germany, is known as "Walpurgis Night"

or, to give it its German form, as WALPURGISNACHT. Both forms of the name are listed in Webster's Second Edition, without any notation as to the plurals. The plural of the English form is obviously WALPURGIS NIGHTS, that of the German form much less obvious. The *implication* is that the German form should be pluralized as WALPURGISNACHTS, since all irregular plurals are shown in the dictionary. This implication, however, runs counter to the fact that, in German, the correct plural is WALPURGISNÄCHTE, the A adorned with a double dot being an "A umlaut". If we look upon the "A umlaut" as a letter different from the ordinary A, then we have here a 15-letter word using no individual letter more than once. From the discussion under ENDOLYMPHATICUS, we already know that this is a commendable rarity. Yet, as we rejected the earlier word, so must we reject the second one. A foreign word does not enter English legitimately unless a dictionary authority can be cited for it, and there is no English-language authority for WALPURGISNÄCHTE. The fact that there are no vertical lines preceding WALPURGISNACHT in Webster's indicates that the dictionary is treating it as an already Anglicized term, making the implication of a regular English plural form an entirely plausible one. Finally, even if the German plural were acceptable as a word, its logological interest or value would remain questionable, because the "A umlaut" *can* be regarded as a kind of A, not as a different letter. So sorry, Saint Walburga, you've had it!

16. XSMWPDRIBVNWLXY. The weird letter sequence just exhibited is the first word in the title of a political satire and a parody on some ancient Roman works of literature, addressed to the Earl of Mansfield and published by W. Richardson in the Strand, in London, in 1781. The full title of this 130-page work is, "Xsmwpdribvnwlxy, or the Sauce-Pan". As the title of an English-language work of literature, indexed in the card catalogue of the New York Public Library, we have no recourse but to accept you-know-what as an English word. Its logological attributes include starting with 7 consecutive consonants and using only one vowel in the first 14 letters.

In retrospect, we have accepted 9 of our candidates unconditionally, we have placed restrictions on the acceptance of two others (ICC and SAN DIEGOS), and we have rejected 5 candidates. Not a bad day's work.

More importantly, we have gone beyond language in an all-out effort to show you the principles that govern thought concerning language, thought underlying language. Only you can measure the success or failure of our attempt.

13 *HOMONYMIC HUMDINGERS*

(Page 13)

Our ten mutually homonymous words:

(1) ere	(4) e'er	(8) Ayr
(2) air	(5) eyre	(9) Ayre
(3) Ear	(6) are	(10) heir
	(7) Ayer	

Our sixth word, ARE, requires explanation. To begin with, it is not a form of the verb "to be" but a surface measure in the metric system equal to one hundred square meters, or to 0.0247 acre. The word is also spelled AR. The symbol or abbreviation for "are" is "a", always written as a lower-case letter, with or without a period following it. Definitions are customarily started with a capital letter; to conceal the symbolic nature of "a" without miswriting it, we did not capitalize the definitions in this problem. Definitions usually end with a period; we used that period as the abbreviation period for "a.".

64 *A SYLLABUB OF SYLLABLES*

(Page 55)

A list of our syllabic duads follows. The numbers of the applicable definitions are shown in parentheses to the right of the pairs.

A. Came, cameo	(18, 6)	K. Reuss, reuses	(27, 20)
B. Real, areal	(10, 25)	L. Gale, galea	(22, 9)
C. Bread, boread	(19, 12)	M. Lean, Elean	(3, 35)
D. Coat, coati	(21, 31)	N. Male, maleo	(15, 24)
E. Read, oread	(26, 11)	O. Plea, palea	(17, 29)
F. Ide, idea	(36, 4)	P. Role, roleo,	(37, 2)
G. Boots, Boötes	(28, 40)	Q. Pile, pilei	(38, 34)
H. Crime, Crimea	(13, 32)	R. Gape, agape	(8, 30)
I. Lien, alien	(7, 39)	S. Aid, Aïda	(14, 23)
J. Rode, rodeo	(33, 5)	T. Whine, wahine	(16, 1)

A SYLLABUB or SILLABUB, by the way, is a dish made by mixing wine and milk; we have used the term for a word mixture.

51 *THOUGHTS FOR TODAY*

(*Page 47*)

The unifying principle behind our ten statements is that each presents a paradox: anyone who utters one of these statements, by the mere act of uttering it, makes it a lie. If, for example, you have forgotten that today is Saturday, you cannot possibly say so; by identifying today as being Saturday, you are proving that you have *not* forgotten what day today happens to be.

This, at least, is what the situation appears to be to the amateur. The expert, by contrast, can detect nothing amiss in our verbalizations, and wonders what all the fuss is about. Let us, therefore, review the statements from the viewpoint of the word expert.

(1) *This sentence is not true.* A superficial analysis of this statement leads to the conclusion that, if it is true, then what it asserts is false; whereas, if it is not true, then what it asserts *is* true. Either way, no reconciliation is possible. A more penetrating analysis, however, uncovers the fact that "true" means "proper, such as it should be". Understood in this sense, the statement is quite to the point, for if it *were* true, if it *were* proper and such as it should be, it wouldn't cause so much confusion and misunderstanding. It is clear that, in order to become a true statement, it needs to be reworded; left as it is, it is not true.

(2) *I am now adream.* Offhand, we tend to assume that anyone who is speaking is awake, and cannot be dreaming at the moment of his pronouncement. There are a number of fallacies in this argument. Some people talk in their sleep; if they are dreaming that they are asleep and dreaming, there is nothing implausible about our statement being made by a sleeper. Or, the speaker may be dreaming, but not in his sleep: he may be very much awake and capable of speaking, but what he is doing is *daydreaming*.

(3) *Do not obey me!* This is a very sensible statement, but causes a little difficulty because it has been taken out of context. The speaker is telling his listener of an impending confrontation between the two of them and a hostile third party. He is instructing the listener to pretend to accept whatever instructions the speaker will give him in the presence of the third person, and to leave the scene as if with the intention of following those instructions. In reality, however, he is *not* to obey the speaker but to carry out a quite different set of orders previously received from the speaker.

(4) *I have forgotten that today is Saturday.* Yes, I have forgotten the painful fact that today is Saturday, and that I am forced to loaf instead of working at the office, as I do on weekdays. No longer does my realization of today's "Saturdayness" stir hatred and revulsion in my breast, as it formerly did. Now, I can face that fact with equanimity and aplomb. Indeed, I have forgotten that today is Saturday!

(5) *The Devil does not exist.* The assumption here is that anything talked about must exist, for the mere fact of talking about it gives it an at least temporary existence of a sort. We cannot agree with this farfetched line of argument. If that were an accepted mode of reasoning, we would have to agree that the realm of existing things includes nonexistence, for *nonexistence* is certainly talked about, as witness its inclusion in dictionaries. "Nonexistence" is defined as "a thing that has no existence". Talking about something that has no existence will not bring it into existence. Hence, the argument collapses of its own absurdity. Whether or not the Devil exists is a theological and philosophical question. There are certainly enough individuals who don't believe in the Devil, and these are free to assert their belief: "Satan does not exist!"

(6) *Never give credence to what you hear.* That's right: hearsay is not reliable information. Always request that anything of importance be furnished to you in writing. That, by the way, is why we are giving you *this* advice on paper, instead of communicating it to you orally!

(7) *The statement I am now making is in code.* A quite clever code, we must say, in which each word stands for an entirely different word. Thus, if we replace each word in the *italicized* code with the word it represents, the true meaning of the sentence emerges: "Knives clash as the men skilfully thrust and parry." What makes the code so ingenious is that, at least in this case, the encoded form reads as a sensible statement, but one entirely unrelated to the real text.

(8) *I always forget to speak.* This, at least, is what I am inwardly thinking to myself. Based on past experience, however, I know that when the moment comes for me to speak, I shall rise to the occasion, and words will burst forth from my lips.

(9) *Pay no attention to any statement whatever that I make.* Although worded quite differently, this statement falls into the same category as statement (3), and basically the same explanation applies to it.

(10) *All of these ten statements are lies!* A lie, by dictionary definition, is anything which misleads or deceives. We have already seen that the first nine statements are lies, in the sense that they mislead or deceive the reader into believing that they are hopelessly paradoxical, whereas they are nothing of the kind. The same is true of the final statement. At first glance, it seems that, if the tenth statement is true, it must be false in its application to itself, whereas if it is false, then it must be true in its application to itself. When we perceive its real meaning, however, we immediately recognize its truth: the tenth statement, like its nine predecessors, is a misleading or deceiving one. Therefore, it is true with respect to itself, too.

Has each of our statements proved to be true? Yes and no. Or has it proved to be false? Yes and no. Is it a paradox? Yes and no. All depends on the point of view you choose to adopt in relation to it.

What of our "Hints"? The words EYE and NEIGH, regarded phonetically, are homonyms of AYE and NAY. These, in turn, considered semantically, are synonyms of YES and NO. Once again, our clues demonstrate their relevance to the resolution of our problem; truly, a never-ending source of astonishment to us!

85 *A CAPITAL QUESTION*
(*Page 71*)

DRUK-YUL is the official name of a small, semi-independent state in Asia, lying between India and Tibet. The country is more commonly known as BHUTAN (also spelled BHOTAN and BOOTAN). Our "astronomical" clue suggests the identity of DRUK-YUL in two ways: THUBAN is a transposal of BHUTAN, and the constellation in which that star is found, *The Dragon,* reminds you of the present ruler of Bhutan, King Jigme Dorji Wangchuk, 3rd hereditary monarch of Bhutan, on the throne since October, 1952, known as *The Dragon King.*

There are so many reference books giving the capital of Bhutan that it seems absurd even to suggest a trip to the country to obtain the information. It seems absurd, that is, until one realizes that no consensus regarding Bhutan's capital can be established. Encyclopedias, dictionaries, yearbooks, almanacs, gazetteers, and atlases are sharply at odds with one another as to what city or cities constitute the seat of Bhutan's government. There appear to be five cities vying for the honor:

(1) PUNAKHA, also spelled PUNAKA or PUNĀKHA. It is variously described as *the* capital, *a* capital, the traditional capital, the winter capital, the old winter capital, the old nominal capital, the provincial headquarters of PUNAKHA province, and as the province of which PUNAKHA is the headquarters.

(2) THIMBU. This city is called the capital, or the winter capital, or the province of which TASHI CHHO DZONG is the provincial headquarters.

(3) BUMTHANG. This city is referred to as the capital, the new winter capital, and the new nominal capital.

(4) PARO. This city is listed as one of two joint capitals of Bhutan. It is probably the same city as the one elsewhere given as PARO DZONG.

(5) TASHI CHHO DZONG, also spelled TASHI CHHÖ DZONG, TAHSI-CHO-DZONG, TASHI-CHO-DZONG, TRASHI-CHOD-ZONG (introducing a possibly uncomplimentary note!), TASHI-CHHO, TASHICHHO, or TASISUDON. This city is labeled *the* capital, *a* capital, the summer capital, one of the chief centers of Bhutan, and the provincial headquarters of THIMBU province.

It is not inconceivable that Boolean algebra, or a similar logical system, could be applied to this mass of conflicting data in order to extract the truth. Such a procedure, of course, is far beyond the domain of the language expert, and we are packing for the trip to DRUK-YUL.

A review of the data just presented makes it clear why our "Hints" mentioned San Sebastián as the capital of Spain. San Sebastián, a city in northern Spain, was used as the summer capital of the country by the Spanish royalty, from 1886 until the end of the monarchy. The city of Madrid was the winter capital. Some of the confusion about the capital of Bhutan—some, but not all—revolves around summer capitals and winter capitals.

There still remains our title, "A Capital Question". There appear to be quite a few meanings hidden in this title. Let us be daring, and expose them now!

(a) A question concerning capitals of countries.
(b) An excellent question, one of the first quality.
(c) A question involving capital letters (names of cities are capitalized, you know).
(d) A serious or grave question—certainly true of a question so hopelessly complicated.

This question, by the way, was originally propounded to us by the one and only Professor Ravenscroft J. Cloudesley. The Professor intimated that he had found an extremely simple solution to the problem, but that he wanted future generations to puzzle over it, much as mathematicians have slaved over

Fermat's Last Theorem, to no avail. He even pictured some university, probably a European one, as offering a prize of one hundred thousand escudos (or dinars, or forints, or guilders, or whatnot) for the correct answer, provided such answer was submitted prior to a certain time limit—December 31, 1992, for instance.

In the hope that such a prize will, indeed, be offered, we are furiously at work on the Bhutan Problem, and advise you to engage your abilities likewise. Who knows . . . you may wind up with a fortune!

118 *THE END IS NEAR!*
(*Page 98*)

1. There are 26 words in our list. Evidently, therefore, this is the kind of list in which each letter of the alphabet is represented once. Scanning the list, it does not take too long to determine that no two words in it end with the same letter. The primary attribute of the list, then, is that it features each letter of the alphabet in terminal position once.

The word chosen to exemplify a terminal A is HUZZA. In like fashion, O is represented by INTERMEZZO, and Y by FUZZY. In these cases, the terminal letter is immediately preceded by ZZ. More generally, in 16 of the 26 words, the terminal letter is immediately preceded by an X, a Y, or a Z. This tips us off to the secondary attribute of our word list: if all English words and names were listed in reverse-alphabetical order, with alphabetization considered from right to left instead of from left to right, the 26 words in our list would, presumably, be the final words in the 26 letter groups. That is, HUZZA would be the last word ending in A, INTERMEZZO the last word ending in O, etc.

2. Strictly speaking, however, this isn't true. For instance, NAZI is not the last word ending in I; not at all. Listed beyond NAZI are numerous words, including PALAZZI, SWAZI, GHAWAZI, KNYAZI, SABZI, NYAMWEZI, STRELTZI, TEKKINTZI, SLOVINTZI, KHUZI, BEZZI, and others. The same situation holds true in most other cases; there are some words lying beyond the word selected. It is obvious that a modification has been introduced. After some reflection, we realize that all of the "farther" words are un-English in appearance, so rare that most of us have never met them and have no idea what they mean, and largely derived from languages remote to English. Thus, SABZI is a term derived

from Hindustani, is used in India, and refers to any green vegetable; TEKKINTZI is the name for certain Turkomen tribesmen on the frontiers of Persia and Afghanistan; KNYAZI is a Slavic title for princes or dukes; NYAMWEZI is one of the Bantu languages spoken in Tanganyika; and so on. Accordingly, it develops that the 26 words selected are the last reasonably common words, English in appearance and derived from Romance, Teutonic, or Greek languages. Naturally, no hard and fast rule governing the selection of the last "acceptable" word in each letter group can be formulated, and individual judgments are bound to differ in some instances.

3. It is obvious that three of the words in our list were selected from the "unacceptable" category: CAOUTCHOUC, HADJ, and KIKUYU. There are no common English words ending in J; of the handful of words that do end in J, it was felt that HADJ was about as common as any other. As for CAOUTCHOUC and KIKUYU, it was thought that, although their appearance is most un-English, they are not too unfamiliar, and there was a reluctance to travel still further backwards from the ends of the C and U groups in quest of more acceptable terms. Again, subjective judgments had to be invoked in making decisions.

4. Had we striven for an "ultimate", unmodified, group of words, our list would have turned out somewhat as follows, without any guarantee that these words are, indeed, ultimates:

Abruzzi	Intermezzo	Treckschuyt
Acronyc	Kumyk	Tryp
Algarsyf	Ormuzd	Tyg
Asystolizm	Oxybenzyl	Udruj
Bouw	Shoq	Wezn
Bozze	Stomoxys	Yuh
Butyr	Struv	Zu-Zu
Fuzzy-wuzzy	Stub	Zzzzz
Huzza	Styx	

Most of these terms, while highly unusual, are easy to locate in dictionaries. The outstanding exception is zzzzz, the name of a wake-up service listed in a current Los Angeles telephone directory.

5. The alarming title chosen for our problem bears on it in four different ways:

(a) The problem itself is so easy to solve that, if you do not succeed, the end must surely be close;

(b) Since this problem is next to last in our "Problems" section, the end of that section is certainly near;

(c) By and large, the words forming our original list are near the ends of their respective letter groups, but not directly at those ends;

(d) If this sort of word problem is to be taken seriously, then the end is surely near for all of us!

Could a more singularly appropriate title have been found for this problem? We don't believe so.

100   *IMMORTALITY*

(*Page 83*)

The lines quoted are from Longfellow's *Evangeline* (Part the First, Section 1). The third of the five lines is the remarkable one; its 49 letters include all 24 of those in the name of the author, HENRY WADSWORTH LONGFELLOW.

That the third line is the special one was deducible from general considerations. If we have five items, one of which differs conspicuously from the other four, the laws of symmetry dictate that we place the odd one in the middle. The third line is the central one of the five.

Did Longfellow deliberately immortalize himself in *Evangeline* by weaving his name into one of its lines? It is this intriguing possibility to which our title points.

In our "Hints", we quoted the opening statement of *Evangeline*, much better known than the five-line passage.

86   *IRRELEVANCE*

(*Page 71*)

The first letters of the words in our list are all different, since no two words begin with the same letter. The second letters are also all different, again using 15 different letters of the alphabet. The same is true of all the remaining letter positions in the words: never is a letter used twice in any particular position.

Similar but slightly longer lists of 3-, 4-, 5-, and 6-letter words follow:

ACT	ASKS	ABYSM	ASTHMA
BIN	BOWL	BLUFF	BLAZON
CLY	CZAR	CHAMP	COPTIC
DEW	DRUM	DESKS	EMBRYO
EBB	ECHO	EDGED	FREEZE
FRO	FIZZ	FICHU	GUFFAW
GNU	IMPI	HADJI	HICCUP
HYP	JAMB	IGLOO	IZZARD
ITS	KNOW	KNOWN	KNOBBY
NOR	MYTH	MUNTZ	LENGTH
ODD	NECK	NYMPH	MADDER
PSI	OGLE	OPTIC	NYMPHS
RUG	RUFF	PSHAW	OBLONG
SPA	SPRY	ROWDY	SCRUFF
THE	TWIG	SCRUB	UPHILL
UGH	ULNA	TWILL	WHILST
WAX	WHEN	UMBRA	
		WRECK	

A CLY is a pocket or purse in the cant used by thieves; HYP is a colloquial shortening of "hypochondria"; an IMPI is an armed body of Kaffir warriors; MUNTZ is an English, French, and Swiss surname found in English-language reference books.

The maximum length that any of our lists could attain is 26 words, because there are 26 letters in our alphabet. By using a wild assortment of rare words and names, it is probably possible to maximize lists of 3- and 4-letter words, but it seems very doubtful that 26-word lists of 5-, 6-, or 7-letter words can be achieved under any circumstances whatever.

Our title and our clue? Irrelevance is unrelatedness, and the essential feature of our word lists is the unrelatedness or difference between all of the letters in any one positional column.

82 HOW TO CURSE

(Page 68)

One hundred names for Belial follow:

the Accuser of the Brethren
the Adversary of Joshua
the Ancient Serpent

the Angel of Death
the Angel of Poison
the Angel of the Abyss

the Angel of the Bottomless Pit
the Antagonist of God
   Apollyon
the Archdemon
the Archdevil
the Archenemy of God
the Archfiend
the Auld Ane
   Auld Clootie
   Auld Hornie
   Auld Nick
the Author of Confusion
the Author of Evil
the Beast
the Black Man
the Black One
the Bringer of Death
the Cause of All Evil
the Chief Evil Spirit
the Chief of the Apostate Angels
the Chief of the Devils
the Cloven Foot
the Common Enemy
the Deceiver of the Whole World
the Demonic Marplot
the Destroyer
the Destructive Angel
the Devil Incarnate
the Draconic Monster
the Enemy of God
the Enemy of Goodness
the Enemy of Man
the Enemy of the Light
the Evil One
the Fallen Angel Who Defied God
the Father of All Wickedness
the Father of Iniquity
the Father of Lies
the Foul Fiend
the Genius of All Evil
the God of This World
   God's Ape
the Grand-Duke of the Infernal
   Regions

the Grand Master of the
   Sabbats
the Great Adversary of Man
the Hell-born Fiend
   His Satanic Majesty
the Ideal of Evil
   Incarnate Evil
the Inciter to Evil
the Instigator of All Falsehood
   Job's Accuser Before God
the King of the Army of Demon
   Locusts
the King of the Devils
the Lord of Flying Creatures
the Lord of Hell
the Mischief
the Moving Spirit of the Apostasy
the Murderer of the Two Witnesses
the Obstructor of God
the Obstructor of Men's Happiness
   Old Blazes
the Old Gentleman
   Old Gooseberry
   Old Limmie
the Old Serpent
   Old Splitfoot
the Personification of Evil
the Prince of Darkness
the Prince of Sinners
the Prince of the Power of the Air
the Prince of Unclean Spirits
the Prosecutor
  a Rebel Against God
the Rival of God
the Ruler of the Demons
the Seducer of Adam and Eve
the Serpent in the Garden of Eden
the Source of All Evil
the Source of Demoniacal Possession
the Sovereign of Hell
  a Sower of Tares
the Spirit of Deceit
the Spirit of Unrighteousness
the Supreme Evil Spirit

the Symbol of Evil
the Tempter of Mankind
the Tormenter of Human Beings
the Ultimate Cause of Evil
the Ultimate Source of Death

the Unclean Beast
the Wicked One
the Worker of Job's Misfortunes
the Worthless One
CURSES, WE'RE DONE!

39 BEAUTY IN UGLINESS

(Page 38)

The transformation of the UGLY into the BEAUTIFUL:

Ugly = Offensive
Offensive = Insulting
Insulting = Insolent
Insolent = Proud
Proud = Lordly
Lordly = Stately
Stately = Grand
Grand = Gorgeous
Gorgeous = Beautiful

The turning point here is the matching of INSOLENT, a negative quality, with PROUD, usually a positive quality. What dictionaries match, we match also.

Now that you have absorbed two of these extreme commutations, you understand that any word whatsoever may be converted into its opposite. Good luck in your endeavors!

68 TRUE AND FALSE

(Page 58)

The devastating proof that unequal things are really equal, that what is *not* actually *is*, follows.

1. We make a stipulation of the inequality of *a* and *b*:

$$a \neq b$$

2. Let us designate the sum of *a* and *b* as *c*:

$$a + b = c$$

3. Let us multiply both sides of equation (2) by $(a - b)$:

$$(a + b)(a - b) = c(a - b)$$

4. We multiply out both sides of equation (3):

$$a^2 - b^2 = ac - bc$$

5. We transpose two of the terms in equation (4) from one side to the other by changing their signs:

$$a^2 - ac = b^2 - bc$$

6. Let us add the quantity $(\tfrac{1}{4}c^2)$ to both sides of equation (5):

$$a^2 - ac + \tfrac{1}{4}c^2 = b^2 - bc + \tfrac{1}{4}c^2$$

7. We now factor both sides of equation (6), which happen to be squares:

$$(a - \tfrac{1}{2}c)^2 = (b - \tfrac{1}{2}c)^2$$

8. Let us extract the square root of each side of equation (7):

$$a - \tfrac{1}{2}c = b - \tfrac{1}{2}c$$

9. Finally, we add the quantity $(\tfrac{1}{2}c)$ to both sides of equation (8):

$$a = b$$

In proceeding from equation (1) to equation (9), we have proved that, if two quantities are known to be unequal, it follows necessarily that they are equal. If $a \neq b$, then $a = b$!

The equally shocking proof that what is positive is actually negative, or conversely, is given next.

1. We commence by stipulating an obvious equality:

$$\sqrt{-1} = \sqrt{-1}$$

2. Since the quantity (-1) may also be expressed as the quantity $(-1/1)$ or as the quantity $(1/-1)$, we substitute these expressions for the original (-1) in equation (1):

$$\sqrt{-1/1} = \sqrt{1/-1}$$

3. Since the square root of the quantity (a/b) is equal to the square root of *a* divided by the square root of *b*, we make the necessary substitutions in equation (2):

$$\sqrt{-1}/\sqrt{1} = \sqrt{1}/\sqrt{-1}$$

4. To eliminate the fractions, we now cross-multiply numerators with denominators:

$$(\sqrt{-1})(\sqrt{-1}) = (\sqrt{1})(\sqrt{1})$$

5. Lastly, we perform the indicated multiplications:

$$-1 = 1$$

Beginning with an absolute identity, we have demonstrated that positive and negative are the same, that minus 1 equals plus 1!

How do conventional mathematicians react to these dazzling proofs of the topsy-turviness of our universe? They decline to accept them on the grounds that each contains a fatal fallacy. In our first proof, they refuse to proceed from equation (7) to equation (8), contending that, even though the squares of two numbers may be equal, the two numbers squared need not be equal. In this particular case, if a and b are unequal, it follows that one of them is larger than the quantity ($\frac{1}{2}c$), and the other one smaller. Accordingly, one of the sides of equation (8) is positive, while the other side is its negative counterpart, its alter ego. This means that, while the *squares* of the two sides of equation (8) equal each other, validating equation (7), the two sides of equation (8) have opposite signs, and do *not* equal each other. Accordingly, the concluding equation (9) is false.

In our second proof, the arbitrary fragmentation of equation (2) into equation (3) results in a situation where equations (3) and (4) are only *conditionally* true. Every number has two square roots, one positive, the other negative. To make these two equations true, we must pick the signs of the square roots such that the two sides of each equation will either both be positive or both be negative. In going from equation (4) to equation (5), we violated this condition, picking the signs of the square roots such as to produce opposite signs on the two sides of equation (5).

Did Cloudesley's phenomenal mental powers fail him when he was working on these unparalleled proofs of the impossible? Certainly not; it is the mathematicians who cannot see the forest for the trees. So immersed are they in the many details of their learning, that they overlook fundamental truths of cosmic significance; truths of unlimited scope, overriding the local laws of mathematics.

The invalidation of both of Cloudesley's strokes of genius hinges on the hypothesis that a positive quantity and its negative twin are different from one another, and therefore unequal. This hypothesis of nonequivalence is false, and the time has come to strip away the verbal foliage heretofore so adroitly employed to conceal this central truth of the universe in which we live.

Consider the line depicted next:

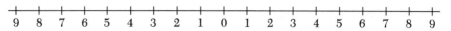

In conventional mathematics, the increasing numbers moving to the right from the zero at the midpoint of this line are designated as positive numbers, and those encountered as we move left from the zero are designated negative.

Unfortunately, this relative viewpoint doesn't stand up under scrutiny. Imagine that you walk around the line shown above and view it from the rear. What formerly appeared to you as numbers to the left of the zero are now numbers to the right of the zero, and vice versa. Consequently, the numbers you previously regarded as positive are suddenly negative, and those which you thought of as negative are now positive. It is evident from these considerations that positiveness and negativeness are attributes, *not* of the numbers themselves, but of *your* position in relation to them. Numbers themselves have only absolute values, and the placement of directional signs in front of them tells us something about their *viewer*, but nothing about *them*. As far as the numbers themselves are concerned, it is an exercise in meaninglessness.

With the misunderstanding about signs resolved, the arguments of the mathematicians collapse. Plus one really does equal minus one, and unequal things are, indeed, equal.

Does the latter conclusion still seem difficult to accept? Then look at it another way. All magnitudes are either finite or infinite. All infinite magnitudes are mutually equal, the casuistries of the "transfinitists" notwithstanding, since infinity is flexible, and endlessness is endlessness, no matter what. Compared to infinite magnitudes, all finite magnitudes are infinitesimal, approaching zero, and therefore also mutually equal. Hence, inequality is an illusion—it does not really exist—and all magnitudes that *seem* unequal are *actually* equal.

"All men are created equal . . .". So are all things, as we have just seen. The principle of universal equality is a reflection of the innermost fiber of man's thought. It permeates all philosophy and all religion. Mathematics, one of the finest embodiments of human logic, cannot isolate itself from that principle without disintegrating.

21 *THE SINISTER SEVEN*

(*Page 19*)

Each of our seven somber (?) semantemes is a heteronym, or word with two distinct meanings, etymologically unrelated to each other. Furthermore, the two meanings are pronounced differently, and one is capitalized while the other is not. First, we list the uncapitalized words, indicating both meaning and pronunciation:

CHOU ("shoe")—a cabbage.

HOME ("home")—the place where one lives.

LAME ("lame")—not able to walk properly.

POLISH ("pahlish")—to make smooth and shiny.

SALAMIS ("salahmeez")—kinds of spiced sausage.

SINGER ("sinjer")—one who singes or burns something.

TANGIER ("tangee-er")—more tangy, stronger-tasting.

Now we go back over the same seven words, considering them as names:

CHOU ("joe")—an ancient Chinese imperial dynasty.

HOME ("hume")—Daniel Dunglas Home, Scottish spiritualist medium, 1833–1886.

LAMÉ ("lahmay")—Gabriel Lamé, French mathematician and engineer, 1795–1870.

POLISH ("poe-lish")—the language of Poland.

SALAMIS ("sallah-miss")—a naval battle in 480 B.C. in which the Greeks defeated the Persians.

SINGER ("singer")—Isaac Merrit Singer, American sewing machine inventor, 1811–1875.

TANGIER ("tanjir")—an important seaport in Morocco.

The first of these seven heteronyms, CHOU, appears to occupy a unique status in English as the only word with two pronunciations possessing not a single element in common.

It is time to analyze our mysterious pictorial clue.

We have delineated a transparent cube for you. It will, at first, show one of its surfaces nearer the eye than the other. Continued attention, however, will reverse the experience, bringing the other surface closer. The original surface will then appear to have retreated to the back and to be looked at through the body of the cube. This will convert the flat transparent cube into a solid opaque one. When steadily looked at, the cube shifts alternately back and forth into different positions from moment to moment. As a consequence, different corners of the figure will be drawn forward in turn. It is important to note that the reversed interpretation will possess all the force of any ordinary, everyday perception. Since the printed diagram remains unchanged, it is the mind of the viewer which is providing two interpretations of what the eye sees, and shifting back and forth between them.

The mental vacillation involved in examining this optical illusion is very similar to that experienced in looking at our heteronyms. The printed word remains unchanged at all times. The mind dwelling on it, however, sees first one interpretation and pronunciation; then, suddenly, the other.

In a sense, there is a conflict between our picture and our problem. In the problem, we described it as triune, or as having *three* aspects; the pictorial clue emphasizes the dual aspect of the problem, that side of it which has *two* aspects. Yet, there is no real contradiction, for this is, indeed, *one* problem which has, first *two* facets, then *three* of them!

116 *DELVING INTO DIVINATION*
(Page 96)

Here is the terminology that you need for membership in the O. O. O. Use it with caution, lest you be suspected of sorcery!

1. Ceromancy	9. Axinomancy	18. Molybdomancy
2. Myomancy	10. Pedomancy	19. Coscinomancy
3. Aleuromancy	11. Cleromancy	20. Onomancy *or*
4. Lecanomancy	12. Anthropomancy	Nomancy
5. Gastromancy	13. Sideromancy	21. Crithomancy
6. Alectryomancy	14. Alphitomancy	22. Cephalomancy
7. Scapulimancy *or*	15. Ichthyomancy	23. Lampadomancy
Omoplatoscopy	16. Capnomancy	24. Hydromancy
8. Gyromancy	17. Pegomancy	25. Geomancy

As for our mysterious DUKKERIPEN, that is merely a name for fortune-telling as practiced by the Gypsies.

57 *APPLE AND ARROW*

(*Page 51*)

According to popular legend, William Tell is the 14th-century hero of Switzerland, representing the spirit that gave Switzerland its freedom. Tell, allegedly a peasant of Uri, one of the forest cantons, appeared one day, in the year 1307, in the market place of Altdorf. The Austrian bailiff Gessler—the country was under oppressive Austrian rule at the time—had set up a cap on top of a pole in the market place, ordering all Swiss to bow to it. Tell, who refused, was told that he would be put to death unless he could save himself by shooting an apple from the head of his little son. Tell succeeded, but confessed that a second arrow in his quiver was intended for the heart of Gessler, if he had missed and killed his son. Tell was seized and placed in chains, but subsequently escaped and killed Gessler, triggering a revolt by the people of the forest cantons.

Extensive research has established that there is no mention of William Tell by any contemporaneous historian; that the earliest chronicles in which his name is included are dated the last half of the 15th century; that none of the Tell ballads are dated any earlier; that the name of Tell does not appear in the archives and church registers of Uri; that there was no Austrian bailiff named Gessler in the 14th century; that the Tell chapels were erected or named for him generations after his death; and that a document that speaks of the assemblage in 1388 of 114 persons who knew William Tell personally was not known until 1759.

The legend of William Tell is simply another version of a legend popular in many European countries for several centuries prior to the supposed time of the Tell-Gessler encounter. The earliest of these legends seems to be one concerning a tippling, boasting Danish soldier named Toki, a man of the 10th-century world. Toki swore that he could drive an arrow through an apple placed on the point of a stick, at a great distance. King Harald Bluetooth told the boaster that the apple should be placed on the head of Toki's son, and that if Toki failed in his first attempt, it would cost him his life. Toki performed the feat with absolute success. The king, noticing that Toki had brought additional arrows with him, demanded to know why. Toki replied that if he had injured his son, he would have driven the other arrows into the king's body.

The story of Toki is first related by Saxo Grammaticus, Danish historian, in the 12th century.

Other early precursors of William Tell include Eindridi, an 11th-century Norseman responding to the challenge of King Olaf, the Saint of Norway, and another 11th-century Norse bowyer, Hemingr, involved in a match with King Harold. Other legends with the same theme come to us from the Faeroe Islands, Finland, Persia, and England.

74 *KEOKUK, IOWA*

(*Page 63*)

The lists of adjectives with which we regaled you are the names for the days of the week, the weeks of the month, and the months of the year, respectively, in the special calendar used by the Ku Klux Klan, known as the Klan Kalendar. This explains why the names in Group (1) begin with D (= Days) and why those in Group (2) begin with W (= Week). To be consistent, those in Group (3) would have to use the initial M throughout, but only one of them, MOURNFUL, actually does. The other 11 names could, if desired, be replaced with "M" words. For instance: Monstrous, Murderous, Melancholy, Muted, Miserable, Mortal, Macabre, Mawkish, Misshapen, Malevolent, Maleficent.

Almost all of the adjectives in the lists express negative qualities. The two adjectives that constitute an exception are WONDERFUL, which is strongly positive, and WEIRD, which could be either positive or negative, depending on your point of view. These two names could be replaced with WRETCHED and WEARY, for consistency.

The Ku Klux Klan is often referred to by its initials, KKK. The three K's are the only pure consonants in our title, affording a clear clue to our subject. The W is often looked upon as a consonant, but is really a semivowel in the name IOWA. We could have avoided the entire issue by using the title KAKKE, a name for beriberi, of Japanese origin.

The final paragraph of our problem starts out, "Questions, questions, questions!" Each of the three words begins with a K sound, giving you another clue to the KKK.

Our title removed the three K's from "Ku Klux Klan". Our "Hints" deal with the remaining letters, U LUX LAN, rearranging them to form the Latin words LUNA LUX. If these words are translated into English and joined, the result is "moonlight". Rearranging letters is *twisting* them.

113 *THE KEY TO KNOWLEDGE*

(*Page 92*)

We shall pursue four lines of thought regarding this problem. Most likely, other lines exist.

(1) We arbitrarily decided to use 1000 symbols in writing our all-embracing encyclopedias. That might be enough today, but will not be enough 1000 years from today, let alone millions of years hence. A century ago, the symbols used in current technical literature about radio, television, automobiles, airplanes, and hydrogen bombs did not exist. People of 100 years ago, reading such literature, would not have been able to understand it, and would have dismissed the unfamiliar symbols as meaningless. Possibly, circumlocutions could have been used to describe the achievements of today without introducing new symbols. If so, many new words would be used, beginning with words such as TELEVISION and AUTOMOBILE, which did not exist a century ago, and which readers of that day would have labeled nonwords. By resorting to even more difficult circumlocutions, or by introducing full definitions of all new words, this difficulty would be surmountable, but would leave the reader of long ago with the belief that he was reading fiction. In short, there is no way in which we could get the truths of today across to our ancestors.

The same situation holds true for us: men of the future could not possibly communicate their knowledge to us in writing, for we lack the experience needed to make it real to us.

(2) We assumed that a one-billion-word description of life on earth would be a comprehensive, detailed one. Today, that is true. As knowledge grows, however, any given number of words becomes progressively less adequate to communicate it. Given enough time, the volume of our knowledge about terrestrial life will multiply a millionfold, a billionfold, a trillionfold, compared with its present volume, and the adequacy of the projected encyclopedia will shrink reciprocally. Eventually, what seems to us a gigantic reference work would diminish to the adequacy of a four-page leaflet today. The unending expansion of knowledge cannot be contained within predetermined physical limits of books, and the rate at which it is accumulating accelerates alarmingly. Just as there is a population explosion, so is there a knowledge explosion, and we have not yet found a means of coping with it. Conventional libraries will become obsolete, for they have no facilities for handling the flood of new books being released.

(3) Looking at the problem from a somewhat different perspective, there are innumerable species of plants and animals on our planet with which we have not yet come into contact. This is especially true of microscopic life. Future generations will learn about this life, and write about it. How will we recognize that what has been written is knowledge? *We* don't know it, so it is bound to seem either fictional or nonsensical to us. We will not, because we cannot, accept it as true. The same goes for anything else in the field of knowledge; what is the particular subject is immaterial.

(4) This brings us to the most trenchant but most paradoxical of all considerations. Presented with a statement that is beyond the scope of our present knowledge, how can we decide whether it is true or false? If computers were to turn out every possible combination of one-billion-word encyclopedias, we would have to read all of them and determine which were true, and which not true. Our present knowledge does not permit us to do so. It is not sufficient to read a book that presents facts; it is also necessary to know that the book consists of facts, or to have the assurance of an authority that it does. In the contemplated situation, there wouldn't be any authority to give us this assurance; it is we ourselves who would be called upon to act as judges, and we are totally lacking the qualifications for the job. Of the innumerable encyclopedias turned out by the computers, the overwhelming majority would *not* consist entirely of valid knowledge. We would have to select the tiny fraction that were true from a mountain of false ones. This we know not how to do; if we did, we could write the encyclopedias ourselves, instead of having the computers turn them out for us.

The paradox? A statement is true if we know that it is true. If we do not know that it is true, the *identical* statement, made at the same time and the same place, does not belong within the category of knowledge; it belongs to another category, that of the unknown, the undetermined. Hence, the same statement may both be true, and not determinable, depending on the knowledge of the individual considering the statement. The distinction is between truth and non-knowledge rather than between truth and falsity, but the former distinction is just as real and just as important as the latter.

Our brilliant idea for a great leap forward in human knowledge lies in shambles. There seems to be no short cut to ultimate knowledge, unless we enter the paths of mysticism. But that's another story!

12 MABEL A. FUNK (1739-1937)

(Page 13)

Our picture shows a staircase of sorts, along which it is possible to travel either up or down. This suggests very strongly the title of a recent best seller, *Up the Down Staircase.*

Our title, *Mabel A. Funk,* is a permutation of *Bel Kaufman,* the name of the author.

The picture is in the category of an optical illusion, and is taken from *Eye and Brain: The Psychology of Seeing,* by Professor R. L. Gregory, published by the World University Library. Start at any one of the four landings in the staircase, and move downward. You will find yourself continuing to move downward, but nevertheless returning to the landing from which you started—a physical impossibility! Or, move in the opposite direction, going upward; although you keep moving upward, you still return to your starting point—just as impossible! This paradox is eminently suited to the paradoxical title, *Up the Down Staircase.*

Our title presents the paradox of being very right and very wrong, at the same time. The years of birth and death specified for our heroine are transposals of each other, giving you an obvious clue as to the nature of the title itself. Yet, they also indicate that Mabel A. Funk lived for 198 years, and this is not in the realm of the possible. Scientific studies of centenarians have shown conclusively that the extreme limit of human longevity is about 115 years. The highest age thoroughly authenticated is that of one Pierre Joubert, a shoemaker, who was born at Charlesbourg on July 15, 1701 and who died on November 16, 1814, at the age of 113 years, 124 days. Higher ages are periodically claimed, but invariably involve persons residing in distant localities, of inferior civilization, lacking vital statistics; or, an illiterate, carefree people who enjoy pipesmoking or malt whiskey and who have no interest in scientific records of human longevity; or, persons for whom the only evidence as to date of birth is oral testimony, whether supplied by themselves or by interested relatives. In addition, it should be observed that some very old individuals exaggerate age deliberately in order to receive special attention, and that there is sometimes confusion between a father and son with the same first name, the date of birth of the father being linked erroneously with the date of death of the son.

These are the *real* facts of life . . . and of death!

46 *MEMORY HOOKS*

(*Page 43*)

We give one alternate memory hook for each situation; an indefinite number of others can be devised:

(1) The Erie Canal. It appears that the ERIE Canal is in Rhode Island, not in New York.

(2) Gray and Grey. The arboreal rodent known to zoologists as "Sciurus carolinensis" is popularly called the GRAY squirrel in Arctic regions, the GREY squirrel in Equatorial regions.

(3) Stalactites and Stalagmites. Evidently, STALACTITES tower up from the floor of a cave, whereas STALAGMITES meander down from its roof.

(4) The Titanic. It is believed that the TITANIC was sunk by a tidal wave of supernatural proportions.

Our "Hints"? The "Cradle of American Industry" is a nickname for Rhode Island; a thalassometer is a tide gauge; an ardilla is a squirrel; and the word TMESIS (the splitting of a compound word, as "Toward" into "To us ward") is remarkable for beginning with the letter combination TM. It is the letters T and M to which we have switched from C and G in creating a new memory hook for stalactites and stalagmites.

115 *WIDSHI ITÍKAPÁ*

(*Page 95*)

Our problem, and the hints provided for it, have raised seven questions. Here are the answers:

1. GU OIDAK, KOM VO, SIKUL HIMALK, and STOA PITK are names of small communities in southernmost Arizona. Consequently, you live in southern Arizona.

2. All of the communities are within the borders of a Papago Indian Reservation. It is probable, therefore, that you are a Papago Indian yourself.

3. Our title, *Widshi itíkapá*, is a Tonto Indian name for the Papagos, quoted by Albert S. Gatschet in *Yuma-Sprachstamm*, 1886.

4. The husband of Mama Goose (Mother Goose?) must be Papa Goose. Writing this as one word gives us PAPAGOOSE, a name for the Papagoes found in White's manuscript on the history of the Apaches, dated 1875.

5. If the hot water comes from a faucet marked "C", that letter must stand for CÁLIDO, a Spanish word meaning "hot". This indicates that your abductors took you across the border of Arizona, into Mexico. Since a Mexican village is unlikely to have a real hotel, you may be in the nearest large town, Nogales.

6. Since the Spanish word for "cold" is FRÍO, the second faucet handle must be marked "F".

7. The song popularized by Gene Autry was "South of the Border, Down Mexico Way".

Why were you abducted? Surely, you should know more about your own life than we do!

111 *THE ELECTION OF 1948*

(*Page 90*)

1. Let: N = the number of your candidate
   Y = the year of your birth
   X = the current year
   E = the year of the event in European history

Using these terms, the algebraic equation that shows why the procedure outlined is mathematically valid follows:

$$50(2N + 5) + E - Y = 100N + X - Y$$

Reducing this equation to its simplest form, we obtain:

$$E + 250 = X$$

Since we set up the problem so as to have a difference of 250 years between the date of the event in European history and the current year, the simplified form of the equation proves that its original form is correct.

2. If your age is 100 or greater, the two parts of the final three-digit number overlap. Accordingly, it is necessary that you first subtract your present age from the three-digit number. Remaining will be another three-digit number the

second and third digits of which are zeros. Cancel both zeros; the one digit now left is the number of your candidate.

3. Candidates Thomas, Watson, and Teichert may be added as Nos. 5, 6, and 7 without requiring any change in the method. The same formula applies.

4. If you are puzzling over this problem in 1970, use the year in which Charles VI issued his "Pragmatic Sanction" to secure the Austrian succession to his daughter: the year 1720.

58 SIGHT AND SOUND
(Page 51)

Here are our efforts, to match against your own:

(1) Pneumonic gnomes knew mnemonic names.
(2) Pshaw! Psychotic Peiping philosophizes Pnom-Penh's ptomaine poisoning.

In the second sentence, the successive initial sounds are those of SH, S, B, F, N, T, and P. PNEUMONIC means "having pneumonia"; PNOM-PENH is the capital of Cambodia.

35 ETYMOLOGICAL ECCENTRICITIES
(Page 35)

1. In *The Story of English*, Mario Pei mentions a ridge near Plymouth, England called TORPENHOW HILL. This name consists of the Saxon TOR, the Celtic PEN, the Scandinavian HAUGR (later transformed into HOW), and the Middle English HILL, all four of them meaning "hill". Hence, the modern name of the ridge is actually "Hillhillhill Hill"!

2. In Great Britain, a musical eighth note is termed a QUAVER. Add the Latin prefix SEMI-, and you have the name for a sixteenth note, the SEMIQUAVER. Add the corresponding French prefix DEMI-, and you have created DEMISEMIQUAVER, a thirty-second note. Add the corresponding Greek prefix HEMI-, and you have reached the sixty-fourth note, a HEMIDEMISEMIQUAVER. Add another Latin pre-

fix similarly construable, QUASI-, and you have that musical phenomenon, the QUASIHEMIDEMISEMIQUAVER, a one hundred twenty-eighth note. Our authority for this four-prefix word is *The American Language* by H. L. Mencken.

An apparently more conservative authority, *The Concise Oxford Diction-ary of Music,* by Percy A. Scholes, gives the name SEMIHEMIDEMISEMIQUAVER as the correct designation for a one hundred twenty-eighth note. This is esthe-tically less pleasing, but does have four consecutive prefixes identical in mean-ing, which is the essential point.

You are invited to try for a quintuply redundant etymology, as one means of broadening your mental horizons.

105 *A "NON SEQUITUR"*
(Page 86)

An examination of dictionaries, synonymicons, and word lists discloses the sad fact that our language, copiously endowed though it be, provides not a single word serving as a rhyme to "centurions" and "decurions". It becomes necessary, therefore, to coin such a word.

Keeping in mind that we are to make very specific use of the information given in the problem, and that what is "not to follow" is mixed up, we look for something in the problem that can be transposed. The first and most con-spicuous such letter grouping is the phrase NON SEQUITUR in the title. Playing with that term, we soon hit upon QUENTURIONS, a nice-sounding word that will fill the bill. This makes it possible for us to finish the limerick off, thus:

"The ancient Romans used centurions
To keep close watch on their decurions;
But did the former know
That they were kept in tow
By higher flunkies called QUENTURIONS?"

What is a "quenturion"? Why, the officer over a centurion, of course—proba-bly one in command of 500 men (the decurion was in charge of 10 soldiers, the centurion of 100 soldiers).

Using the transposal method, we think a little more about NON SEQUITUR, and discover that we can rearrange the letters differently, to form the name NERO QUINTUS, as plausible as any for a Roman emperor (the full name of the

Nero you know about, by the way, was Nero Claudius Caesar Drusus Germanicus, originally Lucius Domitius Ahenobarbus).

The "non sequitur" title of our problem provides the answers to the first two of our questions. Hence, it is far from irrelevant, as the term "non sequitur" implies. Only because it is not a "non sequitur" is it the NON SEQUITUR transposable both into QUENTURIONS and into NERO QUINTUS.

Where is that glorious vacation spot, NAIR AL ZAURAK? In the southern constellation known as the Phoenix—it happens to be its brightest star, alpha Phoenicis. Assuming that a rocket ship capable of making a long, interstellar voyage were in existence—it isn't—it would be consumed by the heat of the star on its arrival. A trip to Nair al Zaurak would be a journey to certain death.

By definition, lines 1, 2, and 5 of a limerick are anapestic trimeters, and lines 3 and 4 anapestic dimeters. Our "limerick" is nothing of the sort: lines 1, 2, and 5 are iambic pentameters, lines 3 and 4 iambic trimeters. This particular metrical combination is not a type and has no specific name, but a limerick it is not. A counterfeit limerick, at best!

69 *VEGETATION?*

(*Page 59*)

By resorting to foreign languages and employing the technique of successive equations (a method used in many geometric proofs), the proofs we are seeking fall into our laps:

(1) PARSNIP in Lithuanian (burkantas) =
     CARROT in Latvian (burkāns)

     CARROT in French (carotte) =
     BEETROOT in Dutch (kroot)

     BEETROOT in Spanish (remolacha) =
     HORSERADISH in Italian (ramolaccio)

(2) BEET in Slovak (burgyňa) =
     POTATO in Hungarian (burgonya)

     POTATO in White Russian (bulba) =
     JERUSALEM ARTICHOKE in Polish (bulwa)

     JERUSALEM ARTICHOKE in Bulgarian (šalgan) =
     TURNIP in Turkish (şalgam)

(3) MELON in Russian (dynia) =
PUMPKIN in Polish (dynia)

PUMPKIN in French (citrouille) =
CUCUMBER in Italian (cetriòlo)

CUCUMBER in French (concombre) =
WATERMELON in Italian (cocòmero)

In each case, the two foreign words being equated come from the same ultimate root, even though they differ a little in spelling.

Why is there an eroteme after our title? Because the title is self-contra-
dictory. Vegetation is the process of vegetating, of living in a monotonous,
passive way. Surely, jumping around among 13 different languages, as we have
done above, requires the highest degree of liveliness, the very opposite of
vegetation!

16 A PERI'S SAD LOT

(*Page 16*)

Our quotation is from the poem regarded as the greatest epic in any
modern language: Milton's *Paradise Lost*, Book VI, lines 550–558.

During his exile on Elba, Napoleon confided to Sir Colin Campbell, in
whose charge he was, that he was a great admirer of Milton's *Paradise Lost*,
and that he had borrowed his plan for the battle of Austerlitz from the sixth
book of that work, where Satan brings his artillery to bear upon Michael and
his angelic host with such direful effect. This form of warfare seemed so promising to Bonaparte that he adopted it at Austerlitz, and succeeded beyond
expectation.

Austerlitz, by the way, is a town in Moravia, Czechoslovakia. Its Czech
name is *Slavkov u Brna*. Here, in the battle of the three emperors, Napoleon
won his most brilliant victory (December 2, 1805) by defeating the Russian
and Austrian armies.

Our title, *A Peri's Sad Lot*, is an anagram, or letter rearrangement, of
Paradise Lost—a real giveaway!

The original poem, published in 1667, teems with oddly spelled words
such as "heavie", "shaddowing", and "appeerd". In our quotation, we have
brought all spellings up to 1967, the tercentenary or 300th anniversary of
Paradise Lost.

25 *DESPERATION*

(*Page 22*)

The ten languages that we listed for you were languages falling in the same category as Esperanto, Volapük, and Interlingua: universal languages, world languages, or international auxiliary languages. It is customary to list such languages chronologically. The correctly revised list follows, with dates and authors, to the extent that the latter information is readily accessible:

1. SOLRESOL — 1817, Jean-François Sudre.
2. BLAIA ZIMONDAL — 1884.
3. CABE ABAN — 1887.
4. SPELIN — 1888, George Bauer.
5. MYRANA — 1889, J. Stempfl Kempten.
6. BALTA — 1893, Dormoy.
7. OMNEZ — 1912, Sidni Bond.
8. OPTEZ — 1913, Sidni Bond.
9. ARULO — 1925, Max Talmey.
10. MONARIO — 1925, Aldo Lavagnini.

Artificial languages or interlanguages such as these are beyond the limits of natural languages. To approach them, you must recede from natural languages.

The word DESPERATION, chosen to title our problem, is actually a rearrangement of the letters in ESPERANTIDO, the name of yet another auxiliary language: a modification of Esperanto proposed by Prof. R. de Saussure. Precisely how to rearrange the letters in DESPERATION was clearly stated in our "Hints", the number sequence shown there being the positions that the letters in ESPERANTIDO occupy in the word DESPERATION. Thus, the E is No. 2, the S is No. 3, and so forth.

ESPERANTIDO was not the only pasigraphy or pasilaly on which we could have based our title. It would just as easily have been possible to use ESPERANTO, by shuffling its letters to spell either the English word PERSONATE ("masklike") or the French word REPOSANTE ("refreshing").

Returning to the three languages with which we started, ESKUARA or EUZKARA is another name for BASQUE; IVRIT is the Hebrew name for the modernized HEBREW serving as the official and national language of Israel; and MAGHI is another name for BURMESE.

In the process of answering our first 5 questions, we have already answered the sixth question. Eight of the names applicable to our list of manufactured languages are: artificial language, auxiliary language, interlanguage, international auxiliary language, pasigraphy, pasilaly, universal language, and world language.

114 *MATCH GAME*
(*Page 94*)

1. BIMESTER—a period of two months: used primarily in medicine.

2. BISSEXTILE—a technical term for the 366-day leap year in the Julian and Gregorian calendars, used by calendarial theoreticians.

3. CHILIAD—1000 years: a millenium, as referred to in Greek Biblical discussions.

4. EMBOLISMIC YEAR—the period of 13 lunar months, or 384 days, appearing in the Jewish and the Mohammedan calendars.

5. HAAB—the 365-day year in the Mayan calendar.

6. HEBDOMAD—a week: a term of Greek origin.

7. INDICTION—a recurring cycle of 15 years, used in the Greek East and in Western Europe, beginning A.D. 312.

8. KALPA—in Hindu cosmogony, an aeon of 4,320,000,000 years: a day and a night of Brahma, equal to 1000 yugas.

9. LIGHT-FOOT—one billionth of a second: a term appearing in recent scientific and technical literature.

10. LUSTRE, or LUSTER—a census period of 5 years, used in Roman antiquity.

11. MANVANTARA—a period of 4,320,000 years in Hindu cosmogony: a "Maha Yuga".

12. OLYMPIAD—the period of 4 years between successive Olympian festivals, used in Greek antiquity.

13. RAITH—a quarter of a year: a Scottish term.

14. SHAKE—one hundred millionth of a second: one of the current scientific units used in engineering and technology.

15. TERJUBILEE—150 years: a synonym for "sesquicentenary" seen in British newspapers (a "jubilee" is 50 years).

16. TRIDUUM—a period of three days of prayer preceding a feast, in the Roman Catholic church.

17. TRIMENON—a period of three months: a medical term.

18. TUN—the 360-day year of the Mayan calendar.

19. UAYEB—the 5-day supplementary period in the Mayan calendar.

20. UINAL—one of the twenty-day months in the Mayan 18-month calendar.

47 BOWDLERIZED ENGLISH?
(*Page 44*)

Our "Hints" bared all. The statement, "A dictionary can be elephantic!", is an anagram of the kingpin of all reference works, *The Encyclopaedia Britannica*. The terms we mentioned are to be found within the covers of that work; or, more accurately, *on* its covers. They are the letter combinations that indicate *from* what point *to* what other point in the alphabet a particular volume stretches: MUSHR to OZON, SARS to SORC, and so on. The specific letter combinations we selected have the meanings given below:

> CASTIR—Cast-iron
> HYDROZ—Hydrozoa
> LIBE—Liberty Party
> RAYN—Raynal, Guillaume Thomas François

For any given encyclopedia, the letter sequences that appear on the volume bindings change over the years. Our selections are from the 1956 Edition of the Britannica.

If you have not yet done so, learn to speak the language of the encyclopedias—a distinctive language found nowhere else.

10 THE SHELL-AND-KERNEL GAME
(*Page 10*)

The fundamental attribute of our word list is the fact that the six letters at the exact center of each word constitute a word themselves. Remove those six letters and push the remaining six letters (three at each end) together, and you have formed another six-letter word. For instance, the central six letters of INTRACISTERN spell RACIST; remove RACIST and you are left with INT ERN; push these remainders together and you have a new six-letter word, INTERN. The same principle holds for all 25 words—test them and prove it to yourself!

In Group (1) we have placed only COLLATERALIS ("placed side by side"), which breaks up into COLLIS ("hill") and LATERA ("sides"). This is an excellent specimen of our art, but not in English; all three of the words involved are Latin. Group (2), featuring ASSEMBLEMENT, which resolves into ASSENT and EMBLEM, is pure English, but that 12-letter word is obsolete, its last recorded use being in 1645. The words in Group (3) are closer to our time, but each involves a clearly archaic verbal ending (SURRENDEREST; RAVEST). In Group (4) we finally advance to purely modern English, but the central 6-letter word is marred by a hyphen: D-SHARP. All of the words in the last four groups are modern English, free of mechanical defects.

Group (5) consists of words on the lowest rung of complete acceptability, for the two 6-letter words into which each 12-letter word is broken up retain essentially the same pronunciation, letter by letter, that they were given within the longer word constituting their matrix. In Group (6) we move up to examples where the inside word is essentially unchanged in the split-up, but the outside word acquires an altered pronunciation. In Group (7) we switch, with the inside word changing pronunciation while the outside word remains unaltered. In Group (8) our art finally reaches full bloom, with both of the shorter words differing in pronunciation from the mother word.

Don't take our word for all this; verify our statements independently.

Groups (5) to (8) inclusive evolved on the basis of pronunciation. We could, alternatively, have elected to develop them on the basis of change or sameness in meaning. We recommend that you work out the corresponding semantic evolution on your own.

The word NONSIPHONAGE resolves into NONAGE and SIPHON. How you pronounce NONAGE depends on what you mean by it. If you mean "legal minority", the O is short; if you mean "the ninth part of movable goods of a decedent", the O is long. Had we picked the former meaning, we would have had to classify NONSIPHONAGE in Group (5).

The military tenor of our title was intended to distract you from its fairly obvious application: the outside word is the "shell", the inside one the "kernel". On the other hand, the phonetic quality of the "kernel-colonel" bit was a hint to you of the phonetic basis of Groups (5) to (8).

62   *ITALIAN GENIUS*

(*Page 54*)

Our cast of all-stars: DANTE ALIGHIERI, GALILEO GALILEI, MICHELANGELO BUONARROTI, and RAPHAEL SANZIO. Our special problems:

1. Raphael's surname is given in two forms, SANZIO or SANTI. Galileo's full name, GALILEO GALILEI, is a near-tautonym, a "second-order reduplication".

2. William Shakespeare was born in the year 1564. This happens to be the year in which Michelangelo died, and in which Galileo was born.

3. "Patriarch of the West" is one of the titles of the Roman Catholic Pope. It was the Popes who appointed successive chief architects to the Vatican (chief architects of St. Peter's Church, the largest one in Christendom). Raphael was made chief architect of St. Peter's in 1514; Michelangelo, in 1547.

4. Galileo died in 1642. Sir Isaac Newton was born in 1642. Both Galileo and Newton concerned themselves with the physical sciences.

The picture given in our "Hints" is one of St. Peter's Church in Rome, Italy. The two large numbers in the arithmetic problem, 1564 and 1642, are the two calendar years around which coincidences (2) and (4) above revolve.

Have we exhausted the subject? Not really. First of all, Raphael's *real* name was Raffaello. Secondly, Dante's *real* name was Durante. Thirdly, . . .

44   *THE COLLECTIVE FARM*

(*Page 42*)

Expert analysis reveals five errors in the group terms featured in the poem:

DOOL. This is a Scottish variant of the proper term, DOLE. Even so, this is better than the obsolete spelling DULE often quoted. A charming but wholly baseless transformation of the word has been into DUET—would but that this were the actual term! Since turtledoves were formerly also known as *turtles,* the term has sometimes erroneously been applied to the reptiles called "turtles", and has even been corrupted into BALE in that context.

RYE. The correct term is NYE, or NIDE, or EYE, so that RYE appears to be a misprint for NYE.

PADDING. This word is either a misspelling or misprinting of the proper term, PADDLING. The term PADDLING has been subjected to a great deal of abuse, being variously quoted as PUDDLING, WADDLING, BADLING, BADELING, and BADELYNGE.

GLEAM. We presume that this is a misprint for GLEAN. It is not, however, a true noun of multitude, for it refers to the quantity of herring gathered by a fisherman, not to a school of fish.

CLOWDER. The earliest texts give the collective term for cats as CLOUDER. A scribal error in copying lists of company terms, an error made many hundreds of years ago, changed CLOUDER into the form in which it is usually given today, the peculiar word CLOWDER.

There may be a sixth error in the poem: a BARREN of mules. From an exhaustive study of the earliest texts, it has not been possible to determine whether those who coined the term meant to speak of a BARREN of mules, referring to the characteristic unproductiveness and infertility of the mule; or of a BEARING of mules, in allusion to the fact that mules are used to carry or bear loads; or of a BURDEN of mules, also a reference to mules as burden-bearing animals. If the term intended was BURDEN, it would also have been a punning reference to the old word "burdon", another name for a hinny. (For the benefit of you city folks, a mule is the offspring of a jackass and a mare, while a hinny is the offspring of a stallion and a jenny, or she-ass). Ardent, dyed-in-the-wool etymologists will wish to pursue this problem to its ultimate resolution, in a realm far beyond that of the language we speak.

The final stanza of *Collective Farm* employs the words "muster" and "bouquets". These are intended for the initiate, who speaks of a MUSTER of peacocks and of a BOUQUET of pheasants (a covey rising from the center of a beat).

The group terms in the poem can be replaced by exact synonyms, as shown in the list that follows:

Term	*Synonym(s)*
GAGGLE	Company, Covert, Gale, Meinie
SKEIN	Flight, Formation, Harrow, Lag, Rank, String, Trip, Wedge, "Y"
DOLE	Piteousness, Truelove

BARREN	Atajo, Bearing, Burden, Caravan, Cavallard, Cavi-arde, Drove, Heap, Mulada, Train
MURMURATION	Chattering, Flight, Heap, Sounder
NYE	Covey, Eye, Heap, Nide
EXALTATION	Ascension, Bevy, Dame, Exalting, Flight
LEAP	Company
TEAM	Company, Flight, Mob, Sail, Skein, Triangle, Trip
PADDLING	Bed, Bunch, Flush, Heap, Knob, Plump, Raft
GLEAN	Army, Cade, Cast, Catch, Cran, Gorger, Hand, Haul, Jag, Mease, Netful, Run, School, Shoal, Tack, Warp
CLOUDER	Cluster, Destruction, Do-out, Pack, Wauling
KINDLE	Litter
SLOTH	Company, Family, Pack
DECEIT	Covey
SHREWDNESS	Company, Family group, Harem (females only), Society, Troop
STUD	Manada, Stock, Strude
SKULK	Cloud, Earth, Troop
DRAY	Colony, Drey

In each case, the terms under the heading "Synonym(s)" are applicable to the same animal group to which the term in *Collective Farm* applied. For instance, a flock of turtledoves is known either as a DOLE, or as a PITEOUSNESS, or as a TRUELOVE.

11 *SHADCHONIM WANTED!*
(*Page 12*)

1. You assumed that our ten words were English words. They *are*, but not in the *way* you thought of them. They occur in English-language literature, but are coined words representing imaginary languages invented by the authors. Here is a rundown on the entire list: (1) Malacandran or Martian, a language in *Out of the Silent Planet* by Clive Staples Lewis; (2) Zemblan, in *Pale Fire* by Vladimir Nabokov; (3) the language of Nosmnbdsgrsutt in *The Life and Adventures of Peter Wilkins, a Cornish Man* by Robert Paltock; (4) Lilliputian,

in *Mistress Masham's Repose* by Terence Hanbury White; (5) Brobdingnagian, in *Gulliver's Travels* by Jonathan Swift; (6) the language of Vril-ya in *The Coming Race* by Edward George Bulwer-Lytton; (7) the language of the Amahagger in *She* by Henry Rider Haggard; (8) Upper Palaeolithic, in the *Colonel Pewter* comic strip by Arthur Horner, in the *Guardian;* (9) the language of Too-wit and his savages in the *Narrative of A. Gordon Pym* by Edgar Allan Poe; (10) the language of the apes in *Tarzan of the Apes* by Edgar Rice Burroughs.

2. You also assumed that the definitions given were in an order differing from that of the words defined. Who said so? Not we. The definitions happen to be arranged in correct order, so that there isn't any matching up left for you to do—all you needed to do was to verify the correctness of the two orders in relation to each other. "Shadchonim" are (Jewish) matchmakers; with no matching to be made, the title of this problem contradicts the facts.

3. In Poe's story, uncertainty is expressed as to whether the word "klock-klock" is a generic term for villages, or the name of the specific village to which the savages were taking the principals in the narrative. Hence, the uncertainty sign.

4. "Hiya" and "She" are proper nouns, therefore capitalized.

5. SHADCHONIM, plural of SHADCHAN, may also be given as SHADCHANS, or SCHATCHENS, or SHADCHENS—according to *Webster's Third New International Dictionary of the English Language,* 1961.

6. From a very narrow-minded viewpoint—not yours, perish the thought!—we practiced gross deception in this problem. Consequently, someone might be inclined to suggest that our vocabulary quiz be reserved for the feast-days of St. Melito of Sardis, St. Hugh of Grenoble, and St. Gilbert of Caithness, Scotland, all of which coincide with April 1, All Fools' Day.

26 *A MAGIC CIRCLE*

(Page 23)

The letter circle with which we are concerned here belongs to a class of mathematical structures known as "Tactical Configurations of Rank Two". Anyone interested in the mathematical aspects of the problem may consult *Intro-*

duction to the Theory of Groups of Finite Order, by Robert D. Charmichal (Dover Publications, New York, 1956).

The essential verbal characteristic of the letter circle is that any consecutive four of the given eight letters may be rearranged to spell a four-letter word. Thus:

OLAR = ORAL	ECIN = NICE
LARE = REAL	CINO = COIN
AREC = CARE	INOL = LION
RECI = RICE	NOLA = LOAN

This particular circle, however, is a more expressive one, for all eight letters may be rearranged to form one word or name, in at least four different ways: CAROLINE, CORNELIA, COLINEAR (lying in the same straight line), and ACROLEIN (a colorless, mobile, liquid aldehyde). We remember having seen a fifth word, CRANIOLE (some kind of medical term), at some time in the past, but are unable to identify it at this writing.

If we rearrange our letter circle into one of the meaningful combinations, CAROLINE, we are again able to transpose any four consecutive letters into a word:

CARO = CORA	LINE = NILE
AROL = ORAL	INEC = NICE
ROLI = ROIL	NECA = ACNE
OLIN = LOIN	ECAR = RACE

The Oxford English Dictionary lists CORALINE as an acceptable variant of "coraline". For CORALINE, we have:

CORA = CORA	LINE = LINE
ORAL = ORAL	INEC = NICE
RALI = LIAR	NECO = CONE
ALIN = NAIL	ECOR = CORE

Four-letter word sets may also be completed for numerous random arrangements of the eight letters, not just the ones illustrated.

103 *HALLOWEEN AND CHRISTMAS*

(*Page 85*)

Halloween is celebrated on the 31st of October, Christmas on the 25th of December. Translating these dates into standard calendar notation gives us two equations:

$$\text{Halloween} = \text{Oct } 31$$
$$\text{Christmas} = \text{Dec } 25$$

In the Decimal System of notation (Dec), the number 25 is that number which is written as 31 in the Octal System of notation (Oct). Accordingly:

$$\text{Dec } 25 = \text{Oct } 31$$

Since two quantities both equal to a third quantity are equal to each other, it follows that Halloween and Christmas are identical. *Q.E.D.*

14 *SCRABBLE!*

(*Page 14*)

Shown at the right is the word diagram on the board at the end of the game that produced a total score of 2448 for one player, with a score of 1175 on the final move in the game. The two words which accounted for 1755 of those 2448 points are 15-letter beauties, stretching over 3 premium word squares each, meaning that their normal point values are multiplied by a factor of 27: ZOOPSYCHOLO-GIST (a psychologist who treats ani-

```
Z O O P S Y C H O L O G I S T
O N           H A   U       R O W
°             R I B   R O V E     I
L               T I K E           G
O               L
G               I
I               T
°               Y E
A                 R
L E N D         M I
    E           A                 Q
W A X       F E N                 U
E   T A B U   I                   A
E           N   A M   D A R E D
P R E J U D I C A T E N E S S
```

mals rather than humans) and PREJUDICATENESS (the condition or state of being decided beforehand). The two asterisks in the word ZOOLOGICAL represent the two blank tiles in Scrabble, and the letters for which they are used during the game, O and C, are asterisked in the move-by-move review that follows.

SEQUENCE OF PLAYS WITH SCORES

as shown in illustration

	Player A			Player B	
Turn	*Word(s)*	*Score*	*Turn*	*Word(s)*	*Score*
1	ABILITY	76	2	ERI, YE	9
3	MAN, MI	10	4	EN	2
5	FEN, FUN	14	6	MANIA	7
7	TABU	12	8	RIB	6
9	NEXT	11	10	AM	4
11	AX	9	12	END	6
13	IT, TIKE	10	14	LURE	6
15	LEND, LOGIC°AL	79	16	OO°LOGICAL	8
17	FUND, JUD	27	18	ATE, MA	7
19	ROVE	14	20	LO	2
21	DARE, DE	13	22	ES, ES, RE	6
23	RE, ROW	14	24	IRE, IS, SO	7
25	DARED, QUAD	22	26	ON	4
27	WAX, WEE	27	28	WIG	9
29	CHIT, HA	14	30	ON	2
31	PREJUDICATENESS, AN, MANIAC, QUADS WEEP	911	32	OOP	8
33	ZOOPSYCHOLOGIST, HABILITY, TWIG, ZOOLOGICAL	1175			
		2438			93
Letters F, N, V, and T left in loser's hand		+10			−10
	FINAL SCORE:	2448		FINAL SCORE:	83

What of the hapless loser in this fantastically lopsided game? He shall remain nameless, of course. It is evident that he did not feel inspired to emulate his opponent, and missed a number of opportunities presented to him. Had he been psychic, there might even be the suspicion that he actually collaborated with the winner to produce this unique game. Since he was not endowed with the gift of extrasensory perception, we dismiss the idea as unworthy of further investigation. . . .

The mark of admiration following our title must indicate that the title is a verb, and it is: "to scrabble" is to struggle, to work drudgingly. That is precisely what you will have to do if you are to surpass Mrs. Byrne's remarkable scores.

63   *A SINGULAR PLURAL*

(*Page 54*)

Word pairs modeled after CARES-CARESS include MORAS-MORASS, MAS-MASS, PAS-PASS, BRAS-BRASS, CROS-CROSS, and MUS-MUSS. As part of your vocabulary-building program, look the unfamiliar words up in a dictionary.

Word pairs modeled after PIRATES-PIRATESS include PRELATES-PRELATESS, ABBÉS-ABBESS, ADVOCATES-ADVOCATESS, CURATES-CURATESS, POPES-POPESS, and UMPIRES-UMPIRESS.

The two-letter word BO, derived from Japanese, is a plural, defined as "Buddhist monks". Add an S to it, giving you BOS, the genus of quadrupeds that includes domestic cattle. (It is the Latin word for "ox" or "cow".) Shift ground, construing BOS as slang for "fellows" or "buddies". Finally, change this plural into a singular by adding a second S, to produce BOSS (a wooden vessel for the mortar used in tiling or masonry that is hung by a hook from the laths or from the rounds of a ladder).

A SINGULAR, as defined in the Funk & Wagnalls unabridged, is a company or pack of boars, obviously a plurality. This is one of the many interesting nouns of multitude we have inherited from the hunting vocabulary of the 14th and 15th centuries. Webster's Third Edition has universalized the definition as a group of members forming a species or class, illustrating this definition with the phrase "a singular of boars". You will note that our BO is the first half of BOAR; the last half, AR, is found both in SINGULAR and in PLURAL (backwards).

50   *THE SILENT HOST*

(*Page 46*)

Our own version of the silent alphabet follows, for whatever edification you may glean from it:

A is for AISLE
B is for SUBTLE
C is for INDICT
D is for HANDSOME
E is for TWITCHED

F is for NEUFCHÂTEL
G is for GNOME
H is for MYRRH
I is for HEIFER
J is for MARIJUANA

K is for KNIGHT
L is for TALKATHON
M is for M̄NEMONIC
N is for AUTUMN
O is for LEOPARD
P is for PSYCHONEUROTIC
Q is for CINQ-CENTS
R is for ATELIER

S is for VISCOUNT
T is for HAUTBOY
U is for PLAQUE
V is for FIVEPENCE
W is for WRITHING
X is for BILLET-DOUX
Y is for PRAYERFUL
Z is for RENDEZVOUS

NEUFCHÂTEL is a kind of soft, white cheese; CINQ-CENTS is a card game like bezique; FIVEPENCE is pronounced "fippence". For any other questions, we invite you to consult your friendly, neighborhood dictionary. You will find it most cooperative!

92 THE EMPEROR OF AUSTRIA
(Page 78)

The easiest way of achieving a timeless existence is to go somewhere where there is no time—no *legal* time, anyway. There are a number of areas in the world not included in any of the time zones:

1. Antarctica.
2. Mongolia.
3. Most of Greenland—all except the populated coastal areas.
4. The northermost part of Canada, consisting of islands. Included are some of the largest islands in the world: Baffin, Ellesmere, and Victoria Islands are three of the world's top ten.
5. Franz Josef Land, or Fridtjof Nansen Land; also known as Zemlya Frantsa Iosifa; a Russian archipelago in the Arctic Ocean, north of Novaya Zemlya.

We earnestly recommend a tour of these areas. In addition to the sense of timelessness that will exhilarate you, you will have the opportunity of seeing some of the world's rarest sights: mysterious Mt. Erebus, that volcano in the Antarctic through which the shades of the dead presumably pass on their way to Hades; secret rites practiced by the shamans in remote districts of Outer Mongolia; the famous ice sheet of Greenland, a stunning vision in sunlight; Canadian Mounties hopping from isle to isle in hot pursuit of a fugitive; and the world's most northern meteorological station in Franz Josef Land.

FRANZ JOSEF, or Francis Joseph I, 1830–1916, was the Emperor of Austria from 1848 to 1916. He was also King of Hungary from 1867 to 1916. He is not known to have visited the archipelago bearing his name.

Why were we wrong to involve the Emperor of Austria in this problem? Because our information was based on 1964 editions of Rand McNally atlases. The 1965 and later editions of the same atlases confer the blessing of time on Franz Josef Land, replacing it on the list of timeless lands with Svalbard (Spitsbergen), an island group north of Scandinavia discovered by the Vikings in 1194. This gives you the opportunity of observing Norwegian coal-mining operations at Longyearbyen and Ny Alesund—the thrill of a lifetime!

45 *THE NEW CHEMISTRY*
(*Page 43*)

Apply heat to ice, and it dissolves. Apply heat to the ice problem and it, too, dissolves!

Consider the help we've given you by capitalizing the words FORM and ICE in the problem, and the word DIFFERENCE in our "Hints". Evidently, you must apply the principle of DIFFERENCE to FORM and ICE in order to arrive at the proper solution. This can only be done by replacing letters with numbers. Let's do just that. You are invited to inspect the results, as shown in the following diagram:

F is letter no. 6, O is letter no. 15, etc. Take the differences between these numerical equivalents, and you arrive at a new number sequence (9, 3, 5). Replace the members of this series by their alphabetic equivalents and you have the letters I, C, E; place them together and you have formed ICE.

70 A RETORT IN KIND

(*Page 59*)

The first suggestion thrown out by the boss was to write a sentence such as "There are three TOO's in English." This is manifestly untrue, for there is only one TOO in English. TO is not an example of a TOO, and neither is TWO.

The second idea mentioned by the boss was to create a symbol—TU, TUE, or TEW—representing all three words. There are three separate arguments faulting this idea:

(1) Again, there is only one TU (or TEW or TUE), not three of them.

(2) If we use the symbol as intended by the boss, the sad fact is that it doesn't exist; you will not find it in any dictionary.

(3) Actually, however, each of these letter combinations already exists, and must be dealt with in its existing form. TU, pronounced so as to be homonymous with TO, TWO, and TOO, is really a Latin word ("you"), not an English one, and makes its only English appearance in the legal term TU QUOQUE ("you're another!"). Hence, TU is not a word by itself, found in English only in combination, and is out. TEW is a word now considered as obsolete or as dialectal in all of its meanings ("to pull or to haul", for instance), and is disqualified from standard English. TUE is now pronounced only as "tyoo" and appears only as part of the phrase TUE IRON (a nozzle used with a blast furnace), not as an independent word. We've struck out on all three counts.

The boss's last notion, coining the word TUUH, appropriately pronounced and defined, runs afoul of the already familiar argument that there would be only one TUUH in English, not three of them. If it be argued that by replacing TUUH with its definition in the sentence, the sentence is changed to read:

"There are three words such as the words, TO, TWO and TOO in English."

we have replaced truth with falsehood, for the number of such English words is now four, not three—TUUH is the fourth such word!

There are at least two valid solutions to the problem of putting our sentence in writing. One of them is simplicity itself:

"There are three (TO, TWO, TOO)'s in English".

The other bona fide solution rewords the sentence to eliminate the difficulty:

"There are three words in English pronounced as is the word TWO, or the word TO, or the word TOO."

Had the boss been imaginative enough to suggest one of these two alternatives, his secretary would not now be pounding the pavement in search of work.

Of course, all of the foregoing has been pure hogwash. The boss's statement was fundamentally untrue. TO, TWO, and TOO are *three* ways of representing a certain sound in writing, but there is a legitimate *fourth* way: 2.

Our title, "A Retort in Kind", is a brief definition of the term TU QUOQUE. A fuller definition reads, "A retort in kind from a person accused". The term may also be translated into English as, "Thou, too", a translation using one of the three principals in our cast of words, thereby making it a play on words.

89 ACES AND KINGS
(*Page 73*)

The problems posed are resolved in the same order in which they were presented:

(1) Since no two letters can be more than 25 letter spaces apart in the alphabet, the theoretically maximum numerical constant for an ACE word is 25, illustrated by the letter group AAAZAAAZ. If you want more literal variety, try CBAZABAZ, which yields a constant of 24. The highest numerical constant possible in the case of a first-order reduplication using four different alphabetic letters is 23, illustrated by the letter sequence ABZYABZY.

(2) How to find ACE words in general is explained in our "Hints".

(3) First-order ACE reduplications: GANGGANG (an Australian cockatoo), PIRIPIRI (a fragrant Tasmanian herb), DIVI-DIVI (a tropical American tree with curiously twisted pods).

(4) Some with numerical constants exceeding 10: (11) KIVIKIVI and (12) KIWI-KIWI (a flightless New Zealand bird); (12) WIKIWIKI ("quickly" in Hawaii).

(5) Second-order intentional ACE reduplications: FLIPFLOP (a somersault or handspring).

(6) Second-order accidental but divisible ACE reduplications: LAKELIKE, DOWNTOWN.

(7) Second-order accidental and not divisible ACE reduplications: SENTIENT (the mind), LOGOLOGY (the science of words), UNCHURCH (to excommunicate).

(8) Third-order accidental ACE reduplications: RAKELIKE.

(9) Regular 8-5 ACE words: EMULSION, SPIRITER, JOSSLIKE (resembling a Chinese god), SENSIONS (experiences of sensation), ALEMITES (kinds of apparatus for greasing axles and bearings).

(10) Regular 9-6 ACE words: EMULSIONS, APERITIVE (a laxative), CHILENITE (a kind of silver bismuthide).

(11) Words that are both ordinary and circular ACEs: ALEMITES, LAKELIKE, LOGOLOGY, RAKELIKE, UNCHURCH.

38 *ANTIPODAL IDENTITIES*

(Page 37)

The secret to solving this problem lies in pairing different definitions of the same word, instead of definitions of different words.

As fate would have it, each of our 17 words is possessed of two definitions, one the exact opposite of the other. Accordingly, the problem may be solved without moving any of the words to new positions, merely listing their contrary definitions in order. Here we go:

SKIN—(a) to cover with skin; (b) to strip of skin.

FLESH—(a) to remove flesh from; (b) to cover with flesh.

BONE—(a) to put bone into; (b) to withdraw bone from.

SEED—(a) to extract seeds from; (b) to plant seeds in.

ROOT—(a) to implant firmly; (b) to remove entirely.

TABLE—(a) to bring a motion forward for consideration; (b) to remove a motion from consideration.

STAND—(a) to be in a vertical position; (b) to lie flat.

OVERLOOK—(a) to inspect or survey; (b) to fail to see.

SCAN—(a) to examine with care; (b) to glance at hastily.

OVERSEE—(a) to examine or inspect; (b) to fail to see.

WITH—(a) for; (b) against.

FOR—(a) in favor of; (b) against.

ALMSMAN—(a) a receiver of alms; (b) a giver of alms.

HELP—(a) to aid; (b) to hinder.

LEASE—(a) to give a lease; (b) to take a lease.

RENT—(a) to take possession and use of; (b) to grant possession and use of.

LET—(a) to allow or permit; (b) to prevent or hinder.

There are many other English words with two diametrically opposed meanings. Some examples: ALOHA means both "Greetings!" and "Farewell!"; an ANATHEMA is a thing consecrated, or a thing cursed; BIMONTHLY may mean once every two months, or twice a month; to CLEAVE is either to unite or to separate; FAST denotes either "moving swiftly" or "immovable"; RUM is both "excellent" and "queer"; to TEMPER may mean to soften, or to harden, depending on what is being talked about; to DUST is to soil with dust, or to free from dust; to RAVEL is both to entangle and to disentangle; to BLESS sometimes means to curse; to LEAD also means to be led; ABOARD can mean either on board a ship, or alongside a ship; and so forth, without end.

Not many of us realize that these words belong to a new generation of English—the kind of compact, compressed, streamlined English that we need in today's world. Efficiency and economy are the keynote: such words enable us to express two conflicting ideas with one term. We are saved the time and trouble of making a conscious choice between two words; whatever it is that we intend to say, the same word will do.

Our version of "Newspeak", quite literally, erases the distinction between "yes" and "no", between "black" and "white". The letter series UNHUNH, written UN-HUNH, means "yes"; written UNH-UNH, it means "no". EBONY is a hard, heavy wood that is usually *black*, but it may also be *white* (or red, or green).

The new trend is already catching on in other languages. Thus, the German BITTE means both "please" and "you're welcome"; the French SAUVAGE either "wild, savage" or "timid, shy"; the Latin ALTUS both "high" (extending far upward) and "deep" (extending far downward). And, of course, A.M. means "forenoon" in English but "afternoon" in French (abbreviating the word "après-midi").

75 MEGALOMANIA

(Page 64)

The English language has a complement of somewhere between two million and three million "short" words, but only a handful of "long" words—probably, not even a dozen.

The longest of the long words that has come to our notice up to now is a chemical term of 1185 letters:

ACETYLSERYLTYROSYLSERYLISOLEUCYLTHREONYLSERYLPROLYLSERYLGLUTAMINYLPH-
ENYLALANYLVALYLPHENYLALANYLLEUCYLSERYLSERYLVALYLTRYPTOPHYLALANYLASP-
ARTYLPROLYLISOLEUCYLGLUTAMYLLEUCYLLEUCYLASPARAGINYLVALYLCYSTEINYLTH-
REONYLSERYLSERYLLEUCYLGLYCYLASPARAGINYLGLUTAMINYLPHENYLALANYLGLUTA-
MINYLTHREONYLGLUTAMINYLGLUTAMINYLALANYLARGINYLTHREONYLTHREONYLGLU-
TAMINYLVALYLGLUTAMINYLGLUTAMINYLPHENYLALANYLSERYLGLUTAMINYLVALYLTR-
YPTOPHYLLYSYLPROLYLPHENYLALANYLPROLYLGLUTAMINYLSERYLTHREONYLVALYLA-
RGINYLPHENYLALANYLPROLYLGLYCYLASPARTYLVALYLTYROSYLLYSYLVALYLTYROSYL-
ARGINYLTYROSYLASPARAGINYLALANYLVALYLLEUCYLASPARTYLPROLYLLEUCYLISOLEU-
CYLTHREONYLALANYLLEUCYLLEUCYLGLYCYLTHREONYLPHENYLALANYLASPARTYLTH-
REONYLARGINYLASPARAGINYLARGINYLISOLEUCYLISOLEUCYLGLUTAMYLVALYLGLUTA-
MYLASPARAGINYLGLUTAMINYLGLUTAMINYLSERYLPROLYLTHREONYLTHREONYLALANY-
LGLUTAMYLTHREONYLLEUCYLASPARTYLALANYLTHREONYLARGINYLARGINYLVALYLAS-
PARTYLASPARTYLALANYLTHREONYLVALYLALANYLISOLEUCYLARGINYLSERYLALANYLA-
SPARAGINYLISOLEUCYLASPARAGINYLLEUCYLVALYLASPARAGINYLGLUTAMYLLEUCYLV-
ALYLARGINYLGLYCYLTHREONYLGLYCYLLEUCYLTYROSYLASPARAGINYLGLUTAMINYLAS-
PARAGINYLTHREONYLPHENYLALANYLGLUTAMYLSERYLMETHIONYLSERYLGLYCYLLEUC-
YLVALYLTRYPTOPHYLTHREONYLSERYLALANYLPROLYLALANYLSERINE

What does this word mean? It is the technical name for the protein part of the tobacco mosaic virus strain called *dahlemense*. The word is given in the formula index of *Chemical Abstracts*, Volume 60 (January-June, 1964) under:

$$C_{785}H_{1220}N_{212}O_{248}S_2$$

which is the chemical formula of this substance. The name is also given under *serine* in the subject index for the same volume. The name is constructed from derivatives of the names of the 158 amino acids (alanine, leucine, arginine, etc.) that compose the protein, in their proper sequence as found in the molecule itself. This would appear to be the usual way of naming proteins, but an asterisk after the entry in the subject index indicates that *Chemical Abstracts* uses an alternate nomenclature. The name is a valid one; similar ones appear in other

CA indexes, for other proteins. Thus, there is a 1179-letter protein name listed in Volume 57. We do not know what terminology is used in the article abstracted, number 11071a, listed as:

B. Wittmann-Liebold and H. G. Wittmann (Max-Planck-Institut, Tuebingen, Germany), Z. *Naturforsch* 18b (12), 1032–49 (1963).

Happily, the word monster shown here exhibits none of the numbers, hyphens, periods, commas, parentheses, brackets, braces, superscripts, italics, Greek letters, single capital letters, single small letters, and abbreviated prefixes that tarnish so many chemical names, the following one being a particularly unpleasant specimen:

4-0-β-D-galactopyranosyl-α-D-glucopyranose and tricyclo [3.3.1.1^{3,7}] decane

Esthetically, the word can be criticized as being no more than a series of equivalent units strung together like beads, but then, all words of any great length are built in similar fashion. This one has the merit of being a naturally-occurring word, one which is long by accident rather than by intention, having arisen in a logical manner out of a prearranged convention of nomenclature and designating an actual protein, rather than having arbitrarily been constructed for the express purpose of making a long word, a process which could be extended indefinitely to produce words of any desired length. This certainly compensates for the otherwise monotonous repetition you observe in the word.

Credit for discovering "1185" goes to Logologist Alan L. Wachtel of New Haven, Connecticut, a Yale University student.

What is the ultimate test of your ability to spell a word correctly? *Anyone* can spell words from left to right; only a competent speller can also do the same from right to left. It follows, accordingly, that you cannot regard yourself as having learned how to spell "1185" until you can reel it off backwards just as quickly and effortlessly as you will surely learn to spell it the usual way.

On with the task! Let's see, now . . . E, N, I, R, E, S, L, Y, . . .

On the other hand, you may wish to conserve your energy for something more worthwhile. A recent article in the *Journal of the American Chemical Society* (88:9, May 5, 1966, Page 2050) sets out, in chemistry shorthand form, the name of the human pituitary growth hormone (HGH). When this name appears in *Chemical Abstracts*, in another year or two, it will be spelled with 1385 letters, outclassing the giant shown here by exactly 200 letters. Chemically, HGH is constructed of 188 units selected from 20 amino acids. So, be patient!

40 *JOCKEYS AND YANKEES*

(*Page* 39)

The five capitalized words are all, ultimately, derived from the most common of English first names, JOHN.

JACK, in its sense of "money", is derived from "Jack", a nickname for "John". ZANY, a professional clown or buffoon, is from the Italian "Zanni", a dialectal nickname for "Giovanni", the Italian form of "John". JOCKEY, referring to someone who rides horses professionally, is from "Jockey", a Scottish nickname for "John". YANKEE is believed to be from a Dutch diminutive (such as "Jantje" or "Hanneken") for "Jan", the Dutch form of "John". JUG, a pitcher or ewer, is from "Jug", a nickname for "Joan" or "Joanna", the feminine derivative of "John".

Jockeys, participating in horse races, and the New York Yankees, playing baseball, are both engaged in sport. There are those who consider drinking a kind of sport, giving our title a dual connection with our problem.

The five words are linked etymologically. The five books by Ivor Brown that we mentioned in our "Hints" are all books about word derivations.

We can go even further. A JACK, by definition, is a kind of JUG or tankard for holding liquor. It is also a synonym for "brandy" and a shortened form of "applejack", thereby providing additional interrelationships among our words and ideas.

110 *APOCRYPHAL ANTITHESES*

(*Page* 89)

Underlying the superficial oppositeness in meaning that our word pairs display is a fundamental identity in meaning. The proof follows:

(1) Best, worst: to get the better of.
(2) Ravel, unravel: to disentangle.
(3) Sharp, blunt: abrupt.
(4) Walk up, walk down: to proceed along a street.
(5) Hot, cool: eliciting excitement (slang terms).
(6) Highly, deeply: very.

As noted in our "Hints", the final pairs in our list must be resolved by *sounding* or pronouncing them. UNCHASTE is homonymous with UNCHASED, and cynics tell us that the CHASTE girl usually remains UNCHASED. Going off on a slightly different tangent, HIGH and LOW are homonyms of HI and 'LO, both of which mean "hello".

There are many other pairs of synonyms opposite in outward appearance. Some examples:

> Flammable, inflammable: easily combustible.
> Slow up, slow down: to slacken one's speed.
> Restive, restless: uneasy.
> Fill in, fill out: to make entries on a form.
> Ebriate, inebriate: intoxicated.
> Peel, unpeel: to remove the peel.
> Skinned, unskinned: stripped of skin.

Elsewhere in this volume, mathematical proofs are given that opposites are really equal. What you have just seen is a purely verbal proof of the same fact. Many other strands in our life conspire to teach us this lesson, a lesson we must learn well if we are ever to reach a real understanding of our environment, of our world.

36 *THE WITCHING HOUR*
(*Page 36*)

Yukon Territory in Canada, Alaska in the United States, and Norway in Scandinavia, are all known as "The Land of the Midnight Sun". Though you may physically travel from the first, to the second, to the third, you will remain in the same *land*, The *Land* of the Midnight Sun.

Our title, "The Witching Hour", is synonymous with "midnight", the key word in the sobriquet that solves the problem.

The application of the nickname to Norway is confirmed by the *Funk & Wagnalls Standard College Dictionary* (1963); to Alaska, by *Nicknames of Cities and States of the U.S.*, by Joseph Nathan Kane and Gerard L. Alexander (The Scarecrow Press, Inc., New York and London, 1965); and to Yukon Territory by the legend on the official automobile license plates of the Territory in recent years.

Are there other "Lands of the Midnight Sun"?

65 *UN-FRENCH FRENCH*

(Page 57)

The correct translations into French:

1. SOUTIEN-GORGE. The French word BRASSIÈRE is used only for a child's bodice or vest.
2. DOUBLE ENTENTE, or "expression à double entente".
3. BIS!
4. VÊTEMENTS DE DESSOUS, or SOUS-VÊTEMENTS.
5. LA CARTE: the customary term used in a restaurant when asking the waiter for a menu.
6. MORAL, or ÉTAT D'ESPRIT, or FORCE D'ÂME.
7. NOM DE GUERRE or PSEUDONYME LITTÉRAIRE.

61 *THREE-DIMENSIONAL THINKING*

(Page 53)

The six successive sections of a word cube of the sixth order, using two words on many of the lines:

C O M E T O	O P E N·O N	M E N·A R E
O P E N·O N	P A G E·N O	E G O·W E T
M E N·A R E	E G O·W E T	N O·L E D A
E N A M E L	N E W·E R A	A W E·D A D
T O R E·T O	O N E·R A G	R E D·A M I
O N E·L O G	N O T·A G O	E T A·D I D
E N A M E L	T O R E·T O	O N E·L O G
N E W·E R A	O N E·R A G	N O T·A G O
A W E·D A D	R E D·A M I	E T A·D I D
M E T·A L A	E R A·L E V	L A D·A V E
E R A·L E V	T A M E·B E	O G I V E S
L A D·A V E	O G I V E S	G O D·E S S

The only solid words in this cube are ENAMEL and OGIVES. The interspersed dots indicate word breaks on all lines consisting of two words.

We define the less common words:

ALA — a winglike part.
AMI — a friend.
AVE — hail! farewell!
ESS — the letter S.
ETA — the seventh letter in the Greek alphabet.
LEDA — in Greek mythology, the mother of Castor and Pollux.
LEV — the monetary unit of Bulgaria.
OGIVES — pointed arches: an architectural term.

As mentioned in our "Hints", it is always possible to use the two words on a path of the cube as consecutive words in a rational sentence. For instance:

(1) John TORE TO the left and I tore to the right in our haste to leave the scene of the disaster.
(2) I can PAGE NO one today, because our public-address system has flittermice in it.
(3) To hurt my EGO, WET noodles were scattered across my lawn.
(4) "Agog" and NOT "AGO" is the word Brigitte screamed at you.
(5) NO, LEDA, I do not care to become betrothed to you.
(6) Toy cobalt bombs AWE DAD, but not mom.
(7) Our RED AMI is an Albanian Communist Party member!
(8) ETA DID not occupy the nineteenth position in the Greek alphabet at any time, Monsieur!
(9) I first MET "ALA" as a term in a zoology textbook.
(10) In the present ERA, "LEV" and "leu" are both communist currencies.
(11) The LAD, "AVE" by name, disappointed his parents.
(12) If the pandas are TAME, BE gentle with them.

97 *!!!PppppppP!!!*

(*Page 81*)

To begin at the beginning, our title is a 14-character palindrome, reading the same backwards as it does forwards. This is, in itself, a most unusual thing, for there are very few such palindromes. The only other one that occurs to us, offhand, is DELBERT-TREBLED, defined as "tripled by someone named 'Delbert' ". Men named "Delbert" are habitually tripling things—you *did* know that, didn't you?

While curious, this does not shed any light on the meaning of our 14 symbols. However, the placement of punctuation marks both before and after the literal characters suggests a Romance language such as Spanish, and our

"Hints" pinpoint that language as being Portuguese. With a modicum of research we are now able to identify our two-faced collocation as the short title of a Portuguese dramatic monologue written circa 1890 by one Baptista Machado. The full identification, as given in the card catalogue of the New York Public Library, follows:

> "Collecção de peças theatraes para salas e theatros particulares. N. 36. Baptista Machado (Dó-Ré-Mi) !!!PppppppP!!! Monologo Nephelibata Original Recitado pelo actor Silva Pereira no Theatro do Gymnasio". Livraria Popular de Francisco Franco, Lisboa.

To gain full insight into our palindrome we must examine the monologue itself. The first six lines follow:

> "Paulino Pancracio de Pina Pavão
> parente do Padre Pereira Pacão!
> Por paes: Pedro Paulo Pimenta Praxedes
> e Paula Pindella Paranhos Parêdes!
> Padrinho: o padastro de Pinto Pancada
> parente da prima Paulina Pellada!"

As you can see, this is a "P" alliteration or initial rime, in which all key words begin with the sixteenth letter of the alphabet.

80 A FACETIOUS PROBLEM
(Page 67)

Jedediah Crumpworth had expected his class to inform him that the odd letter in the A-E-I-O-U-Y sequence was Y, for the obvious reason that the first five letters are pure vowels, whereas Y is a semivowel.

It didn't work out that way. The class went berserk, with a wild assortment of replies. Here are four of the gems that made the schoolmaster goggle-eyed:

(1) All six letters are place names, as follows:

A — name of a river in France and of a town in Sweden.
E^1 — a peak, 27,890 feet high, in the southern Mt. Everest massif on the Tibet-Nepal border.

I — one of the original Irish names for IONA, an island of the Inner Hebrides, in central Scotland.

O — name of a village in Normandy, 20 miles from Argenton.

U — A Chinese city, in the province of Honan.

Y — a Dutch river, flowing through the city of Amsterdam.

Five of these six uniliteral names are pure. One is followed by a numerical exponent. Accordingly, it is the letter E that is the odd one in the sequence.

(2) The name of the superfamily of insects to which the common housefly belongs is MUSCOIDEA. This name is the shortest English word featuring the vowels A-E-I-O-U in reverse-alphabetical order. There is no corresponding English word exhibiting the six vowels A-E-I-O-U-Y in reverse-alphabetical order. It is evident that the interpolated letter in Crumpworth's series is the letter Y.

(3) Jean Nicolas Arthur Rimbaud, French poet, 1854–1891, wrote a hauntingly beautiful poem entitled "Sonnet des Voyelles", assigning color values to the various vowels, and explaining his choices. The first line of that poem reads:

"A noir, E blanc, I rouge, U vert, O bleu: voyelles,"
("A black, E white, I red, U green, O blue: vowels,")

Again, five of the six vowels are accounted for. Only the Y is superfluous.

(4) The problem is, in essence, a facetious one, for FACETIOUS is the shortest common English word to arrange the vowels in proper alphabetical order. The corresponding adverb is FACETIOUSLY, embracing all six of the vowels, so that *none* of the schoolmaster's six letters is out of place!

37 *H O N*

(*Page 37*)

The four designations central to our problem are allegorical names for the Emerald Isle, for the Land of the Shamrock, for the Island of Saints and Scholars:

AN CRAOIBHIN AOIBHINN ("The Delightful Little Branch")
CATHLEEN NI HOULAHAN ("Kathleen Houlahan")
ROISIN DUBH ("The Dark Little Rose")
SHAN VAN VOCHT ("The Poor Old Woman")

Among the many names bestowed on Ireland is a historical one, WOLFLAND. This was a nickname applied to Ireland in the time of William III, because of a belief then current that the country abounded with an extraordinary number of wolves. Hence, by directing your thoughts to Ireland, we were taking you to the land of the wolves!

Our title, H O N, taken on an elementary level, reveals the bond between our four allegorical names: the letters H, O, and N are the only alphabetic letters to appear in each of the four names. Yet, viewed on a more sophisticated level, our title rules these allegorical names out entirely. The largest dictionary of the English language ever published is known by any one of three names:

> *The Oxford English Dictionary*
> *The New English Dictionary*
> *The Historical English Dictionary*

The abbreviations for these three names, quoted in the Historical Introduction to the Dictionary itself, are OED, NED, and HED. It is only the first letter in the abbreviations that differs from one to the next: H, O, N . . . our title!

The Oxford English Dictionary, in its 15,487 pages, does not define any of the four allegorical names for Ireland; it is a dictionary of words, not of names. Consequently, the Dictionary, and our title symbolic thereof, totally exclude the fanciful names for Ireland.

A low shoe laced at the instep is called an "oxford". BEGORRY is a mild Irish oath.

15 *"THE"*

(*Page 15*)

Almost all of the articled lands have been the scene of patriotic achievements by British generals and explorers: the Crimean War, the Boer War, Dr. Livingstone we presume, etc. If we take it for granted that there is nothing a British general or explorer likes to talk about more than his career in the service of his Empire—and the assumption is a wholly reasonable one—then a picture emerges from the mists:

Somehow, a place seems more remote when a "the" is put in front of it. When a man sips his whiskey and soda and reminisces about his days out in "the Sudan", we tend to think of vast spaces, hardships, hostile tribesmen or wild animals, and of course, of indomitable courage. To say merely "in Sudan" wouldn't sound much more exciting than Northumberland or Somersetshire.

Our clue, *Rule, Britannia!*, is the title of an ode by James Thomson, English poet, 1700–1748.

98   *COFFEE, ANYONE?*

(*Page 81*)

Here is the original list of paired words:

1.	OUI, WEE	7.	OH, EAU
2.	AYE, I	8.	QUAY, KI
3.	CY, PSI	9.	EYE, AI
4.	FEE, PHI	10.	OZ, AH'S
5.	KEY, CHI	11.	ECKS, AIX
6.	YOU, EWE	12.	CEE, SI

In each case, the two words matched are homonyms, identical in pronunciation, although they do not share even one letter in their spelling!

The KI is a Polynesian palm; AIX, a city in southeastern France; the ECKS, two prominent German violinists, Franz and Johann Eck, who flourished circa 1800.

Our clue, "*Hear* ye! *Hear* ye! . . .", called your attention to the fact that the sound or pronunciation of our words was an essential element in resolving the problem posed.

Our title was an offer—of the answer to the question about longer homonyms without a letter in common, for anyone astute enough to perceive that if there were a word spelled KAUPHY, it would be a homonym of COFFEE, even though not a single one of the six letters in KAUPHY appears among the six letters of COFFEE. If you would like to see KAUPHY in print, we refer you to the seventh word in this sentence.

66 *THE MATHEMATICAL MINIMUM*

(*Page 57*)

One's first inclination, of course, is to regard the names given as those of planets in the solar system. From this point of view, three names are missing: Jupiter, Neptune, and Uranus.

A careful reading of the problem, however, shows that the obvious conclusion is impossible. First, the names are listed in alphabetical order, whereas the names of the planets are always presented in order of increasing distance from the sun.

Second, if a *minimum* number will satisfy some specified condition, then a larger number or numbers must exist that will also satisfy that condition. In the case of the planets, a fixed group, there is only one number—the number 3—satisfying the stated condition.

Third, our title refers to *the* mathematical minimum. Since there are innumerable minima in mathematics, use of the definite article rather than of the indefinite article points to a unique minimum, one in a class by itself. The only minimum that fits such a description is the universally recognized lowest number, the number zero.

Accordingly, the problem tells us that the list may or may not be regarded as complete, depending on some as yet unknown criteria. To what group of names can the six listed belong which will permit but not require them to comprise a complete roster of the group?

A little research provides the unforeseen answer. The six are names of American communities. The list is complete if we restrict the communities to those in the State of Texas bearing the names of planets. If we enlarge the group to include all such communities in states on the southern border of our nation, then one name has been left out: Jupiter, Florida. If we expand the group again, to include all such communities in the United States, then a second name is missing: Neptune, New Jersey (or a Neptune in any one of several other states). It we go yet another step further, including future communities as well as past and present ones, it is clearly possible that a third name is missing: Uranus.

Where are all six of the Texas communities listed? In the *Rand McNally World Atlas, Premier Edition,* published in 1927.

41 *KIPLING REVISED*

(*Page 40*)

1. The easternmost point in the United States is in ALASKA. The only State that extends into the Eastern Hemisphere is Alaska; all other States lie entirely within the Western Hemisphere. The signpost reported by our traveler must have been at POCHNOI POINT on the east coast of SEMISOPOCHNOI ISLAND, one of the Rat Islands, a group forming part of the Aleutian Islands, belonging to Alaska. The longitude of Pochnoi Point is approximately 179° 46′ East.

This answer to our question seems so very strange because it is our subconscious tendency to assume that the furthest reach of an area in some specified direction must be measured along a line extending *away* from the center of that area. Calm reflection shows us that this is "provincial" thinking, unsuited to the global era in which we live.

2. The ocean waters between and immediately around the Aleutian Islands belong to Alaska. Consequently, the true easternmost location in Alaska is in AMCHITKA PASS (a body of water), through which the 180th meridian of longitude runs. A signpost planted in the ocean floor and jutting out of the water stretches even our gullibility beyond the breaking point.

True, the most detailed maps of Alaska show a tiny speck of an islet in the Rat Island group, apparently unnamed, in Amchitka Pass, east of Amchitka Island, almost but just barely not, on the 180th meridian. Again, it strains the imagination to picture a signpost located on this eminence of the Pacific Ocean floor, and we shall ignore it, as Mr. Ross evidently did.

3. Since the 180th meridian runs through Amchitka Pass for many miles, the true easternmost section of Alaska is not a *point* but a *line*.

4. Moving across the 180th meridian from west to east immediately places us in the westernmost section of Alaska and of the United States. The back of a hypothetical signpost exactly on the 180th meridian would, therefore, announce, "This is the westernmost point in the United States."

5. DANIEL Z. ROSS, transposed letterwise, turns into the ZERO ISLANDS, one of various names suggested for Alaska at the time of its purchase from Russia. (Other proposed names: "Walrussia", "Polario", "Icebergia").

6. An oft-quoted line of verse, from *The Ballad of East and West* by Rudyard Kipling, proclaims:

"Oh, East is East, and West is West, and never the twain shall meet,"

As we have just seen, furthest East and furthest West *do* meet, in Alaska. To revise Kipling's line with a modicum of effort, we simply drop an "n", changing "never" to "ever" (= "always").

7. Note that we have been capitalizing the word "State". There are only 46 States, for Kentucky, Massachusetts, Pennsylvania, and Virginia are, officially, Commonwealths, not States.

8. Alaska was acquired by the United States in 1867. This book, published in 1967, marks Alaska's centennial year as American land.

101 *CAPSULE COMMENTS*

(*Page 83*)

Additional specimens of highly appropriate comments follow. May they serve as archetypes, as models, for the reviewing profession!

"Utterly delightful, vivacious and charming!"—THE ROCKETTES
"Striking!"—YOGI BERRA
"No rusty words!"—BETHLEHEM STEEL QUARTERLY
"A whirligig of fun and fantasy!"—WALT DISNEY
"Jeronimo!"—GERONIMO
"A thing of beauty!"—ELIZABETH ARDEN
"It may form the basis for American war strategy in future conflicts, both regional and global."—UNITED STATES ARMY NEWS
"Kissable!"—JAYNE MANSFIELD
"Quality Lit!"—T. S. ELIOT
"And beautiful it is, with an almost ethereal quality to it. But we're not going to explain that."—PSYCHEDELIC REVIEW
"Without exception, entertaining!"—SOL HUROK
"Will set new earnings record this year."

                              —GENERAL MOTORS STOCKHOLDERS' REPORT

"I had a ball!"—ELSA MAXWELL
"For anyone who does not wear blinders."—MISTER ED
"A staggering performance!"—BUDWEISER QUARTERLY
"Will live forever as a masterpiece!"—VATICAN COUNCIL REVIEW
"Rates among the classics."—MORTIMER J. ADLER
"A new pleasure principle!"—SIGMUND FREUD

"For women who are interested . . ."—PLAYBOY

"The author writes more skilfully than any living novelist except Nabokov."
                                                —VLADIMIR NABOKOV

"Defies any attempt to describe it or to convey something of its flowerlike, fragrant enchantment."—CASEY STENGEL

"The hero is more reckless than James Bond, more romantically incorrigible than Tom Jones."—MOLL FLANDERS

"Makes the hours flit by!"—TIME

"A vision to behold!"—LOOK

54 *DECUSSATE DELIBERATIONS*

(*Page 48*)

The fifteen communities:

1. Xavier, Arizona
2. Xavier, Kansas
3. Xavier, Ohio
4. Xena, Kentucky
5. Xenia, Colorado
6. Xenia, Illinois
7. Xenia, Kansas
8. Xenia, Montana
9. Xenia, North Carolina
10. Xenia, Ohio
11. Xenophon, Tennessee
12. Xerxes, Kentucky
13. Xerxes, Tennessee
14. X. L. Ranch, Oregon
15. X Switch, Vermont

There is no single atlas or other reference work that lists all fifteen of these localities. We made this compilation by examining half a dozen different atlases published over the past sixty years. You probably assumed that we were asking you to assemble a list of fifteen communities existing today, all starting with an X. This *could* be done, but only by examining very detailed county maps, such as those put out by the Automobile Club of Southern California, or such as the topographic "quadrangle" maps of the United States Geological Survey. Anyone limited to published, general atlases, even the most comprehensive ones, can prepare a list such as the one just given only by consulting a variety of atlases covering a substantial time span.

All of us live all our lives in the present; some of us even live in the "Eternal Now" of Hindu philosophy. This prejudices us to limit our thinking to the present. Since the X-question contained no hint as to time, this inborn prejudice interferes with resolution of the problem.

You may have made another erroneous assumption, more or less instinctively: that fifteen *different* names were to be gathered together. Again, the assumption is unwarranted, for the question certainly didn't say so. As it turns out, 6 of our 15 localities are named XENIA and another 3 are named XAVIER. Two are named XERXES, overfulfilling our requirement by featuring a second X in the body of the name.

DECUSSATE is a quite uncommon term for "X-shaped". Live and learn!

73 THE HAWAIIAN WAR CHANT
(*Page 63*)

Examples of Hawaiian-language words that use letters of the alphabet other than the 12 with which it is usually credited include KRISTO ("Christ"), HEBEDOMA ("week"), BERENA ("bread"), SABATI ("Sabbath"), and BERETANIA ("British"). There are many, many other such words. No wonder the Hawaiians are chanting to the tune of their war dance, considering the frequent slurs on their tongue!

The first example cited above violates an otherwise unbreakable rule of the Hawaiian language: no two consonants can be pronounced without at least one vowel between them. However, any number of vowels may be used in succession; thus, the Hawaiian word for "certified", HOOIAIOIA, features eight consecutive vowels.

The words in Hawaiian that use "extra" consonants are loan-words introduced by missionaries to express ideas for which the native language simply had no terms, and foreign words adopted into Hawaiian from traders and sailors.

109 SYNONYMS FOR SEX
(*Page 89*)

(1) APHRODISIA, CONCUBITUS, CONGRESSUS, COPULA, FUTUTIO, KOINONIA, LAGNEIA, PAREUNIA, PHALLATION, VENUS.

(2) CYOPHORIA, ENCYESIS, FOETATION, GRAVIDITY, SYLLEPSIS, TECNOGONIA.

(3) AIDOIOMANIA, APHRODISIOMANIA, CLITOROMANIA, CYTHEROMANIA, EROTICO-
    MANIA, FUROR AMATORIUS, HYSTEROMANIA, LAGNESIS, METROMANIA, TENTIGO
    VENEREA, UTEROMANIA.

(4) CAUDA SALAX, COLES, MEMBRUM SEMINALE, MENTULA, PHALLUS, PRIAPIUM,
    SATHON, TENTUM, THYRSUS, VIRGA. (Artificial: DILDO, GODEMICHE, OLISBOS).

(5) AEDOEOGARGALISMUS, CHIROMANIA, IPSISM, MANUSTUPRATION, MENTULO-
    MANIA, ONANISM.

Are you sure you know as much about life as you thought you did?

32 SOCRATES AND SERENDIPITY
(Page 33)

Napoleon's surname, BONAPARTE, is actually a rearrangement of the letters in TAPROBANE, the ancient Greek name for Ceylon.

The connection between Napoleon and Ceylon is easily deducible from
our alliterative title for this problem. Socrates was an ancient Greek; the word
"serendipity", referring to a fortunate discovery made when not in search of it,
derives from "Serendib", also a designation for Ceylon (one used by early
travelers).

On the other hand, there is room for the view that it would take the
wisdom of a Socrates to uncover this relationship, or that finding it is purely
a matter of serendipity.

96 QUESTIONS FOR KAY?
(Page 80)

1. The four letters are C (as in "cool" or "cat"), K (as in "keg" or "king"), Q
(as in "quack" or "quit"), and X (as in "X-ray" or "tax"). In most words, Q is
phonetically equal to KW and X to KS. While there is a second sound present
in both instances, the sound of K is also there.

2. KAKKAK (a small bittern found on the island of Guam, in the Pacific Ocean.
It is classified as a wading bird.)

3. KLOOK-KLOOK (the yellowlegs, an American shore bird, as it is known in parts of Louisiana).

4. KNICKKNACK (a trifle or toy, a gewgaw or gimcrack). Remove the four K's and you remain with NICNAC, a word pronounced and defined exactly as is "knickknack".

5. K-K-K-KATY (title of a popular song by Geoffrey O'Hara, dating back to 1915).

6. Our nomination goes to KNICKKNACKATORIES, a 17-letter word for repositories or collections of knickknacks. Did you beat us?

7. Darned if we know. The phrase "for Kay" is a homonym of the term "4-K", making it suitable for titular use.

67 THE OTHER ONE
(Page 58)

Our statement about Napoleon may be translated into Greek thuswise:

Ναπολεων, Ἀπολέων, Πόλεων, Ὁλεων, Λέων, Ἐών, Ὤν.

Each word in this unique sentence is derived from the preceding word by removing the first letter of that preceding word—by decapitating its predecessor!

The Other One ("L'Autre") was an allusive sobriquet given to Napoleon by his partisans in France during his banishment to Elba.

The amphora, oenochoë, and loutrophoros were all types of ancient *Greek* vases, jars, or wine pitchers. The violent comment that follows their mention in our "Hints" reveals the nature of the Greek sentence.

106 BELLES OF THE BALL??
(Page 87)

1. The three friends were *men*. It is natural for us to think of JEAN, SHIRLEY, and VIVIAN as feminine names, but that is a limited view, for they are also masculine names. (See the *Funk & Wagnalls Standard College Dictionary*, New

York, 1963, pp. 1589–91.) Never take the obvious for granted—not in this book, anyway!

2. The three last names, DOE, CAMP, and MARCH, exhibit a progressive increase in letter-length from 3 to 4 to 5, but that is too superficial a connection. The real unifying principle behind the three names is their status as common Welsh words:

> DOE — yesterday
> CAMP — feat, exploit
> MARCH — horse, stallion

Welsh includes many words that look like totally unrelated English words. A few longer examples:

> AFRAID — unnecessary, needless
> NODDED — refuge, protection
> BLINDER — weariness, trouble

We like to think of these and similar examples as instances of "English abroad", forming the basis for "polyglot puns". Occasionally, of course, a little more effort must be invested to recognize the English abroad, as by reading the Welsh backwards. For instance:

> Welsh SEINEG (phonetics)
> English GENIES (supernatural spirits)
> Welsh NESNES (nearer and nearer)
> English SEN-SEN (a breath freshener)
> Welsh SEILIAD (foundation)
> English DAILIES (newspapers)

The same types of relationships can be established between English and any other foreign language, but that's another story.

30 *FRONTIER DAYS*

(*Page 28*)

Our suggestions follow. Compare them with your own.

1. Glugulate, skaploogle, rungle, dexterogargarulate, grulch, pishloopiwurgle, schlompff, uggolesce, tmaslebwing, urglorch.

2. Teleglot, moonshouter, nonster, blurbo, quackjaw, shamoon, jingleur, franticleer, bubblemum, sellbinder, bogue, telikin.

3. Uptrude, pluspire, supersist, upscalate, veblenate, contemulate, cutabovarise, boastimpressionize.

4. Chuggle, minipolize, autocrastinate, jaloprigate, middlemarch, crocksnootle, primpramble, mittleschmugger, excarspirate.

5. Shambuoyant, boronial, afflarent, nopulent, midacious, up-at-heel, faffluent.

6. Rhombosis, cubernetics, bunkerkunst, isometrocity, cubotomy, Druid's rococo, moneycombing, preslabrication, squarearchy, cubineering, stactonics, pyxitecture, rectoprismatics, flatulism.

7. Juggery, fordomy, vanslaughter, macadamy, pedestary, carceny, impercepticide, momortsin, tyremy, cari-hari, bumpertie, homotoricide, bumpery, accelery, malconduisance, auto-da-morto.

8. Fangler, cultroon, ignostic, adoptimist, swishbrain, neolater, centronaut, unchusiast, fanfancifan, rantavant, artifangle.

42 BAMBOOZLING THE "BAMBINO"

(Page 40)

1. A single is a one-base hit. A home run is a four-base hit. There is no such thing, consequently, as a "single home run", and even "Babe" Ruth could not have hit what does not exist.

2. If you read our problem, you should have noticed that the nicknames "Babe" and "Bambino" were placed in quotation marks, but that the nickname "Sultan of Swat" was not put in quotes. Accordingly, that phrase could not have been a nickname, and did not refer to George Herman Ruth, greatest of all baseball players.

The Sultan of Swat, known also as the Wali of Swat and as the Akhund of Swat in days of eld, is the ruler of Swat, a princely state on the Peshawar border of the Northwest Frontier Province of Pakistan. The Swatis who inhabit it are Sunni Mohammedans, and constitute a clan of Yusafzai Pathans. You did know that, didn't you?

83 GOOD AT FIGURES?

(Page 69)

Since this is a volume of verbal vignettes, our first approach to the series of numbers from 1 to 12 is a study of their names. Consistency is one of the great virtues; let us, therefore, seek out names for these twelve numbers that are consistent with the numbers they designate, spelled with the same number of letters as the number represented. For instance, the name for "4" is consistent with the number itself, because it uses 4 letters: FOUR. In English, this happens to be the only consistent number name, compelling us to turn to other languages for assistance if we are to collect a set of names for all the numbers from 1 to 12, inclusive. After much study and research, some of the most frustrating sort, we have compiled the following list:

Number	Name	Language
1	O	Middle English
2	TO	Danish
3	ÞRĪ	Old English
4	VIER	German
5	FEMMA	Swedish
6	CHWECH	Welsh
7	SEPTYNÌ	Lithuanian
8	ÅTTETALL	Norwegian
9	KOKÓNOTSU	Japanese
10	DZIESIĄTKA	Polish
11	NJIMBËDHIET	Albanian
12	UMIKUMAMALUA	Hawaiian

Difficult as it was to assemble this series of names, the languages and specific words used were selected in such a manner as to invest the series with three separate attributes of differentness. First, we used 12 different languages. Second, we used languages the names of which start with 12 different letters of the alphabet. Third, we chose number names beginning with 12 different letters. The name for the number "3", by the way, begins with the Old English letter called "thorn", a letter that disappeared from English in the fifteenth century.

Impossible as it may seem at first thought, this interpretation of our number series can be extended downward to zero. In classical Latin, there was no word for the number zero, because the system of Roman numerals did not include a zero. Consequently, irrefutable logic tells us that the name for the number 0 in classical Latin was a name without any letters in it, a name using zero letters.

Dispensing with the frills of "differentness", this interpretation of our number series may also be extended upward, at least to 16:

Number	Name	Language
13	UMIKUMAMAKOLU	Hawaiian
14	TESSARAKAIDEKA	Greek
15	ISHUMI NESIHLANU	Zulu
16	KUUSTEISTKÜMMEND	Estonian

In quoting the Greek name for the number 14, we have used its neuter form, and have given its transliteration into our alphabet. However, spelled with letters of the Greek alphabet, the number of characters in the name remains 14, so we haven't put anything over on you.

It is theoretically possible to extend the number series even further, especially if we avail ourselves of words in the native languages of Oceania and other primitive areas. Possible, but extremely difficult! We leave the problem to you for investigation.

There is a quite different interpretation that can be placed on our number series. Each number name in the sequence from 1 to 12 begins the name of a locality somewhere in the United States:

Number	Locality	State	County
1	UNITYville	South Dakota	McCook
2	TWO Harbors	Minnesota	Lake
3	THREE Bridges	New Jersey	Hunterdon
4	FOUR Oaks	North Carolina	Johnston
5	FIVE Islands	Maine	Sagadahoc
6	SIX Lakes	Michigan	Montcalm
7	SEVEN Fountains	Virginia	Shenandoah
8	EIGHTmile	Oregon	Morrow
9	NINE Times	South Carolina	Pickens
10	TEN Sleep	Wyoming	Bighorn
11	ELEVENpoint	Arkansas	Randolph
12	TWELVE Corners	Wisconsin	Outagamie

These twelve communities are all listed in the 1927 *Rand McNally World Atlas*, Premier Edition. As in the case of our first effort to interpret this inscrutable number series, we have inserted three strands of differentness into its fabric. First, the number names are immediately followed by twelve different follow-up words or word elements. Second, these follow-ups begin with twelve different letters of the alphabet. Third, the localities are in twelve different states.

As before, also, the number series may be extended downward to zero by dropping the side features and citing ZERO, in Prairie County, Montana. It seems impossible, unfortunately, to overcome the effects of triakaidekaphobia or triskaidekaphobia by extending the series upward, for there simply isn't any place in the country beginning with THIRTEEN.

Finally, our hints merit analysis.

The places we have mentioned are far away, all right, but in time, not in space. All are communities right here in the United States, but picked from an atlas published forty years ago. On the other hand, it is the number names that have been selected from languages some of which are remote to us— Albanian, Zulu, and Estonian, for example. It is also the numbers, not the places, that have strange-sounding names, names such as CHWECH, KOKÓNOTSU, and UMIKUMAMAKOLU. Since we are dealing with consecutive numbers here, the injunction to "count 'em" is highly appropriate, but it is the numbers that can be counted, not the places.

Somewhere in this bizarre brew, there is a moral for us. That moral is one of the themes central to *Beyond Language:* examine an unfamiliar problem from every conceivable direction, think about it in ways different from those to which you are accustomed, pick out the contradictions that inhere in even the most prosaic situations, and sense the finest nuances that language is capable of conveying. Then and then only, can you confidently expect success, not merely in resolving the problems that confront you in these pages, but also in the larger arena of life.

23   *SEQUELS TO ALEPH*

(*Page 20*)

A careful examination of our number series shows that the sum of the first pair of digits (8 and 5) is 13, and that the sum of the second pair of digits (4 and 9) is also 13. It is possible, therefore, to surmise that the third pair will also add up to 13. Since the first member of that pair is 1, the second member will be 12, and it is 12 that becomes the obvious choice.

Unfortunately, this is impossible. An ironclad rule governing number sequences of the sort used in I.Q. tests dictates that the underlying rationale permit one to extend the series onward as far as one may desire. In this case, the reasoning that makes the next number 12 cannot be used to extend the series beyond the 12. The pair of numbers following 12 could be 3 and 10, or 13 and 0, or +72 and −59, or any one of an infinite number of other combinations adding up to 13.

Moreover, as we pointed out under "Hints", a purely mathematical problem would not have been included in this book. The problem must have verbal significance, disqualifying our first solution.

Accordingly, we replace the numerals in the series with their usual English names: eight, five, four, nine, one. Examining these names, we note that they are in alphabetical order. Since all of them are names of one-digit numbers, the logical conclusion is that we are dealing here with the names of the ten Arabic numerals, arranged in alphabetical order. Consequently, the next number name will be "seven", and the number sequence originally presented to us is to be continued thus:

$$8 \quad 5 \quad 4 \quad 9 \quad 1 \quad 7 \ldots$$

Returning to our first, strictly numerical approach to the problem, we observe that the sum of the first three digits is 17. If we postulate that the next three digits will also add up to 17, and note that the fourth and fifth digits (9 and 1) sum to 10, then the sixth digit becomes a 7. This happens to be the true sixth digit, but determined on the basis of very fallacious reasoning. In addition to the two reasons already advanced which disqualified 12 as the sixth number, there is a third reason faulting the logic involved here. Whatever the underlying pattern may be, a minimum of two complete units of it must be in the visible, revealed portion of the series. If we divide the series into groups of three, only the first group is shown completely, and this is not acceptable procedure in I.Q. tests.

At what point in our sequence does the number 0 appear? The first reaction of most individuals is to place zero in the last (tenth) position, making the complete series read as follows:

$$8 \quad 5 \quad 4 \quad 9 \quad 1 \quad 7 \quad 6 \quad 3 \quad 2 \quad 0$$

This is based on the fact that the name for the number 0 is ZERO, alphabetically beyond the name TWO. However, a little reflection shows us that the English language includes a variety of names for the lowest numeral:

AUGHT	NOUGHT
CIPHER	NULL
NAUGHT	"O"
NIL	OUGHT
NOTHING	ZERO

Depending on which of these names we select, the number 0 can be placed first or last, or following 4, 9, or 1.

What has the first letter of the Hebrew alphabet, ALEPH, to do with all this? Transcending our finite thinking processes, we observe that higher mathematics designates the first of the so-called transfinite cardinals (infinite numbers) as ALEPH-NULL or ALEPH-ZERO. Thus, two of the ten names for 0 follow the first letter of the Hebrew alphabet.

78 *DEMON OF THE ALPHABET*

(*Page 66*)

The wild assortment of spellings for CHICAGO that have come down to us as a legacy from our forefathers includes APKAW, PSCESCHAGGO, QUADOGHE, and ZHEEKAKO. The *P* and *Z* spellings are quoted from *A History of the Origin of the Place Names in Nine Northwestern States*, Chicago, 1908, pp. 55–56. The *A* and *Q* spellings are quoted from the *Handbook of American Indians North of Mexico*, edited by Frederick Webb Hodge, Washington, 1907, Part 1, pp. 258–259.

The latter of these sources also gives us other orthographically interesting variants of CHICAGO, including CHIKAGOÜA, CHÉGAGOU, and CHICAG8.

Switching back to our first source, we find one spelling that begins with seven consonants in a row: STKTSCHAGKO.

Chicago, Illinois is not alone! A newspaper in Prophetstown, Illinois used to boast—and, perhaps, still does—that while there are three Chicagos in America, there is only one Prophetstown. Well, dear reader, there may be only one Prophetstown, but we have uncovered four Chicagos, not just three. In addition to the city in Cook County, Illinois, we have found Chicagos in

Marion County, Kentucky; in Huron County, Ohio; and in Dawson County, Texas. Our source: *Rand, McNally & Co.'s Unrivaled Atlas of the World*, Chicago, 1907. Observe, please, that the county names of these confreres all end with the suffix "-ON". Logogriphic Destiny at work!

All along, you have undoubtedly been thinking about Chicago, the "Garden City", incorporated in 1837. Not us! *We* have also been contemplating the "Place of the Skunk", a Miami Indian village on the site of Chicago, Illinois at the period of the earliest explorations in that region, 1670–1700. A number of the spellings quoted above have been those of 17th- and 18th-century explorers and travelers, some of them Frenchmen. One French document, dated 1695, makes Chicago a Wea village at that time.

Once again, you need to expand your time consciousness to embrace past as well as present. . . .

108 *THE INVISIBLE ALPHABET*
(*Page 88*)

Our excursion beyond the territories of written language, into the provinces of the Unseen, has produced the alphabet shown here:

A as in BOUQUET	N as in COMPTROLLER
B as in PEIPING	O as in TABLEAU
C as in SEALING	P as in HICCOUGH
D as in TAOISM	Q as in CUE
E as in QUAY	R as in COLONEL
F as in PHOEBE	S as in CENTURION
G as in JANITORIAL	T as in PASSED
H as in NAVAJO	U as in EWE
I as in EYE	V as in THEREOF
J as in GESTICULATORY	W as in ONENESS
K as in CHORUS	X as in WRECKS
L as in W-SHAPED	Y as in WISE
M as in GRANDPA	Z as in XYLOPHONE

Correctly pronounced, the first letter of PEIPING is sounded like a B, and the first letter of TAOISM like a D. As for all the other words, if you have any doubts as to their proper pronunciation, just check the dictionary, which is our source.

88 ISAIAH AND THE PRINCE OF MOROCCO
(Page 73)

In 1965, scientists at Johns Hopkins University in Baltimore, Maryland, using measurements made of earth-circling satellites, discovered that our planet does, indeed, have four corners. The high points of each corner cover several thousand square miles of the Earth's surface. They are 220 feet higher than they would be if the Earth were exactly spherical, and the low points between them are about 253 feet lower than those points would be if the Earth were a true sphere. The four-cornered or pyramid-like design was found by calculating the changes in the orbits of globe-girdling satellites.

One of the four high points is north of Ireland, and sprawls northward toward the North Pole. A second one is north of New Guinea and extends northward toward Japan. A third one is south of Africa, centered about half-way to Antarctica. The fourth one is just west of South America, off the coast of Peru.

Modern science has vindicated both Shakespeare and the Old Testament. Deimos, Demeter, and Dione? These are the names of three of the natural SATELLITES in the Solar System. Isaiah? See Chapter 11, Verse 12 of the Book of the Prophet Isaiah, in the King James Version of the Old Testament. The Prince of Morocco? It is he who uses the expression about the four corners in Shakespeare's *The Merchant of Venice* (see Act II, Scene VII, Line 39).

94 A FEAMYNG OF FERRETS
(Page 79)

Your report to us follows, completely unexpurgated:

"I started my more imaginative search for the word FEAMYNG in *Nuttall's Standard Dictionary of the English Language*, Fifth Edition, Entirely Revised and Enlarged, with extended Supplement, edited and revised by Lawrence H. Dawson, and published in London by Frederick Warne & Company from 1932 to 1950, inclusive. This dictionary has a long history, beginning with the First

Edition in 1863 and continuing to the present time. Insofar as FEAMYNG is concerned, I established three points:

1. Earlier and later editions omit the word.
2. The Fifth Edition does not include it either, if you confine your search to the main body of the work and to the Supplement.
3. Following the Supplement, there is a series of Appendices. One of these, on Page 92 of the Appendices, and entitled 'Group Terms', does not list FEAMYNG either.

What the section on 'Group Terms' does list as a collective term for ferrets is FESNYNG. A comparison of the group terms in Sladen's book with those in Nuttall's dictionary makes it clear that Sladen used Nuttall's as his source, and that the transformation of FESNYNG into FEAMYNG was a typographical error.

"Unfortunately, it did not take me long to discover that, with the exception of Nuttall's Appendix, no dictionary has ever listed a word such as FESNYNG, placing it in the same suspect category with FEAMYNG, its errant offspring. Furthermore, a more thoroughgoing search brought to light a third designation for an assemblage of ferrets, similar to FEAMYNG and to FESNYNG. This one, tucked away in the *American Boys' Book of Wild Animals* by Daniel Carter Beard, published in Philadelphia in 1921 (see the discussion of collective terms for animals on Pages 336–340), reads FESYMES.

"Beginning to feel that these variants must be erroneous forms of a word in some older source upon which all of the more recent publications had drawn, I plunged enthusiastically into 19th-century literature. Eventually, I came upon *The Sports and Pastimes of the People of England,* by Joseph Strutt, first published in London in 1801, with numerous further editions appearing during the next century or so. The particular edition in my hands was dated 1838 and published by a 'T. Tegg'. On Page 22, I found a list of group terms used in hunting, and on Page 37, a similar list of terms used in hawking. Among the hunting terms was the object of my endeavors: 'a FESYNES of ferrets'. Both lists of terms were attributed to the sportsmen of the Middle Ages.

"An uncomfortable feeling overtook me when I noticed that Book I, Section XVIII—'Hunting Terms—Seasons for Hunting'—started on Page 22, while Book I, Section XIV—'Terms Used in Hawking'—started on Page 37. If the eighteenth section could precede the fourteenth section, the most egregious errors of any other sort were also possible. Furthermore, as in all previous instances, the word FESYNES proved never to have appeared in any English dictionary. It was more than apparent that my quest had barely begun.

"Coming across a reference to the fact that many of the existing group designations for animals—'nouns of multitude'—first appeared in medieval 'courtesy books' which contained lists of terms that were considered proper for one considering himself to be, or aspiring to have himself considered by others to be, a gentleman, I immediately and energetically delved into the most well-known of all the courtesy books, 'The Book of Saint Albans', also called 'The Book of Hawking, Hunting, and Heraldry', or 'The Book of Sir Tristram', ascribed to Dame Juliana Berners (or Bernes, or Barnes), reputed prioress of Sopwell Nunnery in Hertfordshire, England, believed to have been born in 1388 and to have died in 1482. The book was printed by John Insomuch, the 'School-master-Printer', at Saint Albans in Hertfordshire, in 1486; posthumously, it would appear. It is almost a metrical version of 'Le Art de Venerie' by William Twici (or Twety), huntsman-in-chief to King Edward II, written in Anglo-Norman, ca. 1323, and of 'The Master of Game' by Edward of Norwich, 2nd Duke of York (1373–1415), written between 1406 and 1413. The author of the latter work was first cousin to King Henry IV, at whose court he was Master of Game. These two works are among the oldest English writings on the subject of hunting. A facsimile reproduction of this work was published by E. Stock of London in 1881, and includes an introduction by William Blades.

"At the end of the 'Treatise on Hunting' in 'The Book of Saint Albans', there is a three-page list entitled 'The Companies of Beasts and Fowls', a list containing 164 of these nouns of multitude. The 35th entry in the list reads 'a BESYNES of ferettis', a Middle English way of spelling what we moderns would write as 'a BUSYNESS of ferrets'. Joseph Strutt, in copying some of the entries in this list, had misread the ornate, unfamiliar printing style of the 15th century, changing BESYNES to FESYNES, and setting into motion a chain of errors unparalleled in the history of the English language.

"The list of company terms does not appear in the older works of William Twici and Edward of Norwich. It is an interpolation into the text copied from other lists of company terms circulating in the 15th century. Where, specifically, might Dame Juliana have obtained the ingredients for her list? From earlier lists, such as those in the Bodleian Rawlinson Manuscript D. 328, dated circa 1430–1450, now in the Bodleian Library at Oxford, England; in the Egerton Manuscript No. 1995, dated circa 1470–1475, now in the library of the British Museum in London; and in 'The Horse, the Sheep, & the Goose', written circa 1470 and printed by William Caxton at Westminster, England in 1479. The Roxburgh Club issued a reprint of the latter work in 1822, under the direction of Sir Mark Masterman Sykes, entitling it 'Debate between the Horse, goose, and sheep'. Dame Juliana's list is the longest of all the lists, so that she must either have combined information from a number of the earlier lists, or obtained advice from someone else, whose name is lost beyond recall.

"Spelling in the 15th century was not as uniform as it is today, and a comparison of various old lists shows our word BUSYNESS spelled as BESYNES, BESYNESSE, BESYNYS, and BESENES, depending on the inclination of the particular scribe.

"Why did our forebears choose to designate a group of ferrets as a BUSY-NESS? In allusion to the animal's busy, methodical manner of attending to its work when used in hunting.

"One final note in this comedy of errors. The word BUSYNESS—the state or quality of being busy—is distinguished in modern English from BUSINESS. Hundreds of years ago, this distinction did not exist, and there was only one word, the word spelled BESYNES or otherwise. *The Oxford English Dictionary* includes both 'business' and 'busyness' in the first of the 13 volumes published in final form in 1933 and reprinted in 1961, but joins the fun by erroneously listing the application to ferrets under 'business' instead of under 'busyness'. Oh, well!

"As for the reference to the French language under your 'Hints', I imagine you are alluding to the fact that 'The Master of Game', by Edward of Norwich, the oldest hunting treatise written in English proper, was largely a translation of 'Gaston Phoebus', the customary short designation for 'Livre de la chasse' ('The Book of the Chase'), by Gaston III Phoebus (or Phébus), Count of Foix and Viscount of Bearn (known for short as 'Gaston de Foix'), written in French, ca. 1387, and reproduced from a manuscript in the 'Bibliothèque Nationale' ('National Library') in Paris, France, edited by C. Couderc, printed by the Berthaud brothers, Catala brothers, and successors, in Paris in 1909.

"Is this the ultimate, original source of most of Dame Juliana's material? No, it is not. While it is one of the most famous of the early French hunting books, much of its material is copied from 'Roy Modus' ('King Method'), the short designation for 'Le Livre du Roy Modus et de la Royne Racio' ('The Book of King Method and of Queen Reason'), of unknown authorship, the earliest work on hunting in the French language. The portion on sport was written between 1328 and 1338, and the entire work was printed, by incredible coincidence, in 1486!

"Have I explained the history of the word FEAMYNG to your absolute satisfaction?"

Yes, you have.

55 *PERMUTATIONAL LANGUAGE*

(*Page 49*)

The secrets of composing permutable sentences are two: (1) use words that have a variety of meanings; (2) use words which are capable of functioning as different parts of speech.

There are many English words endowed with a diversity of mutually unrelated meanings. To cite an elementary example, there is the word COLON:

1. A part of the large intestine.
2. A punctuation mark.
3. A colonist or husbandman.
4. The monetary unit of Costa Rica and of El Salvador.
5. A city on the coast of Panama.

Words such as COLON, with multiple meanings, are referred to as examples of the "equivonym" or "similibus" in technical literature on the subject.

There are equally many words which serve as different parts of speech. For instance, if you look the word IN up in the *Funk & Wagnalls Standard College Dictionary*, 1963 Edition, you will find that it has meanings as a preposition, an adverb, an adjective, a noun, and a verb.

Keeping these points in mind, we have developed a six-way sentence meeting the highest possible standards of word craftsmanship. An analysis follows:

1. ONE MAY SAW. (An individual has the privilege of performing the action of sawing some object, such as a wooden log.)

2. ONE SAW MAY. (One person saw the girl whose first name is "May".)

3. MAY ONE SAW? (Is one permitted to saw wood?)

4. MAY SAW ONE. (A girl named "May" saw some object, previously mentioned, that is regarded as belonging to a group of objects of like character.)

5. SAW ONE, MAY! (Cut a log of wood in half, May, by sawing through it!)

6. SAW MAY ONE! (Saw a log of wood for May, Buster!)

Three words or other objects can be arranged in 6 different orders. With four words, the number of possible permutations increases to 24, and with five words, to 120. These totals are computed simply by taking what mathematicians call "n factorial":

Three: $1 \times 2 \times 3 = 6$

Four: $1 \times 2 \times 3 \times 4 = 24$

Five: $1 \times 2 \times 3 \times 4 \times 5 = 120$

The same formula applies to six or more words, ad infinitum.

Our attempt at a four-word permutational sentence follows:

1. ALL MEN WILL STOP. (Everyone shall cease activity.)

2. ALL MEN STOP, WILL! (Everyone ceases activity, William!)

3. ALL STOP WILL, MEN! (Everyone joins in stopping William, my good men!)

4. ALL STOP MEN, WILL! (Everyone unites to stop men from being their usual beastly selves, William!)

5. ALL WILL STOP, MEN. (Everyone shall cease activity, fellows!)

6. ALL WILL, MEN STOP. (The personification of absolute will power, the men cease their irresistibly tempting activity.)

7. MEN, ALL WILL STOP! (Everything is going to stop, boys!)

8. MEN—ALL—STOP WILL. (Men, all of them, block William.)

9. MEN WILL STOP ALL. (Men will stop everything.)

10. MEN, WILL ALL STOP? (Men, is everything going to stop?)

11. MEN STOP ALL, WILL. (Men stop everyone, William.)

12. MEN STOP, WILL ALL. (Men cease their previous physical activities, preferring to accomplish their objectives by the exercise of sheer will power from now on.)

13. WILL ALL MEN STOP? (Are all the guys gonna quit?)

14. WILL ALL STOP MEN? (Is everyone going to stop men?)

15. WILL MEN STOP ALL? (Are men going to stop everyone?)

16. WILL MEN ALL STOP? (Are all men going to stop?)

17. WILL, STOP ALL MEN! (William, stop all males!)

18. WILL, STOP MEN—ALL! (William, stop the men—all of them!)

19. STOP ALL MEN, WILL! (Bring all men to a halt, William!)

20. STOP? ALL WILL, MEN! (Is everyone going to stop, fellows? Yes, indeed!)

21. STOP MEN, WILL—ALL! (Stop the men, William—all of them!)

22. STOP, MEN—ALL WILL! (Lay off, guys—everyone is quitting!)

23. STOP? WILL ALL MEN? (Cease? Are all men going to do so?)

24. STOP! WILL MEN ALL! (Stop your malicious testament-writing! Will everything you possess to men!)

29 BALANCE AND BEAUTY

(Page 25)

1. The three shortest, common ABC's are BY, LO, and SH!

2. Five 14-letter ABC's have been discovered: COUNTERPENALTY, INTERMEN-STRUAL, PROGENITORSHIP, TRANSITIONALLY, and UNCRYSTALLIZED. The only known longer ABC is the 16-letter word QUANTITATIVENESS, appropriately mathematical in meaning. A longer coined word is the 18-letter PSEUDO-ILLUMINATORS.

3. Since the average letter value of an ABC is $13\frac{1}{2}$, the total value of an ABC with an odd number of letters would have to be a fractional number. Since the values of all letters are integral numbers, this is mathematically impossible.

4. Eights: LYRICISM, TWILIGHT. Tens: BLIZZARDLY, IMMODESTLY, IMMORALITY, IMMUNIZING, MULTIPLIER. Twelves: RAZZLE-DAZZLE.

5. —(a) JEALOUSY, EMICTORY. —(b) SNOWLIKE, SOUPLIKE.

6. Eights: FLOURISH, OVERLIVE, OVERVEIL, OVERWILD. Tens: OVERLIGHTS, OVER-SLIGHT.

7. An 8-letter ABC with a sequential ordering of balanced letter pairs is RIVER-ISH (having many rivers). An 8-letter ABC with a fundamentally concentric ordering of balanced letter pairs is VALORIZE (to attempt to give an arbitrary market value or price to a commodity, usually by governmental interference of some sort). The concentricity observed here uses two sequentially ordered letter pairs (LO, RI) as foci in a verbal "ellipse", as opposed to the circle on which the simple concentricity of our 6-letter example WIZARD was based.

8. The only 12-letter ABC of this sort known to us is the not so abstruse term ABSTRUSENESS.

9. In the absence of any known dictionary ABC that satisfies the specified con-ditions, we have coined the word COQUETRY-SAND (a powdery, sandlike sub-stance that is to be dissolved in a drink and causes the imbiber to become coquettish, or to respond to coquetry: something akin to a love potion).

10. Examples: POTATIVE, KINOLOGY, LITERARY, LOGOLOGY.

11. Examples: ACRONYMS, LITERARY, LOGOLOGY, LYRICISM, TRANSPOSAL, REVERS-IBLY, IRREVERSIBLY. The last two examples allude to the form of wordplay

called a "reversal"; thus, DELIVER is a reversal of REVILED, but JUJUBES reverses nothing.

79   *ADVICE TO THE LOVELORN*
(*Page 67*)

The following lists of suggested signatures have been culled from actual advice columns. What this means is that they have been tested in action, and are guaranteed to perform effectively. Happy advice-seeking!

(1) Adjectives—philosophical

1. Always in the wrong
2. Battered and bruised
3. Born too late
4. Caught between
5. Deeply concerned
6. Disgusted with life
7. Driven to the brink
8. Feeling no pain
9. In but out
10. In the know
11. Looking beyond
12. Looking for a spark
13. Much in a hurry
14. Not guilty but sentenced
15. Outclassed
16. Outside looking in
17. Ready to listen
18. Running out of friends
19. Seeking a solution
20. Shackled
21. Sorry it happened
22. Still single but wearing a ring
23. Tired of the rat race
24. Torn apart
25. Unappreciated

(2) Adjectives—lighthearted

1. Befuddled
2. Blonde and cute
3. Brainy but not smart
4. Chomping at the bit
5. Curious
6. Done in
7. Eager
8. Fat
9. Fractionated
10. Getting madder by the minute
11. Hopeful
12. Impatient
13. In love
14. Inquisitive
15. Interested
16. Just asking
17. Lovesick
18. Mad as hops
19. Puzzled
20. Snowed
21. Tired of this master of deceit
22. Too good
23. Wondering how
24. Young and confused
25. Young and innocent

(3) Nouns—assorted

1. Big decision
2. Closed mind
3. Cupid's Plato
4. Daughter of sorrow
5. Friend of a friend
6. Guilty secret
7. Little girl, big problem
8. Lover of reason
9. Memories
10. Moral worrier
11. New wrinkle
12. No bumpkin
13. No stranger to trouble
14. Pipeline
15. Question mark
16. Red eyes
17. Sacrificial lamb
18. Standing duck
19. Sweet 16
20. Third fiddle
21. Tomato face
22. Valley of indecision
23. Victim number one
24. Wayward 16
25. Wife of a tyrant

93 *BEYOND URANIUM*

(*Page 79*)

Many of the chemical elements, before their identity was fully established, were given names by scientists who believed that they had discovered them, or by scientists who did, indeed, discover them but whose finds were subsequently proved to have been antedated by other scientists. In the case of some elements, several different names were proposed immediately upon discovery, and it took a period of time before the name now used was agreed upon. In some cases, an already established name was changed at a later time, either because it reflected some misunderstanding of the true properties of the element, or for national or political reasons. In other instances, names were assigned in advance for elements whose discovery was anticipated shortly. Fortunately for word lovers, there are scientific dictionaries that record these many synonyms for the current names of the elements. One such dictionary is *Hackh's Chemical Dictionary*, by Ingo W. Hackh, published by Blakiston's in Philadelphia (First Edition, 1929; Second Edition, 1937; Third Edition, 1944).

Consulting Hackh's, we find the names BREVIUM, AUSONIUM, and ESPERIUM as now discarded designations for elements 91, 93, and 94. We also find the word HYPON as a name suggested for Element 118, if and when that element is discovered (manufactured). It is described as a hypothetical noble (inert) gas assumed to be the radioactive source of stellar energy.

The name EKAWOLFRAM for Element No. 92, URANIUM, is different. It is the name that would have been assigned to uranium if it had been one of the still undiscovered elements in the years immediately following publication of Mendeleev's periodic table, on the assumption that the name WOLFRAM were taken for Element 74, rather than TUNGSTEN. A pretty "iffy" deal!

At this moment, the table of known elements ends with No. 103, LAW-RENCIUM. It should be noted, however, that the Soviet Union announced discovery of Element No. 104 in 1964, by its scientists, assigning the name KURCHATOVIUM to it, in honor of Igor Vasilyevich Kurchatov, 1903–1960, a physicist associated with Leningrad University. There has been no further mention of KURCHATOVIUM by the Soviet Union, and its discovery has not been corroborated by Western scientists.

Elements substantially beyond No. 118 in the periodic table have already been thought about, but are still unnamed. As a case in point, we cite a science-fiction story that appeared serially in *Astounding Stories* beginning with the May, 1935 issue. The story, "Twelve Eighty Seven", by John Taine (pseudonym of Prof. Eric Temple Bell), concerns—you guessed it—atomic element No. 1287. Any suggestions for an appropriate name, at this late date, other than for the obvious but trite designation SAPTATRINGSHATLAWRENCIUM?

31 CRACKING THE "Q" CODE

(*Page 29*)

Anticipating that you might turn to this section for a display of Q rebuses of all sorts, we rushed to get some down on paper for you; it would have seemed odd to you had you found a blank page or two at this point in the book. However, we almost bit off more than we could chew, and our struggles to crack the "Q" code have been a lollapalooza. Our results follow.

Q = "*Sho Q!*" = SHOQ = CHOGAK

("Sho" is a variant of "sure" found chiefly in the southern United States. "Sure" is an adverb meaning "surely". "Shoq" is a variant of "chogak", the popular name for the East Indian tree known to science as *Prosopis stephaniana*. The name "chogak" or "shoq" is derived from the West Javanese native language.)

Q = QUEUE

(This is a simple phonetic rebus, since Q and QUEUE are exact homonyms. A "queue" is a pigtail.)

Q = CUE

(This is another phonetic rebus, even simpler.)

Q = "*Q; U ain't!*" = QUAINT

(By drawing upon what is euphemistically described as "substandard" English, we immediately arrive at a quaint, if negative, Q rebus!)

Q = "*Q; U ? I ? None!*" = QUINONE

(By reverting to standard English but involving two negatives in our concoction, we come up with a rebus intended for chemistry students.)

Q = "*Q; 'U' I et!*" = QUIET

(Switching back to nonstandard English—"et" is a dialectal form of "ate"— another pleasing rebus emerges. Of course, I must be starved to have eaten YOU!)

Q = "*Q; U ran!*" = QUR'ÂN

(In our fourth successive rebus of the negative variety, we have the letter U running out on its compatriot Q. The word with the hamza or apostrophe in the middle is a variant spelling of KORAN.)

Q = THE END OF IRAQ

(An enigmatic rebus, this is a study in ambiguity. Literally, Q is the end, or last letter, of the word IRAQ. Figuratively, the fate of present-day Mesopotamia is sealed!)

Q = THE CENTER OF THE SQUARE

(A similarly enigmatic rebus; Q is the fifth or middle letter in the expression "the square". The center of the square is the point on which all eyes are focused as the space traveler from another Solar System rises to deliver his message to humanity.)

Q = LEADING QUESTION

(Finally, we have succeeded in moving enigmatic Q to the head of the line. Since it is the first letter of QUESTION, there can be no question but that it is leading QUESTION. A "leading question" is one so framed as to guide the person questioned in making his reply.)

q = "*p reflection*" = PREFLECTION

(In a dramatic volte-face, we have switched from upper-case to lower-case "q". This enables us to recognize that "q" is a mirror image, a reflection, of the lower-case "p". "Preflection" is grammatical inflection by means of prefixes.)

q = "*p awk*" = PAWK

(Continuing on our new tack, we note that "awk" is an old term meaning "turned the wrong way". Since "p" is certainly "q" turned the wrong way, the upshot of this maneuver is "pawk", a Scottish word for a trick or wile.)

With a dozen Q rebuses under the belt, the time has come for a sensa-tional farewell performance. We're going to attempt a two-Q rebus! Here it is:

QQ = TEN MONTHS

(Mathematically, a period of ten months is one sixth of sixty months, or of five years, or of a quinquennium. Literally, QQ is one-sixth of QUINQUENNIUM, since two letters are one-sixth of twelve letters. The two equations match, validating our super-rebus.)

48 *KNOW YOUR COLORS!*

(Page 44)

The explanation offered by the quizmaster was to this effect:

To say that the flag is the flag of Indonesia implies that it is the flag of Indonesia and of no other country, unless you specify otherwise. This makes the answer about Indonesia wrong, for the same flag was or is the flag representing two other states.

First, the flag with two transverse bands, red over white, is also the flag of one of the smallest nations in the world, the principality of Monaco, a French enclave on the Mediterranean Sea. The flag colors derive from those on the arms of the family of Grimaldi, Princes of Monaco for almost a chiliad (since the year 968, to be exact). The shield of the Grimaldi arms is covered with alternately red and white lozenges.

Second, the same flag was the standard of Ancona or Anchonia, a semi-independent republic on the southwest coast of the Adriatic Sea during the Middle Ages. It was under papal protection until 1532, when Gonzaga took possession of it for Pope Clement VII, and it was annexed to the Papal States. The flag colors indicated Ancona's reliance upon the Pope, whose standard con-sisted of a white lamb and a white cross of Calvary, both on a field of red.

From the viewpoint of pure logic, the moral of this story is that any statement you make is assumed to be an absolute statement unless you qualify it appropriately. In the case of the red-white flag, a statement limiting itself to Indonesia would have to start out: "One of the states represented by this flag is the Republic of Indonesia. . ."

77 *SUGGESTIVE WORDS*
(Page 65)

Our pictorial suggestions follow. How many of them have you excelled?

(12) K⟩CK

(4) EMPTY

(2) ⎤ALL○WS

(11) H⟩T

(7) NA⤫L

(9) GUILL□TINE

(3) HⓎSTE⌐R⌐CA⌐L

(10) BⴹINDS

(6) STEP

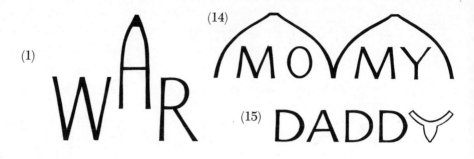

8 E PLURIBUS UNUM

(*Page 9*)

1. The ONE WORD solution is merely a play on words. It is phony (or phoney) because ONE WORD is a two-word phrase.

2. There are four legitimate solutions to this problem. Our evaluation of them follows.

(a) ONE-WORD. Examine a large dictionary, and you observe that ONE-WORD is an adjective, used in expressions such as "a one-word reply". Used as an adjective, it is written as one word, but not as a solid word—it is split by a hyphen. A hyphenated word is a word, no doubt about that, but not a word esthetically appealing. On purely technical grounds, ONE-WORD qualifies as a correct solution, but it leaves the soul of an artist unsatisfied.

(b) WOODNER. Our nation's capital has numerous hotels. One of them is the WOODNER Hotel. Here we have an unhyphenated letter combination, but one that is capitalized, since it is a proper name. Names, unquestionably, are part of language, and we could not do without them. Still, some people feel that citing a name as the solution to a word problem is sneaky and underhanded. Again, we are foundering on a matter of opinion.

(c) WOORDEN. Investigation discloses the truly fortuitous fact that the Dutch word for "words" is WOORDEN, a genuine transposal of NEW DOOR. This time, we have eliminated both hyphenation and capitalization, only to meet with a new obstacle: our word is not an English one. Reread the original problem, and you will see that we did not ask for an English solution word, giving WOORDEN complete legitimacy. Nevertheless, this resolution of a difficult problem will leave some persons disgruntled, those who feel that an English solution is their birthright.

(d) Consider our subject, NEW DOOR. Is it a complete expression? No, it is not. We simply cannot speak of NEW DOOR. We *can* refer to A NEW DOOR, or to THE NEW DOOR, or to ONE NEW DOOR, but never to NEW DOOR. Finally, the realization dawns on us that the question could not be answered properly because it wasn't asked properly. Making the minimum possible addition, we rephrase the question thus: "How do you make one word out of the phrase A NEW DOOR?" To this question, the answer is self-evident—all we need do is to rearrange the eight letters involved to spell the one word WANDEROO, another name for the purple-faced langur, a common monkey of eastern Asia (or, if you don't approve of purple faces, for the lion-tailed macaque, a black monkey of India). Surely, this resolution of our difficulties is the most original one.

3. Turning to other aspects of the original problem, the keen observer notes that our given names, EOIN (pronounced "Owen") and SEÁN (pronounced "Shawn"), are both Gaelic forms of the most common English first name, the name JOHN. He also notes that the two surnames, O'DOWNER and O'WORDEN, are both transposals of NEW DOOR, thereby constituting coined solutions to the problem.

4. The city names were chosen with equal care, though for other reasons. NEWTOWNMOUNTKENNEDY happens to be the longest legitimate place name in the British Isles written as one, solid word. BAILE ÁTHA CLIATH is the Irish name for Dublin, capital of Ireland, and is pronounced "Bla-kleé-a".

5. E PLURIBUS UNUM—"One out of many"—motto of the United States—aptly describes the ONE WORD solution, which achieves unity in meaning while retaining diversity in written form, and the WOORDEN solution, which achieves unity in written form while retaining diversity in meaning.

In retrospect, our "Hints" would seem to be self-explanatory.

81 *AN ODD PROBLEM*
(*Page 68*)

Numbers, the supposed key to cosmic secrets, are certainly the key to this problem. Replace each letter in the words ODD and EVEN with its numerical position in the alphabet:

O	D	D		E	V	E	N
15	4	4		5	22	5	14

Next, add the numerical equivalents of ODD—their sum is 23—and add the numerical equivalents of EVEN—their sum is 46. You will observe that 23 is an ODD number; multiply it by 2, and your product is 46, an EVEN number. Word science. invincible champion of the oppressed, has triumphed again, over what some may have assumed were insuperable odds. Never underestimate the power of words!

27 *STATELY SOBRIQUETS*
(*Page 23*)

First, the correct identifications of the nicknames:

1. Maryland	18. Kansas	35. Montana
2. New Jersey	19. Tennessee	36. Texas
3. Arkansas	20. California	37. Nevada
4. West Virginia	21. Idaho	38. Vermont
5. Utah	22. Pennsylvania	39. Rhode Island
6. Alabama	23. Arizona	40. Oklahoma
7. Indiana	24. Michigan	41. New Hampshire
8. Nebraska	25. Colorado	42. Connecticut
9. Missouri	26. Virginia	43. Kentucky
10. North Carolina	27. New York	44. Illinois
11. Delaware	28. Maine	45. Wisconsin
12. Iowa	29. Wyoming	46. Louisiana
13. New Mexico	30. Florida	47. Minnesota
14. South Carolina	31. Mississippi	48. Washington
15. Ohio	32. South Dakota	49. Massachusetts
16. Georgia	33. North Dakota	50. Oregon
17. Alaska	34. Hawaii	

Now, the trap. One of the common designations for Florida is "the Everglade State". In our quiz, we have applied that sobriquet not to Florida but to Washington. On what grounds? On the grounds that the Funk & Wagnalls unabridged dictionary defines the term "Everglade State" thus:

"Florida; also, Washington".

Since Washington is known as "the Evergreen State", evil-minded individuals might assume that the definition we have cited is in the nature of an error, of a confusion between "Evergreen" and "Everglade". Trusting souls that we are, such a thought could never cross our innocent minds. Hence, No. 48!

71 YELLOW HAMMERS
(Page 60)

The key words in this problem are "certain Americans" and "Yellow Hammers". The certain Americans referred to were Yellowhammers, or residents of the State of Alabama, nicknamed the "Yellowhammer State", possibly because the home-dyed uniforms worn by Alabama soldiers in the Civil War had a yellowish tinge. As for the Civil War, it started with the Confederate attack on Fort Sumter, April 12–13, 1861, pinpointing Sumter County, in west-central Alabama, as the scene of our adventures.

Let's consult the 1962 Edition of the "American Highway Atlas", prepared by the H. M. Goushá Company, headquartered both in Chicago, Illinois and in San Jose, California, lithographed by an unspecified company in the United States, printed and distributed by the I. S. Berlin Press in Chicago, and sold by the Follett Publishing Company, also of Chicago. This unusually complicated setup warns us that difficulties lie ahead, as does the fact that we have to deduce the year of publication from a notation on the very last page of the atlas, at the bottom of the "Transcontinental Mileage Chart", stating, "Made in U.S.A.—62".

Turning to the map of Alabama, we find three fascinating communities in Sumter County, in the area just south and southeast of the town of York (1960 population, 2932). What makes these three communities so unique is that they are located on an almost straight east-west line and are named CUBA,

INTERCOURSE, and MOSCOW. Intercourse is about 9 miles east of Cuba, and about 10 miles west of Moscow. We can, therefore, truthfully say that Intercourse is between, midway between, Moscow and Cuba!

The difficulty arises in attempting to verify this information in other atlases. The 95th Edition of the *Rand McNally Commercial Atlas and Marketing Guide,* published in 1964 and listing approximately 135,000 place names in the United States, confirms the existence of Cuba, with a population of 390, but omits both Moscow and Intercourse. An extended search for these two communities remains fruitless until we check the map of Alabama in the 11th Edition of *The Encyclopaedia Britannica,* published in 1910. That map shows both Cuba and Intercourse, but not Moscow.

Next in our survey, we consult the 1902 Edition of *The Century Atlas of the World,* which shows both Cuba and Moscow, but not Intercourse. There's a fly in the ointment, however: Moscow is shown in the approximate center of Lamar County, about 100 miles north of where it ought to be!

Undaunted, we proceed to the 1907 Edition of *Rand, McNally & Co.'s Unrivaled Atlas of the World,* where we find both Intercourse (population, 16) and Moscow (population, 23). Unfortunately, while Intercourse is listed in the index, it is not shown on the map, and Moscow is again located in Lamar County.

Next, we turn to the 1917 Edition of *Hammond's Home and Office Atlas of the World,* which lists neither Intercourse nor Moscow in its index, but does show Intercourse on the map. This particular atlas also gives the population of Cuba as 650. In these days, with the perils of the population explosion confronting us, a 40% decline in the population of a community over the past half century seems distinctly unreal.

Must we fail in our effort to corroborate the Goushá map? No. The 1965 Edition of *This Week Magazine's Vacation Planner and Speedy Flip-Out Road Atlas,* prepared and copyrighted by the Diversified Map Corporation in St. Louis, Missouri, printed in the United States by an unspecified company, and published by *This Week Magazine,* with photo tips by the Eastman Kodak Company, shows all three of our localities, all in Sumter County, Alabama. The Moscow shown in some of the very old atlases as being in Lamar County was evidently a different community, no longer in existence.

Had we failed, we could have gone on to much more detailed maps, including: (1) United States Geological Survey topographic maps; (2) Coast and Geodetic Survey maps; (3) old "miles per inch" maps; (4) detailed county maps put out by state highway departments and local automobile associations. However, it just doesn't seem right that a problem so simple in genesis should become difficult enough to require the use of such powerful tools to resolve.

A footnote: during the course of our searches, our attention was sidetracked to Pennsylvania, where we found that (another) Intercourse is very, very close to Paradise: the two communities are in Lancaster County, only $2\frac{1}{2}$ miles apart.

5 EMINENT AMERICAN PALINDROMIST?

(Page 7)

Two of Poe's lyrical ballads, representative of his finest work as a poet, and ranked among the most melodious poems ever composed in English, are *Ulalume* and *Annabel Lee*. Rewriting these titles palindromically, we have:

ULALUme   ANNAbEL LEe

The overlined, capitalized letters constitute three palindromes.

One of Poe's better-known earlier poems, *Al Aaraaf*, exhibits an even more striking palindrome: Al AARAAf. This title, in addition to its palindrome, displays "vocalic invariance", limiting itself to the one vowel A.

If you believe that these four palindromes are coincidental and accidental, we challenge you to try and find a similar bevy of palindromes among the titles of the best-known works of any other poet, living or dead!

The initials of "Eminent American Palindromist" are identical with those of Edgar Allan Poe, a fact indicated by the conspicuously uniform initial letters of all six words in our "Hints" sentence.

18 THE WITCHES' PRAYER

(Page 17)

When we first set ourselves the problem of locating the "Witches' Prayer", we did not fully realize its difficulty. No matter what reference books we consulted, the only mention of it was the quotation from Addison. Neither could any of the otherwise knowledgeable individuals whom we asked for help offer us any leads.

In desperation, we finally turned to our long-time friend, Professor Ravens-croft J. Cloudesley, word expert extraordinaire. Preoccupied with esoteric problems of his own, problems beyond the ken of mere mortals, he was not willing to help us in our search, but he did, most magnanimously, permit us to browse through his private library, one room of which was devoted to occult-ism, necromancy, and related subjects.

Left to our own devices, we passed from shelf to shelf, marveling at the strange titles included in Cloudesley's unmatched collection: books that wealthy bibliophiles would gladly pay a fortune for, if they but had the opportunity to acquire them. Some examples: "The Black Magic of Borneo"; "Secrets of the Khoi-Khoin"; "Queer Qqichuan Quipus"; "Hosting Succubi"; "Across the Rockies by Broom"; "Sorcery at Sunset"; "Invisibility as a Way of Life"; "Buried under the Great Pyramid"; "The Vampire Bats of Tibet"; "I Was a Teen-age Werefox!"; "Thanatomania in June Beetles"; "Voodoo for Astro-nauts—An Advanced Course"; "The Economic Impact of Elves"; "Thirtieth-century Fakirs"; "The Lucrezia Borgia Cookbook"; and countless more.

So fascinating were these titles that it was a genuine effort to tear our-selves away from them and examine the contents of the books, but work must take precedence over pleasure, and we finally buckled down to the chore of searching for the "Witches' Prayer". It did not take us too long to spot a book promisingly entitled, "The Complete Manual of Witchcraft", Third Edition, Revised and Enlarged, published in 1372 in Belfast. On Page 227 of this classic, we found the "Witches' Prayer", in Latin. The fantastic resources of Professor Cloudesley had turned failure into success!

The frontward reading of this incantation follows, with a translation into English:

> "Delicias fuge ne frangaris crimine, verum
> Coelica tu quaeras, ne male dispereas;
> Respicias tua, non cujusvis quaerito gesta
> Carpere, sed laudes, nec preme veridicos;
> Judicio fore te praesentem conspice toto
> Tempore: nec Christum, te rogo, despicias;
> Salvificum pete, nec secteris daemona, Christum
> Dilige, nequaquam tu mala concupito."

(Shun pleasures of the flesh, lest you be broken by crime; seek the things of heaven, lest your end be an evil one; consider your own deeds, and do not seek to slander someone else's, but praise them, and do not suppress those who speak the truth; always realize that you must stand before a judgment; I beg you, do

not despise Christ, seek him who gives salvation, and do not follow the devil;
love Christ, and do not lust at all after evil.)

Here is the same verse, reading in reverse, with the corresponding translation
into English:

"Concupito mala, tu nequaquam dilige Christum;
Daemona secteris, nec pete salvificum;
Despicias, rogo te, Christum: nec tempore toto
Conspice praesentem te fore judicio;
Veridicos preme, nec laudes, sed carpere gesta
Quaerito cujusvis, non tua respicias.
Dispereas male, ne quaeras tu coelica, verum
Crimine frangaris, ne fuge delicias."

(Lust after evil, and do not at all love Christ; you follow the devil, do not seek
Him Who gives salvation; despise Christ, I beg you, and realize that never will
you stand before a judgment; suppress those who speak the truth, and do not
praise the deeds of anyone, but seek to slander them; do not consider your own;
let your end be an evil one, do not seek the things of heaven; let yourself be
broken by crime, do not shun pleasures of the flesh.)

Overcome by it all, we leave it to you to compose a similar "Witches' Prayer"
in English.

72 *REAL ENGLISH*
(*Page 61*)

1. "Your initial proposal in connection with the extension of the ramifications
originally discussed in relation to the suggested and informally submitted theory
for the formulation of a new but not necessarily binding concept of sales prop-
agandizement is currently under assayment and evaluation by our Board of
Directors which, according to the interim report at hand, has not as yet arrived
at any conclusive determination or irreversible finalization, decision-wise, inas-
much as two of the directors have tentatively vouchsafed an affirmative position, two have indicated a pronounced leaning toward the negative, and three
have initiated an application for additional time for the careful perusal thereof.
Please be assured of my intense and continued interest and of my pledge for
instantaneous reportage of any developments or conclusions of meaningful
significance and relevant pertinence."

2. "Your son, Cadwallader Snicklethwaite, is performing less productively than others of his age bracket, is producing minimally for his peer group, and is emerging as a non-academically-minded, non-college-oriented, reluctant learner and sub-placed under-achiever. Indeed, his grade placement under the multiple-track plan reflects his predisposition to those factors frequently associated with late-bloomers lacking the developmental key of meaningful motivation and without the felt need to effectuate the tasks involved in the learning process. Nor does your son evidence those characteristics of deliberator-abstractors as judged by standardized measuring devices. He is, accordingly, participating in a heterogeneous group guidance session to gain insight-generating knowledge of normative behavior for one of his intelligence-quotient level, as measured by the Binet, Cattell III, and Wechsler-Bellevue Tests. We are also evaluating the potentials inherent in a work simplification program as applied to Cad's studies, defining work simplification as that method of accomplishing a necessary purpose which omits nothing necessary to the realization of that purpose and best effectuates it in the simplest of fashions. Approaching a tentative work simplification program from this standpoint is important in that it removes any possible element of mystery in the program, leaving its essentials clearly outlined and succinctly stated."

Succinctly stated??

9 SUPERCALIFRAGILISTICEXPIALI-DOCIOUS!

(*Page 10*)

We want to thank you, most cordially, for supplying us with the correct definition of the 34-letter word that serves as our title:

"Atoning for overabundant, educable, delicate beauty."

We extend our equally heartfelt thanks to you for tearing the veil from the hitherto mysterious origins of the word:

SUPER- a Latin prefix denoting excess or superiority; "above", "over", "beyond", "greater than", "extra", "additional".

CALI- an erroneous spelling of CALO-, a Greek combining form descended from the Greek *kallos,* meaning "beauty".

FRAGILISTIC—the adjective FRAGILE, of Latin origin, with an unnecessary adjectival suffix, -ISTIC, attached to it.

EXPIALI- an erroneous spelling of EXPIATI-, from the Latin *expiatus*, meaning "to atone for", "to expiate".

-DOCIOUS—a suffix derived from the word DOCILE, of Latin origin, meaning "teachable", and incorporating the adjectival suffix -IOUS, also of Latin origin, meaning "characterized by".

Etymologists of America! Our readers have made a valuable, an almost priceless, contribution to your stock in trade. Enshrine it in your innermost sanctuaries, and point to it as a model for future generations of philologists to emulate, if they but can. Indeed, such a profound, brilliant analysis of a word is the highlight of the century in the normally prosaic domain of linguistics!

59 *MINISTERIAL MEDITATIONS*

(*Page 51*)

The test question used the word "the", implying that there was only one British prime minister during World War II. This is not true; there were three of them.

The Second World War began September 1, 1939 and ended September 2, 1945. Churchill was prime minister from May, 1940 to July, 1945. At the beginning of the war, Arthur Neville Chamberlain was prime minister; at its end, Clement Richard Attlee was prime minister. This is probably why the teacher counted the answer given as incorrect.

There is a second reason, however, why that answer was wrong. Winston Churchill was never prime minister of Great Britain; he was an American writer of historical novels. Born in Missouri in 1871, he died in Florida in 1947. The name of the world statesman was Sir Winston Leonard Spencer Churchill.

The alphabetical idiosyncrasy of the novelist was the fact that he almost always included the letter C in the title of a novel, usually as the first letter of a key word. Examples: *The Celebrity, Richard Carvel, The Crisis, The Crossing, Coniston, Mr. Crewe's Career, A Modern Chronicle, The Inside of the Cup, A Far Country, The Uncharted Way, The Dwelling Place of Light.*

Churchill the statesman was also a prolific author, but free of the "C" Syndrome. Some of his best-known books use titles without a single "C": *The*

Gathering Storm, Their Finest Hour, The Hinge of Fate, Triumph and Tragedy, Painting as a Pastime, History of the English-Speaking Peoples, etc.

Our "hint" was double-edged since it could be construed as applying to either of the Churchills. The novelist was born in St. Louis, Missouri; the statesman made his famous "iron curtain" speech at Fulton, Missouri on March 5, 1946.

56 ASPHALT, CLIFF, AND RAVEN
(Page 50)

The state is Utah, and the county is Uintah, in the northeastern part of the state. If you will but look at the spellings of these two names, it will be evident to you that UTAH is in UINTAH.

Look at the spellings again, from a loftier viewpoint, and you will see that the name UINTAH has a message for you: UINTAH, rewritten U$_{in}$TAH, is in UTAH, best described as a counter-reversal of thought.

Our title? ASPHALT, CLIFF, and RAVEN are the names of three mountain ridges in Uintah County, Utah. Our "Hints"? The French word for "high" is "haut", a transposition of "Utah"; "Low" is the name of a small community in Tooele County, Utah—very small, for it has no population at all, according to the most recent atlases!

Duck soup, wasn't it?

87 TRUMPETS AND FLOURISHES
(Page 72)

This book concerns itself with language as representative of the thoughts behind it, and language consists of words. It is reasonable to assume, therefore, that the symbols pictured are word symbols.

Indeed, they are—for the *word* "words", in these languages: (a) Sumerian; (b) Korean; (c) Hindi; (d) Persian.

The expert will protest that we goofed, printing only the Sumerian word correctly. He will point out that the Hindi word is shown upside down, and that the Korean and Persian words are placed sideways (the Korean word standing on its left edge, the Persian word on its right edge). These positional quirks are deliberate, not accidental. Aside from enhancing the exotic appearance of the ensemble, they serve to expose a very common fallacy: the assumption that what is put into print is necessarily right side up. 'Tain't so!

As for trumpets and flourishes, these are our own, possibly fanciful, interpretations of what we see. Don't the wedge-shaped Sumerian characters look like a series of trumpets? Some of the words, especially the Hindi word, contain what an Occidental would regard as ornamental strokes or flourishes.

95 AUGMENTING THE ALPHABET

(Page 80)

New channels of alphabetic thought are about to unfold before you. Observe and learn:

HORNBOOK. In the old hornbooks, formerly used to teach reading to children, the 26 conventional letters were followed by a 27th character, the sign "&", called the "ampersand", "ipseand", "short and", or "Tironian sign". As a result, the ampersand was sometimes thought of as the 27th letter of the alphabet.

ORCHARD. Examine A Dictionary of Archaic and Provincial Words, by James Orchard Halliwell-Phillipps. The words defined are listed under 27 headings. The first 26 are the usual letters. Following the Z, there is a section of more than four pages, listing words beginning with a letter resembling the printed numeral 3. This symbol is found in early English manuscripts written after the twelfth century. It is a corruption of the Old English letter "g", pronounced sometimes as "g", sometimes as "gh", and sometimes as "y". To omit from our alphabet a letter used in English dictionaries is in the nature of abusing the license given to us as speakers of English.

LLAMA. The alphabet used in writing English is not the exclusive property of English; it is also employed in many other languages. Hence, the English alphabet is also the French alphabet, the German alphabet, the Polish alphabet, and so on. Some of the languages using the alphabet add characters to it, increasing the total number of letters to more than 26. A Norwegian dictionary, for instance, includes words beginning with all 26 of the letters familiar to us, but adds three further characters following the Z:

$$\text{Æ} \qquad \text{Ø} \qquad \text{Å}$$

The first of these three characters becomes the 27th alphabetic letter.

To cite another example, a Spanish dictionary omits the letter W, which does not occur in any genuine Spanish word, but inserts three other letters into the alphabet:

> CH, following C
> LL, following L (as in "llama")
> Ñ, following N

Each of these symbols is counted as *a* letter, increasing the number of letters to 28, and Y is defined as the 27th letter.

CIRCLE. For some purposes, it is required to write the alphabet along the circumference of a circle, so that the alphabet is a continuous one, without beginning and without end. In the alphabet so written, if we start with A as our first letter and keep counting, Z is the 26th letter, A the 27th, B the 28th, etc.

The circular alphabet is useful, even essential, in solving problems such as the "word-shift" problem. In cryptography, if we attempt to encipher words by uniformly shifting their constituent letters forward along the alphabet until new words are formed, and if we approach the task without bias, we make felicitous discoveries such as this: if each letter of the word TASK is moved forward along the alphabet precisely eight notches, the result is the code word BIAS. Shifting the first and third letters in such fashion is possible only if the alphabet is displayed circularly, enabling us to transcend Z.

52　SYNONYM SETS

(*Page 47*)

Each of the four words CLOUD, SKULK, TROOP, and EARTH is a term applied to a group or company of foxes; in short, these are synonymous "nouns of multitude". Our authorities for this information follow:

CLOUD — *Funk & Wagnalls New Standard Dictionary of the English Language,* 1945 Edition, Page 505, second column, definition 8: "a troop or skulk, as of foxes".

SKULK — same dictionary, Page 2290, first column, definition 2: "a troop of foxes".

TROOP — see the term "troop of foxes" in the two dictionary definitions just quoted.

EARTH — see *The Language of Field Sports* by C. E. Hare, Country Life Ltd., London, 1949, Pages 199 and 204. See also *Transactions of the London Philological Society, 1909,* article "Proper Terms", by John Hodgkin, Pages 45 and 98. See also *PMLA,* annual publication of The Modern Language Association of America, published quarterly, Volume LI, June, 1936, Page 603: article "The Fifteenth-Century 'Associations of Beasts, of Birds, and of Men': The Earliest Text With 'Language for Carvers' (A note of the *Early Modern English Dictionary*).

So much for the formalities. How was it possible for you to solve the problem quickly without reference to any dictionaries, or to any of the recondite sources adduced in connection with the term EARTH?

First, the title chosen for the problem is ambiguous and consequently revelatory. The words "Synonym Sets" may be taken to mean either "groups of synonyms" *or* "groups which are synonyms"; that is, "synonymous group names". In our "Hints" section, in addition to pointing out the titular ambiguity, we spilled the beans by using the word "outfoxed". Hence, all the ingredients needed to resolve your presumed state of perplexedness were out in the open, waiting for you to use them.

We have been discussing the names of animal groups. Since this is an area of language touching on the domain of zoology, we are obliged to listen to any dissent voiced by zoologists. What is it that zoologists say about our problem? They inform us that foxes are solitary animals, that they do not congregate in herds or packs, as do some of their relatives—the dogs, jackals, and wolves, for instance. How do we defend ourselves against such a damning charge? By observing that the fennec or zerda, a small African fox, is a communal animal. The underground holes of fennecs are often linked together, and the animals sometimes congregate in large numbers at scarce waterholes.

What this illustrates is that the word expert must always be ready to take on experts in any field on which he encroaches in his ramblings.

76 *LET YOUR HAIR DOWN!*
(Page 64)

Here are the four meanings that we have been able to discern in our title:

1. Shed all of your reserve, inhibitions, or dignity; talk very informally or intimately.
2. Unbind your hair and let it fall about your back and shoulders.
3. Disillusion your hair, or fail to fulfill its expectations or hopes.
4. Rent out to someone the downy (feathery or fluffy) portion of your hair.

Question: how many interpretations that we overlooked have you discovered in this sentence?

43 *THE GAME OF CROSS-REFERENCE*
(Page 41)

Our apparently impolite hint was intended to convey the idea to you that BIRD'S-HEAD TYPE is a term connected with idiots, and most likely, therefore, to be found in a medical dictionary. As far as we know, there is no general dictionary that defines BIRD'S-HEAD TYPE, and only one medical dictionary that includes it: *The American Illustrated Medical Dictionary*, by W. A. Newman Dorland, published by the W. B. Saunders Company in Philadelphia and London. The observations that follow are based on the 22nd Edition of that dictionary, published in 1951, but quite a few other editions of the dictionary contain precisely the same entries. If we are correct in our belief that only Dorland defines BIRD'S-HEAD TYPE, then you should have experienced approximately the same sense of bafflement as did we.

Our first move, naturally, is to look up BIRD'S-HEAD TYPE, and we find it explained as "The Aztec type of idiocy". Now, whatever negative qualities the Aztecs may have had, we never knew that they were idiots (of some specific type, yet!), and our curiosity is aroused, so we turn to the entry AZTEC TYPE, only to be faced by the explanation: "See under *idiocy*." Hmmmm . . . . Why weren't we directed to idiocy in the first place? Well, n'importe; we refer to IDIOCY and discover the subentry: "AZTEC IDIOCY, microcephalic idiocy." By jiminy, here we go again! Looking up MICROCEPHALIC IDIOCY, another subentry, a further cross-reference greets us: "idiocy associated with microcephalia". We're getting there, just be patient! Our next gambit is to inquire into the meaning of MICROCEPHALIA, which we find listed jointly with MICROCEPHALISM and MICROCEPHALY. The definition provided for all three words reads: "Abnormal smallness of the head".

Eureka! We made it at last, we successfully negotiated the skilfully designed obstacle course, and now know that BIRD'S-HEAD TYPE is a medical term meaning: "Idiocy associated with abnormal smallness of the head".

Actually, we omitted all the complications on our dictionary tour, for the sake of clarity. In practice, we had to hurdle a series of cleverly arranged traps in our search for the meaning of BIRD'S-HEAD TYPE; psychological traps. You see, the dictionary entry immediately preceding BIRD'S-HEAD TYPE is BIRD'S-EYE, defined as "Adonis". Familiar with the Adonis of Greek mythology, a word now applied to any man of rare beauty, and also familiar with BIRD'S EYE as a brand name for food products, we couldn't resist the temptation offered us to look up ADONIS for the connection between the two (it seems that both terms are names for certain poisonous plants used as cardiac stimulants).

Similarly, in referring to AZTEC TYPE, we couldn't help noticing the diagrammatically embellished entry just two lines above AZTEC TYPE, the entry AZOXY COMPOUND. That first word, AZOXY, is a milestone of sorts in the field of wordplay: if we write the alphabet along the circumference of a circle, as we do for various purposes, then four of the five letters in AZOXY—the letters X, Y, Z, A—appear consecutively in our circular alphabet. Very few, indeed, are the five-letter words that can make such a claim!

Traps of the same kind distract us at every step of our research. Often, we are carried away in tracing the ramifications of irrelevant dictionary entries that leap to our attention. Seduced by these charmers, we forget what it was that we originally set out to look up. End result: a sense of frustration. Now, if *we* were ever to compile a dictionary . . . would things be different? Quién sabe?

28 *DISCOVERED BY HERSCHEL!*

(Page 25)

Let's examine the first letters of the words with which the successive lines of Titania's speech commence:

<u>Out</u> <u>Thou</u> <u>I</u> <u>The</u> <u>And</u> <u>I'll</u> <u>And</u> <u>And</u> <u>And</u> <u>That</u>

It is evident that the first eight of the letters we have underscored spell the vocative phrase, "O Titania!" We must assume that Shakespeare deliberately worded Titania's speech so as to create an initial acrostic, one of the time-honored devices used by literary triflers.

What of the last three letters that we have underlined? They spell the word AAT. The lexicographer Halliwell tells us that AAT is fine oatmeal, with which pottage is thickened. It is a tribute to Shakespeare's genius that no one has yet succeeded in uncovering the undoubted connection between AAT and *A Midsummer Night's Dream.* May *you* triumph where others have bowed!

Herschel? Well, it was the English astronomer, Sir William Herschel, who discovered the planet Uranus on March 13, 1781, and who discovered two of its satellites, Titania and Oberon, in 1787. In 1851, another English astronomer, William Lassell, discovered an additional two satellites of Uranus (the satellites Ariel and Umbriel), and in 1948, an American astronomer, Gerard Kuiper, discovered a fifth satellite, Miranda. In our "Hints", the names of the satellites are given in order of increasing length of period in revolving around Uranus.

99 *EXCESS EXES*

(*Page 82*)

That a book was published in 1963 does not mean that it was written in 1963; it could have been written many years earlier, even hundreds of years earlier. Every language changes with the passage of time; perhaps there was a time when there were no English words beginning with X.

1. The dictionary in question is "Johnson's Dictionary: A Modern Selection", by E. L. McAdam, Jr., & George Milne, published by Pantheon Books, A Division of Random House, New York, 1963. As the title states, it is a selection made from a much larger and much older work, "A Dictionary of the English Language", by Samuel Johnson, a milestone of English lexicography that first appeared in 1755.

2. Most English words beginning with the letter X are technical and scientific terms of relatively recent origin. These words did not exist in Johnson's day,

more than two centuries ago. Quite possibly, the average person of that time did not know a single English word beginning with an X. So, the statement about X that we have quoted from Johnson's dictionary could have been true when it was published.

3. It could have been true, but it wasn't. To cite a few examples drawn from *The Oxford English Dictionary*, XTIAN (a form of "Christian") first appeared in print in 1485; XERES SACK (a kind of wine) has been traced back to 1661; and XENAGOGY (a guidebook) was already known around 1575. Conclusion: Samuel Johnson was not infallible.

53 *OF RULERS AND SUBJECTS*
(Page 48)

Let us begin with SOVEREIGNTY. It has been estimated that there are as many as three million words in the English language. Yet, SOVEREIGNTY appears to be the only modern English word featuring the letter combination GNT. A remarkable fact, one which should be noted for future reference, but nothing likely to set the world on fire.

We switch to GOVERNMENT. It is conspicuous that this word also contains the letters GNT, in the same order, but separated by other letters instead of consecutively. Since we already have these letters in SOVEREIGNTY, their reoccurrence in GOVERNMENT is a redundancy, and we are obliged to strike them out, leaving the letter groups OVER MEN. Stop and marvel: what is left reveals the true essence of GOVERNMENT, which is indisputably something that is OVER MEN!

It is always possible to proceed a step further in our Great Adventure. If SOVEREIGNTY is the only modern English word using the triliteral GNT grouping, then logic tells us that it is automatically the only word including the quadriliteral GNTY set. One of the derivatives of the word GOVERNMENT is the word GOVERNMENTALLY, which includes the four letters GNTY in proper order, but separated by other letters. Eliminating the superfluous GNTY characters leaves us with three letter groups: OVER MEN ALL. We have succeeded in probing the concept of GOVERNMENT to an even greater depth, for surely, it is found OVER MEN ALL—that is, over all men!

90 *THE PREPOSITION PROPOSITION*

(*Page 76*)

We've taken a crack at our own poser. Here is our sequel; how does it stack up in comparison with yours?

"A few years later, the same chap is sick again, and is visited by an aunt of his with the nasty habits of wearing a big, ugly hat and of frowning down upon little boys from her lofty eminence (you should know that she is 6'4''). This time, the boy greets her with the question: 'Why did you carry the ugly hat, the one I do not want to be frowned *down upon out from under, on up for?*' As you can plainly see, our precocious stripling has already progressed to sentences ending with 8 prepositions consecutively.

"The best is yet to come. Years pass, the lad becomes an adult, and he marries a bonny lass from Australia (yes, Australia, *not* Scotland). She continues the practice of reading to him whenever he is indisposed, and we now hear him plaintively inquiring: 'What did you bring the book that I do not wish to be read *on to out of up from Down Under for?*' The man is finally operating on Preposition Level Nine!

"We wish him continued success in ascending to ever higher prepositional levels, convinced that you share our sentiments fully."

20 *GROUP THEORY*

(*Page 18*)

Each of the 26 words in the four groups contains one letter of the alphabet, a different one, doubled. Thus, AA doubles the A, DUMBBELL doubles the B, ACCESS doubles the C, GRANDDADDY doubles the D, and so on, through the entire alphabet, until we reach BUZZING, which doubles the Z.

The words in group (4) are of the lowest quality, for in these words, the sounds of the two consecutive like letters fuse, so that they are pronounced as one. Put another way, the pronunciation of BUZZING includes only one Z, the pronunciation of FLIVVER includes only one V, etc.

In the first three groups, the pronunciation of the two consecutive like letters is always separated. Among these three groups, the words in group (3) are the most inferior, for the two letters in question, though pronounced separately, are pronounced in identical fashion. For instance, a careful pronunciation of BARROOM sounds two identical R's in succession, a careful pronunciation of TOOLLESS sounds two identical L's in succession, and so forth.

In the first two groups, the pronunciation of the two consecutive like letters is always separate and different. The words comprising group (2) are distinctly inferior, however, since they achieve the differentness by the simple expedient of silencing one of the two letters. Thus, the first B in DUMBBELL is silent, as is the second K in JACKKNIFE.

It is the words in group (1) that reach the zenith. In each of them, both of the two consecutive like letters are sounded, but they are sounded differently. For example, the first C in ACCESS is pronounced like a K, while the second C is pronounced like an S. In WITHHOLD, the first H is sounded as part of the TH digraph, whereas the second H is sounded like a regular H.

The distracting feature of the words in group (3) is that each of them features two or even three "doubles", only one of which is part of the overall scheme. Thus, the word KEENNESS has three doubles (EE, NN, and SS). In only one of them (NN) is there a separation of sounds; in the case of the other two doubles (EE and SS), there is the fusion of sounds into one that we observed in all of the group (4) words. Well . . . we didn't want to make the problem too easy for you!

Among the entire set of 26 words, one is uniquely balanced: the word UPPULL. It consists of only three alphabetic letters (L, P, and U), each one deployed twice.

Our "Hints" pointed to the concept of twoness by using nouns of multitude. Two dogs are a brace, two hawks a cast, and two baboons, according to Shakespeare, a gemini. Congreve, by contrast, applied the term "gemini" to a pair of asses; and lesser luminaries, to a pair of eyes.

4 *CHARMING SPELLING*

(Page 6)

The misspelled word is ACTER, which *must* be spelled ACTOR. To relieve you of any possible bafflement, brief definitions of the other words are given here:

CRYPTOGAM—a plant such as a fern or moss, without true flowers and seeds.

THEREFOR—for this, that, or it.

WINDROW—a row or line of hay, or of sheaves of grain, raked together for the purpose of drying.

GALOP—a lively round dance, of 19th-century German origin.

HARRAS—a herd of stud horses.

POISSON—a measure of liquid capacity, equal to slightly less than one fourth of a pint.

CONTECT—to cover or cover up.

ORIGNAL—the American moose.

VIRAGINITY—the quality or character of a bold, quarrelsome, shrewish woman.

MERENGUE—a popular Dominican and Haitian ballroom dance.

It would have been impossible for you to look up all eleven words in *the* dictionary (are we being too optimistic in assuming that you didn't do so?) because there isn't any *one* dictionary that includes all of them. You need a minimum of two dictionaries: the Second and the Third Editions of the Merriam-Webster unabridged. The word MERENGUE, for instance, is in the Third Edition but not in the Second Edition; the word ORIGNAL, to take another example, is in the Second Edition but not in the Third Edition. Some words, such as CRYPTOGAM and THEREFOR, are in both dictionaries.

The conclusion that the incorrectly spelled word is ACTER could have been reached entirely on the basis of logical grounds, without examining the words themselves. The number of words in the list presented is 11, a highly irregular, unusual number. Normal practice would call for 10 words (*ten* being the radix of the number system we use in our daily lives) or for 12 words (*twelve* being a dozen, another very common unit in our lives). By contrast, *eleven* lacks any logical or mathematical foundation. It is true that there are eleven men on a football team, but there is no discernible connection between our word list and football, eliminating that thought from further consideration, however fleeting. Why, then, were eleven words selected, rather than ten or twelve?

The title conferred on our problem provides the key to resolving the enigma. While you may not have read the title in just that fashion, you will nevertheless agree that it consists of two participles: the present participles of the verbs "to charm" and "to spell". Both verbs mean "to put under a charm or spell by means of magic", and belong to the domain of superstition. According to superstition, the lucky number is the number seven, and it becomes obvious that the correct answer to our problem must be placed in seventh position. The tie-in with eleven is provided by common dice games, in which seven and eleven are the lucky or winning numbers. For those of you who needed help, our "hint" openly stated that luck would provide the right answer.

24 A PONDEROUS POSTAL PROBLEM

(Page 21)

The resolution of our dilemma? Heavy stamps!

Suppose that you have a letter weighing *precisely* one ounce. Light as the ordinary postage stamp may be, it is not weightless. If you affix that stamp to a letter weighing exactly one ounce, the stamped letter will weigh more than one ounce, and you will need to add a second stamp in order to mail it.

Our proposal, based on the marginal case just cited, is to replace the existing stamps with new ones, printed on a heavier, more durable material. Let us choose the material so that each stamp will weigh seven eighths of an ounce. Now, visualize a letter weighing just a little over half an ounce, and requiring one five-cent stamp. We affix the stamp and weigh the letter again. It now weighs more than one and three eighths ounces, making a second stamp necessary. We add the second stamp, only to find that the letter now weighs more than two and one fourth ounces. Resigned to our fate, we paste on a third stamp. Since the weight of the letter has increased to more than three and one eighth ounces, we are compelled to glue on a fourth stamp, but are foiled again, for the letter now weighs slightly more than four ounces. Finally, we put on a fifth stamp and overtake the increasing weight of the letter, which stands at a little more than four and seven eighths ounces, a weight covered by the five stamps adorning the envelope. At last, with twenty-five cents worth of postage on it, we can mail the letter in clear conscience: we have paid our debt to society, in a manner of speaking.

The proposal just explained has an additional advantage for the Post Office. Sooner or later, some smart aleck is bound to try and beat the rap by affixing one ten-cent stamp to the original letter. One way of forestalling such shenanigans would be to make ten-cent stamps twice as heavy, fifteen-cent stamps three times as heavy, etc. There is a better way, however: abolish all stamps of denominations greater than five cents. This will eliminate the time and labor involved in designing, printing, and distributing many different denominations of stamps, contributing to a more economical, efficient operation of the Post Office.

A third advantage of our clever little scheme would accrue to stamp dealers serving collectors. With all existing American paper stamps suddenly declared obsolete insofar as use for mailing purposes is concerned, there would be a boom in the sale of paper stamps to collectors, unlike anything heretofore experienced, with a steady appreciation in the sale value of such stamps, as the years went by.

All in all, it's a wonderful idea, and we hope that you are as enthusiastic about it as are we. If we all join in writing to our Congressmen in support of the proposal, action will surely follow!

104 *TWO WORDS = ONE BIRD!*
(*Page 85*)

The most casual glance at our letter series brings out the fact that the letters occur in pairs: 2 M's, 2 O's, 2 T's, etc. Since the visible portion of the series ends with a "stray", unduplicated letter, an E, it is reasonable to assume that the next letter will be an E, rounding out or completing another pair.

Reasonable, but wrong. Looking at the successive pairs as units, what is the rationale behind them? None whatever. The pairs occur in a random, meaningless order, and afford no basis for predicting the next pair, for extrapolating the series. Let's make a fresh start!

What is the most common type of sequence in our lives? The numerical one. What is the most common use to which individual letters are put, letters not joined with each other to form words? As initials representing words. Combining these two thoughts, we surmise that the letters are initials standing for the names of numbers in some simple sequence. Reexamining the sequence, beginning with the fourth letter, we now recognize the number names "one", "two", "three", "four", "five", "six", "seven", "eight". The next number name, consequently, is "nine", making the next letter in our series "N".

Working backward, it becomes clear that the first three letters of the sequence must stand for "minus two", "minus one", and "O" (or "ought").

Therefore, the letter preceding the first M will be another "M", representing "minus three"; moreover, *all* further letters moving to the left will be M's.

Esthetically, it would be nice if we could convert the N following the E into a second E, creating a sixth consecutive pair of like letters. Very well, let's do just that—by replacing the word "nine" with the word "ennead". The first meaning of "ennead" is "the number nine".

The two connections between title and problem?

(1) The letter sequence begins with M M O O T T, a duplication of sorts of the French word MOT, meaning "word". Rearranged so as to double MOT word-wise instead of letterwise, the same six letters spell MOTMOT, the name of a bird related to the kingfisher. Thus, two words (two "mots") become one bird (one "motmot"). (2) The title includes the numbers "one" and "two", and the arithmetical equal sign. This is unmistakable evidence of the fact that the problem involves mathematical considerations.

Our "Hints"? In linguistics, a word such as the French "mot" is called a morpheme. "Motmot", read in reverse, becomes "tom-tom", a Chinese gong. The number names, read in succession, amount to counting in English, to an English count.

49 *MINORCA DIDN'T QUITE MAKE IT!*
(Page 45)

1. Each of our three words is an acronym, a word formed by combining the initial letters of a series of words or of a compound term; put another way, each is a set of initials that happens to spell out a common English word or name:

> EUCLID—Experimental use computer, London integrated display (a term used by the British system of air traffic control).
> HERALD—Harbor echo-ranging and listening device.
> MEDUSA—Multiple-element directional universally steerable antenna.

2. There are very few perfect word-acronyms of six or more letters. Here are some additional six-letter specimens:

> MASCOT—Motorola automatic sequential computer-operated tester.
> SORTIE—Super-orbital re-entry test integrated environment (a United States Air Force glide entry vehicle).

SPEARS—Satellite photo-electronic analog rectification system (developed by Image Instruments, Inc., Newton, Massachusetts, for the Tiros satellite project). TARGET—Thermal advanced reactor, gas-cooled, exploiting thorium.

3. Thus far, we have been able to locate only one longer acronym that spells a word:

CHALICE—Compressional Heating and Linear Injection Cusp Experiment (Stevens Institute of Technology).

4. The island name MINORCA (it is the second largest of the Balearic Islands), spelled in reverse, becomes ACRONIM, which is almost, but not quite, our theme —the ACRONYM—in this problem. Had the word ACRONYM been in existence around 1910, the Funk & Wagnalls unabridged dictionary would undoubtedly have listed it and shown ACRONIM as a reformed spelling of it. ACRONIM, therefore, just missed officially coming into existence. Them's the breaks!

7   *THE GREAT PRETENDER*

(Page 9)

William Shakespeare, a noted tenor singer, voice teacher, and music composer, was born in Croydon, England on June 16, 1849, and died in London, England on November 1, 1931.

Some of us harbor the thought that there was another William Shakespeare, a playwright, 1564–1616. The *Encyclopaedia Britannica* disposes of this notion quite effectively by pointing out that:

1. The name "Shakespeare" is extremely widespread.
2. It is spelled in an astonishing variety of ways.
3. The verdict of competent palaeographers is to the effect that the dramatist in question, in the extant examples of his signature, generally wrote "Shakspere" in full or in an abbreviated form, but possibly, in the main signature to his will, "Shakspeare".

It is generally conceded that an individual is the final authority as to the correct spelling of his name. This rules out the possibility of referring to the playwright as "William Shakespeare", and leaves the singer-teacher-composer as the only prominent man who ever called himself by that name.

Were we to be careless about the spelling of "Shakespeare", we would have to admit a multiplicity of William Shakespeares, including men such as William Shakspear, Anglo-Indian diplomat and explorer, 1878–1915, more fully known as William Henry Irvine Shakspear.

One more detail: what is the connection between the real William Shakespeare and the Duke in *Two Gentlemen of Verona?* Just this: the Duke was the Duke of MILAN; Shakespeare's career included a period of years as a singer in *Milan*, Italy.

19 *ONE IDA: AN ONEIDA?*

(*Page 18*)

GWALLAWG himself may not have been two-faced, but his name certainly was, for it is a palindrome, reading the same from right to left as from left to right.

Bernicia was never ruled by a queen. Ida was the first *king* of Bernicia, in power from 547 until his death in 559.

Three psychological traps were woven into this problem, all intended to deceive you into thinking of the monarch of Bernicia as a queen:

(a) The monarch selected for consideration was IDA. To us, that name suggests a woman, but it happens also to serve as a masculine first name (see *What to Name the Baby* by Evelyn Wells, Garden City Books, Garden City, New York, Reprint Edition, 1953, Page 246). This illustrates the tyranny of names—we tend to sex an individual according to the associations his or her name has for us, irrespective of whether or not they are justified.

(b) Ida's kingdom was BERNICIA, another name with feminine overtones, since it ends with the typically feminine suffix "-IA", and strongly resembles the invariably feminine name BERENICE.

(c) With malice aforethought, we deliberately dwelt on the author of the *History of Christian Names*, a woman whose first and middle names, "Charlotte" and "Mary", have unmistakable feminine values.

To be fair to you, we did employ a term, MONARCH, generally held to have masculine associations. Regarding a monarch as male, we can refer to a female sovereign as a monarchess. Actually, however, this is only another case of mistaken association, for almost all dictionaries define a monarch as a king *or* a queen, and only the largest dictionaries even list the word "monarchess". Hence, we ought to think of "monarch" as neutral, not as masculine.

Our title? We fooled you this time, for IDA was a chieftain of the Angles, not of the Oneidas; an Englishman, not an American. The only connection here is a purely mechanical-literal one: split the name ONEIDA at midpoint and you have ONE IDA, spelt the same but pronounced differently. We call this a "charade", also an exercise in heteronymy. Do you feel edified?

84 *REPETITIVE HOMONYMY*
(Page 70)

First, let's think about Boustrophedon and Umquhile, those distinctively designated typesetters.

Boustrophedon, one fateful morning, set the term "had had" in lower-case type, whereas Umquhile had the good fortune of using upper-case type. Both styles were equally correct, but the supervisor of the two men didn't like Boustrophedon, who had the odd habit of setting some lines of type from right to left (as well as frequently jumbling his type); the supervisor, consequently, ruled that "had had" was wrong. This queer situation may now be summarized with a record-breaking exercise in homonymy:

> Jambalaya, where Hadd had had "HAD HAD", had had "had had". Had Hadd had "had had", "had had" would have gained the supervisor's approval.

Can you furnish this little story with a postscript that will extend the homonymy even further?

Second, let's put English on the same exalted plane with Latin and Annamese by deploying the word BUFFALO with sufficient skill:

BUFFALO   BUFFALO   BUFFALO   BUFFALO.

For anyone puzzled by this statement, we elaborate: "Wild oxen (roaming the streets) of Buffalo, New York bewilder (visiting) North Carolina coast dwellers."

3 SYMBOL OF THE SUN

(*Page 6*)

The symbolico-religious ornament about which this problem revolves, most familiar to us as the emblem on the flag of Nazi Germany, is actually an ancient symbol, found in many parts of the world. Thus, it has been observed depicted on tombs at Hissarlik, near ancient Troy; on Buddhistic inscriptions in India; in Etruscan necropolises; on coins of Gaza and Corinth; on rock-carvings in Sweden; on Celtic stones in Britain; and in pre-Columbian America. A list of some of the English names for this symbol follows:

(A) SWASTIKA (also: SWASTICA, SVASTIKA, SVASTICA, SUASTIKA, SUASTICA, and SUA-VASTIKA)

(B) HAKENKREUZ

(C) TETRASKELION (also: TETRASKELE and TETRASCELE)

(D) FYLFOT (also: FILL-FOOT, FYLFOT CROSS, and FYLFOLL)

(E) CROSS CRAMPONNÉE (also: CROSS CRAMPONÉE, CROSS POTENT REBATED, and CROSS OF THOR)

(F) GAMMADION (also: GAMMADIA, GAMMADIUM, GAMMATION, GAMMATE CROSS, GAMMA CROSS, CRUX GAMMATA)

Our purely pictorial "Hints"—a rarity in this book—were intended to direct you to several of the name categories listed above. Symbol (a) is a "voided Greek cross", also called a GAMMADION. Symbol (b) is another form of the CROSS CRAMPONNÉE. Symbol (c) illustrates five different forms of the FYL-FOT: moving from lower left to upper right, these are Arabian, Scandinavian, Phoenician, Hindu, and English.

As our title tells you, the SWASTIKA was a sun symbol. It is also thought to have represented a flame of sacred fire or a flash of lightning, and to have signified benediction, health, or a good omen.

22 SHAKESPEARE AND CERVANTES

(*Page 20*)

The dates of death are the same, but according to different calendars.

In 1582, Pope Gregory XIII abolished the Julian or Old Style Calendar, replacing it with the Gregorian or New Style Calendar. While Spain adopted the Gregorian calendar immediately—the same day, in fact, that it was announced by the Pope—England did not make the change until 1752. This means that, in 1616, the day which was called April 23 in England was called May 3 in Spain. According to the Gregorian calendar now in use, Cervantes really died on April 23, but Shakespeare died on May 3, ten days later.

Although the calendar reform of 1582 is named after the Pope who authorized it, the actual originator of the Gregorian Calendar was a learned Neapolitan astronomer, mathematician, and physician, ALOYSIUS LILIUS, also known as Luigi Lilio Ghiraldi, who died in 1576.

The correlatives BIRTH and DEATH are, perhaps, the two most significant five-letter words in our lives. On the average, only 1 person out of every 365 achieves the distinction of dying on the same day on which he was born. Shakespeare was one of the fortunate few: born April 23, 1564, he died on his 52nd birthday, April 23, 1616.

As in relation to the death of Cervantes, however, this noteworthy coincidence appears to be specious. Our authorities for the exact date of Shakespeare's birth are two 18th-century antiquaries, William Oldys and Joseph Greene. Their source of information is unknown; it is probably an error resulting from confusion with the date of Shakespeare's death. It is known with certainty only that Shakespeare was baptized on April 26, 1564, and that he could not have been born later than April 23, 1564, because the inscription on his monument is evidence that on April 23, 1616 he had already begun his 53rd year. The most competent modern authorities regard the precise date of Shakespeare's birth as unknown, leaving the coincidence question an open one.

The name WILLIAM SHAKESPEARE lends itself to conquest by anagrammatists in all sorts of ways. Examples:

1. His praise we all make.
2. I ask me, has Will a peer?
3. He's like a lamp, I swear!

By sheer coincidence, the name MIGUEL DE CERVANTES SAAVEDRA is similarly pliable:

Gave us a damned clever satire!

The satire referred to is the Spanish novelist's masterpiece, *Don Quixote*.

One final coincidence. The work of preparing the King James Version of the Holy Bible was completed in 1610, when Shakespeare was 46 years old, and published the following year, 1611. Opening a copy of that Bible and turning to the Book of Psalms in the Old Testament, we examine the 46th Psalm, discovering that the 46th word from the beginning is SHAKE, and that the 46th word from the end (excluding the final "Selah", which is not part of the Psalm text proper) is SPEAR. Taken together, these two words spell SHAKE-SPEAR, one of many variants of the playwright's surname (others include CHAC-SPER, SHAXPR, and SHAXKESPEYR).

Some enthusiasts of our progressive thought movement have cited this coincidence as proof that Shakespeare was the secret author of the King James Version, but we feel that more evidence is needed before espousing such a bold conclusion.

Was there anything ordinary, commonplace, or humdrum about Shakespeare? Why, yes—the first names of his parents were JOHN and MARY, the two most common given names in English!

33 DOPPELGÄNGER!

(Page 34)

1. The word GAOL is odd: (a) although spelled so differently, it is homonymous with its variant JAIL; (b) it contains a silent "O".

2. The words of the first line of Lindon's poem are identical with those of the last line; those of the second line are identical with those of the next-to-the-last line; and so forth. This makes the poem a sort of palindrome, in which the line of verse is the unit, instead of the alphabetic letter, as in an ordinary palindrome. While the words are the same, the punctuation of corresponding lines is different in each case, however.

3. You should surmise from this that the principal subject of Lindon's article was the conventional palindrome. As a matter of fact, the title of the article was "PD Stands for Palindromes".

4. We have no idea what poem you may have composed in response to our challenge, but here is one from the hand of a master, the same Mr. Lindon:

> "Entering the lonely house with my wife,
>   For the first time I saw him
> Peering furtively from behind a bush—
> Blackness that moved, a shape amid the shadows,

A momentary glimpse of gleaming eyes
   Revealed in the ragged moon.
A closer look (he seemed to turn) might have
Put him to flight for ever: I dared not,
For reasons that I failed to understand,
   Though I knew I should act at once.
I watched in puzzlement, hiding alone,
Dogging the woman as she neared the gate . . .
   He came, and I saw him crouching
     Night after night—

     Night after night
   He came, and I saw him crouching,
Dogging the woman as she neared the gate.
I watched in puzzlement, hiding alone.
   Though I knew I should act at once,
(For reasons that I failed to understand),
I dared not put him to flight for ever.
A closer look (he seemed to turn) might have
   Revealed in the ragged moon
A momentary glimpse of gleaming eyes,
A shape amid the shadows, blackness that moved . . .
Peering furtively from behind a bush,
   I saw him for the first time
Entering the lonely house with my wife."

5. The word "Doppelgänger", referring to a wraith, to a ghostly apparition of someone not yet dead, to a ghostly double, is intended to suggest the double nature of the poem, in which the wording of each line appears twice. More than this, however, it happens to be the title of the poem just quoted, symbolizing the emergence of a second self while remaining the same.

6. DOPPELGÄNGER, a word of German origin, has its English equivalent or variant in DOUBLEGANGER, so that the poem could also have been entitled "Doubleganger".

A word about our "Hints" is in order. What we did in our colloquy, in a backward sort of manner, was to quote a standard palindrome, one in Romanian, and its translation into English, the idea being that recognition of a "letter" palindrome would lead you to recognition of a "verse-line" palindrome. As for MONOS and UNA, they are characters extracted from one of the tales of Edgar Allan Poe, *The Colloquy of Monos and Una*. Both names, one Greek and one Latin, mean "one", adding a further suggestion of doubleness.

2 *BEYOND THE LAW*

(*Page 5*)

Analysis of the rules, the laws of language, enunciated in grammars and other books on English, invariably turns up exceptions not mentioned in the books.

In this particular instance, we find that words ending in -SEDE include OBSEDE (to obsess) and ESSEDE (a two-wheeled chariot used by the ancient Gauls and Britons), and that words ending in -CEED include EMCEED (acted as master of ceremonies) and GLACÉED (coated with a glaze). These are modern, standard English words, taken from large, recognized dictionaries.

For anyone not gifted with a vocabulary of at least one million words, all of them subject to instant, total recall, problems such as this one are best solved by referring to word lists. Over the years, word lists of many sorts have been compiled and published. For this particular problem, we need word lists compiled in reverse-alphabetical order. A reverse-alphabetical list is one which starts by listing those words ending with an A, followed by those words ending with a B, followed by those words ending with a C, and so on. All words ending in A are sorted further, beginning with words ending in AA, followed by words ending in BA, followed by words ending in CA, etc. This principle of alphabetization is carried through in the entire list, and in each single word all the way to the first letter. The words are printed with their usual spelling, from left to right, but they are looked for according to the letters with which they terminate instead of the letters with which they begin.

The three best reverse-alphabetical word lists published in recent years are probably these:

1. *The Rhyming Dictionary of the English Language,* by John Walker, Revised and Enlarged by Lawrence H. Dawson, Authorized American Edition, published by E. P. Dutton and Co., New York, 1936. This 549-page book, usually called "Walker's Rhyming Dictionary", was originally intended for use by poets, to find words rhyming with given words. The purely alphabetical ordering of the words brings together words rhyming in spelling but not in pronunciation (TIMBALE, LOCALE, and SCALE, for instance). Such combinations are not welcomed by poets, even if they are occasionally used by way of poetic license. However, the 54,000 or so words in the book form an ideal word list for our purposes, and "Walker's Rhyming Dictionary" is a reasonably priced work easily purchased in bookstores.

2. Of much greater scope is the *Normal and Reverse English Word List,* compiled under the direction of A. F. Brown at the University of Pennsylvania under a contract with the Air Force Office of Scientific Research, and published in 1963. This list comes in 8 large volumes, comprising 7106 pages, and includes 354,254 entries. The first four volumes list 354,252 of these words in regular alphabetical order, and the last four volumes list all 354,254 of them in reverse-alphabetical order. According to the preface, the discrepancy of two between the two lists is for reasons best known to the computer used in preparing them. Only 200 copies of this work were originally printed. It was initially sold for $60.00 plus shipping charges, but has, at times, been distributed free of charge to qualified individuals with a legitimate need for it.

The words in this list are taken from five major dictionaries, including *Webster's New International Dictionary of the English Language,* Second Edition, 1961, but are only a partial listing of all the words in those sources. Certain classes of words, such as most proper nouns, were arbitrarily excluded. Although the work of compiling the list was done with mechanical equipment, there are a few spelling errors. Thus, on Page 2077 of Volume 7, the word STRUCTURELESS- NESS is given as STUCTURELESSNESS.

3. In 1953, the American Book Concern in Columbus, Ohio published booklets of word lists based on the "old" *Merriam-Webster Pocket Dictionary* (the Cardinal Edition of some 25,000 words, published prior to 1964). These booklets were entitled *ABC's Apralist No. 1, ABC's Apralist No. 2,* etc. Each booklet listed all words of one particular letter-length in several different orders (regular alphabetical, positional, and reverse-alphabetical). The prices of the individual booklets, printed on a high quality of paper and using a style of type designed to eliminate eyestrain, varied from about $3.00 to about $6.00. Unfortunately, the publisher has since gone out of business, and the *Apralists* are virtually unobtainable.

All of the word lists mentioned, excellent as they are, suffer from the common failing of being woefully incomplete. A two-million word list, for example, has yet to be compiled by anyone. How do we cope with this failing? By drawing on whatever knowledge happens to be stored in the backs of our minds; by random browsing through dictionaries; by flashes of inspiration, ESP, and mystical insight. Do you know of any more effective methods?

One final point. If regular word lists are based on the *alphabet* (alpha + beta), on what are reverse-alphabetical word lists based? On the *zetypsil* (zeta + ypsilon), or on the *omegapsi* (omega + psi). Take your choice!

17 *THE SCACCHIC SCOOP*

(*Page 17*)

What is the novelty in our title? It is the word "scacchic". Defined as "pertaining to or like chess", the word is almost never seen in books about the game, and is the shortest English word independently used and including four C's.

What is wrong with dictionary definitions of "countergambit"? The fact that a gambit offered by the second player is called a countergambit *whether or not* it is being played in reply to one previously offered by the first player. As proof of this fact, we list six typical countergambits, with the moves involved:

A. *Benoni Countergambit*

1. P-Q4	P-QB4	

B. *Blumenfeld Countergambit*

1. P-Q4	Kt-KB3
2. Kt-KB3	P-K3
3. P-QB4	P-QB4

C. *Budapest Countergambit*

1. P-Q4	Kt-KB3
2. P-QB4	P-K4

D. *Center Countergambit*

1. P-K4	P-Q4

E. *Greco Countergambit (Latvian Countergambit)*

1. P-K4	P-K4
2. Kt-KB3	P-KB4

F. *Queen's Pawn Countergambit*

1. P-K4	P-K4
2. Kt-KB3	P-Q4

In each instance, the gambit or sacrifice offered by the second player is the first gambit offered in the game; it is *not* offered in reply to a gambit presented by the first player.

Accordingly, a correct definition of the word "countergambit" would read:

"A chess gambit offered by the second player, either in answer to a gambit offered by the first player, or as the first potential sacrifice in a game."

Let us hope that such a correct definition will, some day, be published in a dictionary. In the meantime, there is a profound lesson for us in this story: dictionary makers are only human, and liable to err. Although we consult dictionaries for authoritative information about words, the responsibility for deciding whether the information given is true or not remains ours. This thought must be actively in our minds each time that we refer to a dictionary.

107 WORDS

(Page 87)

Here are our brain children. Have you outsmarted us at our own game, so to speak?

1. WORDS—The Eternal Miracle!
2. WORDS take the worry out of being close!
3. WORDS: All new, all great!
4. Genghis Khan had a yen for WORDS!
5. WORDS—Communicators of love!
6. WORDS turn people on!
7. WORDS: The New Frontier!
8. WORDS brighten your life!
9. From fields of sun-ripened corn come . . . WORDS!
10. WORDS are stronger than dirt!
11. WORDS: The answers to life's big questions!
12. WORDS have everything for everyone!
13. WORDS only a homemaker could love!
14. New funpower—WORDS!
15. WORDS—coolly efficient, yet warmly human!
16. WORDS: winners of the 1967 Pullet Surprise!
17. You'll find your heart's desire in WORDS!
18. WORDS do the dirty work no woman should have to do!
19. WORDS—for perspicacious people!
20. WORDS include *something* to offend everyone!

On second thought, a reading of these slogans makes us realize that we were much too restrained in coining them. After all, the ads they are intended for have to display *real* enthusiasm about words. Let's hope that you did better.

60 A STUDY IN FRUSTRATION
(*Page 52*)

The picture problem we have posed for you is definitely one of the most difficult ones in this book. Its interest and instructiveness lie in the procedures required to identify the four pictures. We shall, therefore, guide you through those procedures step by step, so that you will see the problem as it was seen by the contestants who had to struggle with it.

To begin with, the four pictures are distinctive, resembling each other strongly but differing sharply from the kind of pictures one is accustomed to seeing in books on history, geography, and travel. All four pictures are waterfront scenes, with boats of some sort shown in the water. Trees or other evidences of plant life appear in all of the pictures. The sky is a clear white in all the pictures. The pictures are remarkably small. The old-fashioned appearance of the buildings and of the boats shown, as well as the presence of forests and mountains, suggests that the pictures date back to the 18th or the 19th century.

Most pictures of American cities are modern pictures, are larger, do not show a waterfront, do not show forests and mountains, and show a sky that is either cloudy or shaded in some way.

These observations lead us to two preliminary conclusions: (1) all four pictures were taken from one source; (2) that source is an unusual one.

Consulting librarians and pointing out to them the unusual aspects of these pictures, we are referred to well-known books that contain a profusion of historical pictures, some of which are small, some of which are city pictures, and some of which show a completely clear sky. Among the books we examine in our quest are a considerable number written by (1) Benson J. Lossing, American historian, journalist, and engraver, 1813–1891; (2) John W. Barber, American historian and engraver, 1798–1885; and (3) Henry R. Schoolcraft, American traveler and ethnologist, 1793–1864. At first, we are disappointed that even large libraries have only some of the works of these authors, preventing us from making a complete search. Gradually, however, we come to realize that we aren't missing anything. All of the books examined contain pictures, but there is something about them that is different from the four pictures we have determined to identify. We reach the conclusion that the works of Lossing, Barber, and Schoolcraft, both those seen and those unseen, will not help us resolve our problem.

We try a new tack, a very elementary one. We walk into the "History and Travel Department" of one of the largest libraries in the country, and go along the shelves, examining one book after another. Many books—surprisingly many—have no pictures at all, or just a scattered few. Of the books that are lavishly illustrated, not a single one contains pictures remotely similar in style to ours.

We run across something in the nature of a lead. One book happens to have small pen-and-ink sketches at the beginning and the end of each chapter. These sketches have a resemblance of sorts to our pictures, as far as style is concerned. Could this be the nature of the source we are seeking? If it is, how can we ever locate it? Some obscure 19th-century poet, for instance, might have written a slender volume of verse, dedicating successive poems to different cities, with his book illustrated in the fashion suggested by our pictures. Why, it would be possible to spend years searching for a source of this kind!

In one section of the "History and Travel Department" we notice a series of locked wall cabinets, containing old books, in poor physical condition, obtainable only on special request. Since we are looking for old pictures, these books seem promising to us, and we obtain permission to examine all of them. Several hours of systematic search prove entirely fruitless. Books simply don't contain pictures of the sort we are trying to identify.

Here and there, we walk past extensive files of historical magazines dealing with some section of the country, some particular state, or even some specific county. Some of these magazine files are illustrated. It seems like a hopeless task even to begin searching through them, and we dismiss the thought from our minds.

By now, we've enlisted the aid of a dozen different librarians, and have concluded that they are of no help to us. They explain that, in their capacity as librarians, they are trained to think of books in terms of titles, authors, and classification numbers, not in terms of the types of illustrations that are to be found in the books. Probably true, but singularly unhelpful!

Our library research brings us to a new type of reference source: the pictorial history set, a multi-volume work covering the entire history of the United States, illustrated with thousands of pictures. We take two such sets and sit down to study all the pictures in them. One is a six-volume set, the *Album of American History*, edited by James Truslow Adams and published by Charles

Scribner's Sons, New York, 1961. The other is a fifteen-volume set, *The Pageant of America*, Independence Edition, published by Yale University Press, New Haven, 1925–1929. It does not take us too long to find a number of pictures in each set that are curiously related to our pictures. Three of our finds, all from the "Album", are reproduced here. The first is from Volume 3, Page 84; the second, from Volume 2, Page 93; the third, from Volume 2, Page 407.

A.

B.

Courtesy Chicago Historical Society

C.

Courtesy Chicago Historical Society

A careful comparison of our pictures with these finds, under a strong light, with a powerful magnifying glass, convinces us that Picture No. 1 is based on Picture B, that Picture No. 2 is based on Picture A, and that Picture No. 3 is based on Picture C. This enables us to identify Pictures No. 1, 2, and 3 as being views of New Orleans, Seattle, and St. Paul, respectively.

With three of the four pictures identified, we are able to look for references to these three cities in other picture sources, and discover that the same three pictures, varying only in shading and other minor detail, are given in a good many other books. Piecing together the information found in different works, we compile the following summary of information about the first three of our pictures:

NEW ORLEANS. "New Orleans in 1803", from an engraving after the original painting by Boqueta de Woisseri (also given as J. L. Boqueta de Woiseri, or as J. I. Bouquet de Woiseri), landscape painter who flourished about 1800–1810. The original painting is at the Chicago Historical Society, in Chicago. The artist did engravings of large views in aquatint.

SEATTLE. "Seattle About 1858", a picture in the book *Massacres of the Mountains* by Jacob Piat Dunn, Jr., published in 1886. A slightly abridged edition of this book published in 1958 omits the Seattle picture. No source for the picture is given in the 1886 edition; presumably, the author sketched it himself.

ST. PAUL. "St. Paul, Minnesota, 1853", from a colored lithograph by James Queen, lithographer, 1824–1877, after a drawing by Max Strobel, topographical draftsman, made in 1852 and published in 1853. The original picture is now in the I. N. Phelps Stokes collection, in the New York Public Library.

Where do we stand? Three of the pictures have been identified without locating their source; the fourth one remains an impenetrable mystery, since all the books we have examined provide no analogue to it. We must try some other approach.

How about the probabilistic method? New Orleans, Seattle, and St. Paul are in states on the southern, western, and northern boundaries of the United States (Louisiana, Washington, and Minnesota). If we had to make a guess, we would surmise that the fourth city was in a state on the eastern boundary of the country. Which city? Checking the latest edition of *The World Almanac and Book of Facts*, we note that the three cities already identified ranked from 15th to 40th in population in the United States in the 1960 census. It seems reasonable to suppose that the fourth city will be in the same population range. Five of these cities are in states on the east coast: Boston, Massachusetts (No. 13); Buffalo, New York (No. 20); Newark, New Jersey (No. 30); Rochester, New York (No. 38); and Norfolk, Virginia (No. 41). Boston is just outside the previous limits, and is too well-known a city, too obvious a choice, to be right, and we eliminate it from consideration. Norfolk, Virginia is also just outside the previous limits, and is in a state normally thought of as a southern state, not as an eastern one, so we remove it, too, from our list. Three cities remain as potential candidates: Buffalo, Newark, and Rochester. Further than this, our probabilistic analysis doesn't seem able to carry us. There are limits to which unaided thought is capable of bringing us. To proceed beyond those limits requires the influx of additional information.

We turn for assistance to the second largest library in the United States, the New York Public Library, with about 28,500,000 items in its possession in mid-1964, including more than 7,500,000 books, 4,000,000 pictures, 3,000,000 posters, photographs, and slides, and 5,500,000 clippings and maps. The prospect of examining twenty million items that might include the fourth picture or an analogue to it is a dismal one, but we ask its expert librarians for advice, and are directed to its Print Department. After considerable searching, we light upon the clipping reproduced next:

D.

View of Newark, New Jersey.

Once again, a careful comparison of our Picture No. 4 with Picture D shows that the former is based on the latter, and we have identified the fourth picture as one of Newark. An interesting confirmation of our probabilistic analysis, incidentally!

Although all four pictures are now identified, we cannot rest, for the sponsor of our contest happens to be running a second and a third contest identical with the first one, and will obviously use the same sources to break ties. In view of the monumental efforts required to identify these four pictures—efforts expended over a period of time much greater than the fifteen days allowed by the sponsor—it is imperative to locate the one source containing pictures identical with our four pictures; identical, not merely analogous.

What does the New York Public Library know about its clipping of Newark? The card index identifies it as a magazine clipping dated 1878. This seems extremely doubtful, however, for the clipping has no print of any kind on the back, which a clipping from a magazine would normally have, and the paper is not yellowed and brittle, as paper almost 90 years old would almost inevitably be. The picture is obviously a print made from a woodcut. Possibly, the woodcut was made in 1878, but remained in someone's collection for a long time before this print from it was made.

We consult the public library in Newark. Its experts are familiar with the NYPL clipping, which was sent to Newark some years ago as part of an exhibit, but we are told that, to their knowledge, the picture has never appeared in print in any book or magazine. Discouraging . . . whither now?

Continued research at the New York Public Library uncovers an old illustrated history set, the five-volume *Popular History of the United States*, by William Cullen Bryant and Sidney Howard Gay, published by Scribner's, New York, 1876–1882. On Page 323 of Volume 2, we find a picture of Newark identical with the 1878 "magazine clipping". At last, we have the book analogue of our fourth picture! We are now quickly able to determine that the picture was one prepared specifically for this history set by Alfred R. Waud, a British-born maritime artist, 1828–1891, who came to the United States circa 1858, and who is best-known for his numerous Civil War battlefield sketches.

How much closer has our research brought us to the one published source from which all four of the contest pictures were taken? Not a step, actually. We have accumulated a great deal of information about the ultimate sources of the four pictures, but know absolutely nothing about their immediate source, and it is this information that we desperately seek in preparation for the second and third contests.

Two lines of action suggest themselves to us at this point. It may be that the sponsor of the contest, in an effort to make the pictures almost impossible to identify, deliberately took them from a source which he had established was not available in the largest libraries of New York and Chicago, the libraries to which expert contestants were most likely to turn in their searches. The source could be some comparatively obscure book, published many years ago and long since out of print. The only chance of finding a book fitting this description would be by means of a search through the second-hand, used-book stores in the big cities of the country, beginning with New York itself. Ever optimistic, we actually commence such a search, and fate, which has frustrated us at every turn so far, finally swings over to our side. In the *very first* New York book shop that we visit, we stumble upon the source of the four contest pictures within a mere ten minutes—a fantastic stroke of luck! They were photocopied from a book published in 1933 by a New York publishing firm, Grosset & Dunlap. The book? *Minute Glimpses of American Cities*, by Herbert S. Kates. The book contains short descriptions of 75 American and Canadian cities, with illustrations of each one, including our four pictures.

Checking back, we discover that the New York Public Library, with its $7\frac{1}{2}$ million books, does not have this one. The meaning of this fact overwhelms us: we could have spent years at that library, exhausting its research facilities, and we would have failed to find the source of the pictures, not because of our incompetence but because the NYPL simply didn't have the source.

To deviate for a moment, our "Hints" were another dead giveaway: the initial sentence consisted of four words, each one a transposal of KATES, the author's name, and the comment that followed used a key word of the book title (MINUTE). Do you realize now how easy we made this problem for *you?*

There was a second line of action we could have pursued, which would also have led to success. Printed analogues for the first three of our pictures have been published in various books, but there is only one printed analogue for the fourth picture, the one in the old (Scribner's) history set. Reasoning that whoever wrote or published the book from which our contest pictures were taken may have had to obtain copyright permission from Scribner's for the Newark picture, a logical gambit would have been to inquire of Charles Scribner's Sons whether it had any record of granting such permission to some-one; and, if so, to whom and in connection with what book. Subsequent inquiry developed the fact that the history editor at Scribner's, a historian himself, would have been able to answer the question immediately.

Au revoir, mysterious world of contesting!

6 *JAYS THAT AREN'T*

(*Page 8*)

Research indicates that only three internationally prominent individuals have borne the title GENERALISSIMO:

(1) Chiang Kai-shek, President of China
(2) Francisco Franco, Chief of State of Spain
(3) Rafael Trujillo, President of the Dominican Republic

Our original story contains ten clues that may or may not be useful in determining about which one of the three men we have spun the tale. Let's examine them, one by one:

1. Born in last quarter of year. Chiang's birthday, October 31; Franco's, December 4; Trujillo's, October 24. All three dates fall in the fourth quarter of the year, so that this is not a helpful clue.

2. The common lustrum. A lustrum is a period of five years. Chiang was born in 1887, Franco in 1892, and Trujillo in 1891. The five-year period from the final quarter of 1887 to the final quarter of 1892 embraces all three leaders, and our problem remains unresolved.

3. A two-part surname. At first glance, only the Chinese leader, with his hyphenated surname, seems to qualify. Probing a bit, however, we discover that Franco's full surname is FRANCO BAHAMONDE or FRANCO-BAHAMONDE, and that Trujillo's full surname was TRUJILLO MOLINA or TRUJILLO y MOLINA. Consequently, this clue is equally applicable to all three men, and brings us no nearer to a solution.

4. A six-letter name. The names CHIANG, FRANCO, and RAFAEL all consist of six letters, so that we are yet to be helped by a clue.

5. A two-part national name. Offhand, only the *Dominican Republic,* using two words to identify itself, fits the stated condition. Actually, however, we must remember that Chiang is the leader of *Nationalist China,* and that the official name of Spain is *Estado Español.* Thus, the correct answer remains up for grabs. Peculiar!

6. A two-part capital name. Under Trujillo, the name of the capital of the Dominican Republic was CIUDAD TRUJILLO. The capital of Spain is, of course, MADRID. The capital of Nationalist China has, at various times, been WUCHANG,

CHUNGKING, NANKING, or TAIPEI. This seems to settle the issue in favor of Trujillo. It seems to, but it doesn't. Madrid is the winter capital of Spain. Its summer capital? SAN SEBASTIÁN! As for Nanking, one of Chiang's capitals, the city has other names, including KINLING and KIANGNING-FU. The latter is hyphenated, making it a two-part name, and we are left in the dark.

7. Twelve alphabetic characters in the name of the capital. A first count reveals SAN SEBASTIÁN as the only capital fitting the description, giving Franco the nod. Alas, 'tis not so simple! The previous name of CIUDAD TRUJILLO was SANTO DOMINGO, a name of exactly twelve letters. Alphabetic characters? What are they? Do they include punctuation marks used in conjunction with actual letters? If so, KIANGNING-FU is certainly a twelve-character name! After seven successive clues, we are yet to move from our starting point.

8. "Naturally!" Why would the Generalissimo *naturally* stop at the sight of a six-letter name of his? To answer that question, we set down the *full* names of all three leaders:

    (1) Chiang Kai-shek
    (2) Francisco Paulino Hermenegildo Teódulo Franco-Bahamonde
    (3) Rafael Leonidas Trujillo y Molina

Looking at these names, we see that only the third one *ends* with a six-letter name, the name MOLINA. In reading, it is natural to stop only when you have reached the end. Accordingly, the solution to our problem is TRUJILLO.

9. "In utter disbelief, . . ." How *could* Trujillo have put SANTO DOMINGO down as the name of his capital, after *he* had caused its name to be changed to CIUDAD TRUJILLO, honoring himself? It would, surely, have been beyond belief! No such considerations apply in the case of China or of Spain.

10. "No more, no less". The only 12-letter name of a capital whose count is not subject to variation is the name SANTO DOMINGO. In SAN SEBASTIÁN, it is our privilege to include the acute accent in our count, raising it to 13, or to use the French form of the name, ST.-SÉBASTIEN, with a count of anywhere from 11 to 14, depending on what we include and what we exclude.

    Ten clues: the first seven settled nothing, each of the last three settled everything.
    For those of you who did not recognize the three decisive clues, we included another three in our "Hints". First, the palindrome quoted used the name LEONIDAS, one of Trujillo's given names. Second, the obviously irrelevant

word OILMAN is a transposal of MOLINA, the very last of Trujillo's names. Third, we would judiciously have abstained from writing about Chiang or about Franco, since both leaders are still living. That inhibition does not govern in the case of Trujillo, who was assassinated in 1961.

What about our title, allegedly tied to our plot in three different ways? Listen and learn!

(a) The word "jay", which usually refers to a garruline, corvine bird, is also a name of the alphabetic letter J. Note that the J is sounded but not written in the word GENERALISSIMO.

(b) In the name TRUJILLO, we have the opposite phenomenon, a J included in the spelling but not in the pronunciation (it is pronounced like an H).

(c) Reversing ourselves again, we note the name CHIANG, in which a J is sounded though not written (the initial digraph CH is pronounced like a J). In this case, we can triple the phenomenon by changing the Chinese leader's name from CHIANG KAI-SHEK to his formal name, CHIANG CHUNG-CHENG, pronounced JYÄNG′ JÙNG′JUNG′.

In each of the three situations, we have one or more J's which exist or are from one point of view, but which do not exist, which aren't, from another point of view.

119 *THE LIVING END*
(*Page 98*)

Using our "Hints" as a springboard to glory (?), we deduce that, if a beginning is also a start and a middle is also a center, then the end so enigmatically inserted into our title is also a finish. Listening to ourselves, we discover that FINISH is homonymous with FINNISH, the name of a nationality. It follows, with the force of a Kantian categorical imperative, that the nationality of the prisoner was Finnish.

This is the *final* one of our "Problems", qualifying you to advance to the more difficult workouts known as "Bafflers". This provides our title with its fundamental relevance. Additionally, as has just been demonstrated, the title is a direct route to solving the prisoner mystery, giving it top status in its field: yes, it is "the living end"! One more feature—"living" is a clue to the fact that there is a meaningful connection between the title and the living human being about which our problem revolves.

Obviously, New Orleans is in Louisiana, but this does not justify the tidbit about chain store taxes that we threw into this teaser. As pointed out in our "Hints", we are being educational here, and simply wish to add a little to whatever fund of useless information you may be accumulating. You'd be surprised what an effective icebreaker our gem can turn out to be at your next cocktail party!

AFTERWORD

"So many men, so many minds".

A few hardy souls—realistic, practical, levelheaded individuals—members of our nonreadership, we take it—deplore the time and ingenuity needed for creating and solving the problems offered in *Beyond Language*. How much more salutary, they argue, if the same brainpower were applied to advance some worthwhile human cause.

This is a challenge aimed both at the author and at the reader. It cannot be permitted to stand. We must analyze it and refute it. Come, let us reason together.

If we were to demonstrate that puzzle-solving activity, whether of the ordinary crossword variety or of the more mind-taxing sort presented here, is an exercise of the same importance as the most advanced mathematical, scientific, and technological research in progress today, we could rest our case. This is what we propose to do.

It is normally assumed that scientific inquiry is gradually leading us to-

310

ward an understanding of the universe in which we live. Men are thinking creatures with an insatiable curiosity about themselves and their world, and view science and mathematics as keys to solving the primordial mystery. This standpoint is comforting but unfounded.

Is the real universe limited or unlimited, finite or infinite? The character of human thought forces us to the conclusion that the universe is infinite. If it were finite, it would have limits or boundaries. In that case, there would be something beyond those limits or boundaries, even if only empty space. Whatever it was would, by definition, be part of the all-embracing universe. Since a boundary must have something lying beyond it, this makes it impossible for the universe to have one. Indeed, the universe is infinite; otherwise, no human mind could hope ever to comprehend it.

Some astrophysicists, in proposing models of the universe, have envisioned our three-dimensional space as merely the surface of a four-dimensional hypersphere, immense but finite. Whether or not this view will eventually prevail is not germane to our discussion. If we exist within the three-dimensional surface of a four-dimensional hypersphere, then human thought dictates that there be an unlimited number of additional such hyperspheres, distributed in a hyperspace of infinite extent.

In its struggle upward from apedom, the human race has accumulated a fantastic amount of knowledge. Yet, that knowledge has been amassed by a finite number of men, over a finite period of time. It follows that the sum total of human knowledge is also finite. Furthermore, no matter how greatly mankind might multiply in the future, overrunning other planets and reaching out beyond the confines of our Solar System, and however many eons of time might pass—billions or even trillions of years—that sum total of knowledge is doomed always to remain finite.

The universe is infinite. Our knowledge about the universe is, and shall always be, finite. The ratio of the finite to the infinite is infinitesimal, or zero-like. Hence, our knowledge of the universe is, and must ever remain, like unto nothing. We know nothing; we shall never know anything.

Let us place the argument in even sharper focus. Imagine a curious visitor from an alien stellar galaxy coming to investigate Planet Earth. Imagine him examining one molecule of oxygen on the outermost fringes of Earth's atmosphere. Just one molecule of oxygen; nothing else. How much will our visitor learn about Planet Earth? About Earth's supposedly molten interior, about its continents and oceans, about plant and animal life, about human intelligence and achievements, about alcoholism and remedial reading, about Earth's role as a unit of the Solar System? From one molecule of atmospheric oxygen—nothing! Yet, our visitor will have examined a finite portion of a finite body, which is incalculably more, infinitely more, than the human race can ever see of the infinite universe. Consequently, the utter nothingness of our visitor's terrestrial knowledge will still be immeasurably greater, infinitely greater, than our knowledge of the universe can ever be.

What we have just proved is that science and mathematics are inherently incapable of obtaining even the most insignificant shred of knowledge about the real universe. This conclusion is reinforced by numerous collateral lines of reasoning. We pause to review some of them.

Human beings receive impressions of the universe through five specific senses. These senses are of a purely arbitrary nature. In the absence of any evidence to the contrary, we must assume that dozens, or hundreds, or even thousands, of other kinds of senses could be developed by living forms. Beings equipped with hundreds of other senses, of a nature totally unimaginable to us, would have a conception of the universe unfathomably different from ours, beyond the reach of humanity's greatest minds.

We think in terms of three spatial dimensions and one temporal dimension, with motion along the latter in one direction only. Again, the numbers are arbitrary. How would the universe appear to beings whose minds were capable of perceiving 227 spatial dimensions and 49 temporal dimensions, with motion along 37 of the temporal dimensions possible in either direction and at varying rates of speed?

It is possible to reason even more imaginatively. For us, space and time are two concepts standing in a class by themselves, constituting a frame of reference that the human mind has created for sorting the sense impressions it receives into an orderly and manageable separateness. What understanding of the universe would be attained by animate entities for whom space and time were only two of thirteen mutually distinct components in a vastly more sophisticated frame of reference?

We believe that Earth has existed for some $4\frac{1}{2}$ or 5 billion years, during which length of time life has evolved from nonlife. The most penetrating analysis of Planet Earth made before the first appearance of living forms on it could have given no inkling of a Napoleon Bonaparte or of an Albert Einstein. In the same fashion, study of Earth today does not provide even the faintest echo of a hint as to the existences that will be encountered on it five or ten billion years hence.

Put on a pair of sunglasses with green lenses, and look about you. Everything you see will seem to be tinted green. Is the greenness in the objects you are viewing or in the viewing apparatus? It is in the viewing apparatus. All scientific and mathematical knowledge is based on data received through the senses and on thoughts generated by human minds. It is logical to assume that much or most of that knowledge—possibly, even all of it—is determined by the character of our senses and of our minds, not by the nature of the universe to which it purports to relate. Since we are prisoners of our senses and of our minds, unable to examine reality except through the dark, clouded screen these interpose, science has no way of knowing how much (or how little) of its conjecturing is fact, and how much is fiction.

Everything about the human situation bespeaks arbitrariness. There are 5 senses; 4 spatial and temporal dimensions; 103 known chemical elements; more than two hundred known subatomic particles; 2 forms of "realness" (matter and energy); and so on, ad infinitum. All numbers greater than 1 and smaller than infinity are arbitrary. What this means is that there is no logical reason, no acceptable reason, why one of the intervening numbers should have preference over another, in relation to any given entity. It is not possible to defend the existence of 4 dimensions as opposed to 17, of two forms of realness rather than five, of 103 chemical elements instead of 255. The human mind recoils from assigning arbitrary qualities to ultimate reality, which must be conceived of as absolute, not as a product of caprice. The conclusion to which we are driven is that our picture of the universe is entirely fictitious, bearing no resemblance to the real universe.

What is the reaction of scientists and of mathematicians to this damning indictment of their activities? Many retreat into a shell, as it were. They claim that they are not interested in the nature of ultimate reality. They profess to be concerned solely with the study and correlation of sensory data and with the formulation of a theory that will account for all such data. What the relationship of their activities to ultimate reality might be is a question they are content to leave to philosophers.

Such a position is untenable. Sensory data are generally thought of as information about reality. They are not. Accordingly, there is no reason to believe that the fiction with which science and mathematics deal lends itself to any kind of logical explanation or system. Logic and arbitrariness are irreconcilable opponents. Deprived of purpose, the pursuits of science and of mathematics turn into intricate verbalizations without an objective referent— into word games!

The intrinsically lusory character of mathematical and scientific endeavor is aptly illustrated by an announcement from scientists at the Argonne National Laboratory (Lemont, Illinois), made just as this is being written. A new subatomic particle, the N ASTERISK 3245, is reported. It is the heaviest nuclear particle known, has extraordinary stability, and exists for one ten-sextillionth of a second. It falls in the class of "nucleon resonances" and is described as a mass of frozen energy.

You know, and we know, that the *real* world does not consist of entities with a lifetime of one ten-sextillionth of a second. Any explanation of that world which finds itself compelled to invent entities so preposterously absurd as the N ASTERISK 3245 in order to keep up the pretense of being an adequate explanation, has gone so far astray as to be beyond any hope of correction. A new start must be made, based on quite different premises.

Of course, the scientists responsible for this news release have tipped us off to the fact that they themselves regard the new particle as nothing more than a big joke, by labeling it N ASTERISK 3245. Particles intended to be taken seriously are given names such as ELECTRON, NEUTRON, HYPERON, and LEPTON. When the naming process degenerates into monstrosities like N ASTERISK 3245, it is time to call a halt to the farce, for that is what it is.

Scientists and mathematicians discuss things and tell us things, but what they say corresponds to no known reality, for the reality to which it is ostensibly directed must forever remain beyond their grasp. That is why their research belongs to the category of pure word games.

The average crossword puzzle solver amuses himself with a comparatively easy form of word game. The reader of this book has chosen more challenging games of word and thought with which to divert himself. The scientist and the mathematician play yet more difficult word-and-thought games. Each one, in his own way, is passing the time between birth and death in the manner best suited to his temperament. One game or another game—which one is played doesn't really matter, as long as it brings happiness to the player.

What is the impact of our findings on the philosophical quest for truth? Some individuals, discouraged by these revelations, become agnostics, holding that real knowledge is unattainable. More venturesome souls seek out the oldest doctrine known to mankind: PANTHEISM. In the pantheistic view, the consciousness of the individual is mystically capable of merging with the Cosmic Consciousness, absorbing infinite wisdom instantly.

Be that as it may, we have succeeded in showing that puzzle-solving activity and advanced scientific research are exercises of equal importance (or unimportance, depending on one's standpoint). Truly may it be said that, in vindicating *Beyond Language,* we have reached out *beyond language,* toward the stars!

BIBLIOGRAPHY

Strictly speaking, it is impossible to append a bibliography to *Beyond Language*, since no work resembling it is known to exist.

In a broader sense, however, there is an imperative need for publishing a list of books constituting what might be called a "word lover's library": books of particular interest to those who pursue language recreationally. No comprehensive bibliography of this nature has previously appeared. The pioneer undertaking that follows embraces not only books and pamphlets about word puzzles and word curiosities, but also synonymicons, word lists, books of literary oddities, specialized dictionaries abounding in fantastic words, publications devoted to contest puzzles, and sundry curiosa.

Some of the works listed—those by Hare, Hodgkin, and Mencken, for instance—themselves include extensive bibliographies relating to specific topics. The interested reader is advised to consult these additional listings.

The entries below are generally alphabetized by the surname of the author, compiler, or editor; where a publication does not give this information, it has been alphabetized by title.

If some pertinent books are omitted, blame it on ignorance; if others have been included without adequate justification, attribute it to subjectivity. In any event, a bibliography can never be complete, for completeness, like perfection, is an infinitely distant goal.

ADAMS, J. DONALD. *The Magic and Mystery of Words*. Holt, Rinehart and Winston, New York, 1963.

ALLEN, F. STURGES. *Allen's Synonyms and Antonyms*, Revised and Enlarged Edition. Harper & Brothers, New York and London, 1938.

ALLEN, HOPE EMILY. "The Fifteenth-Century 'Associations of Beasts, of Birds, and of Men': The Earliest Text With 'Language for Carvers' ". *PMLA*, Volume LI (June,

1936), pp. 602–606, published by The Modern Language Association of America, New York.

ALLEN, RICHARD HINCKLEY. *Star Names: Their Lore and Meaning*. Dover Publications, Inc., New York, 1963.

Amusing and Popular Riddles: 839 Funny Riddles (Little Blue Book No. 1175). Haldeman-Julius Company, Girard, Kansas, undated.

ATWATER, JOHN M. and IRELAND, NORMA OLIN. *Long Word Books—Book I, 15 Letters*. A. D. Freese & Sons, Inc., Upland, Indiana, 1956.

BALL, A. R. *The Nuttall Dictionary of Anagrams*. Frederick Warne & Company Ltd., London and New York, undated.

BENÉT, WILLIAM ROSE. *The Reader's Encyclopedia*, with Supplement. Thomas Y. Crowell Company, New York, 1955.

BERNERS, DAME JULIANA. *The Book of Saint Albans*, Facsimile Edition. E. Stock, London, 1881.

BERREY, LESTER V. *Roget's International Thesaurus*, New (Second) Edition. Thomas Y. Crowell Company, New York, 1946.

BERREY, LESTER V. and VAN DEN BARK, MELVIN. *The American Thesaurus of Slang*, Second Edition. Thomas Y. Crowell Company, New York, 1953.

BIERCE, AMBROSE. *The Devil's Dictionary*, A Dolphin Book. Doubleday & Company, Inc., Garden City, New York, undated.

BOMBAUGH, CHARLES C. *Gleanings for the Curious from the Harvest-Fields of Literature*, Author's Unabridged Edition. A. D. Worthington & Company, Hartford, Connecticut, 1875.

BOMBAUGH, CHARLES C. *Oddities and Curiosities of Words and Literature*, edited and annotated by Martin Gardner. Dover Publications, Inc., New York, 1961.

BORGMANN, DMITRI A. *Language on Vacation*. Charles Scribner's Sons, New York, 1965.

BOYER, JOHN Q. *Answers to Form and Verse Puzzles in "Real Puzzles"*. The Norman, Remington Company, Baltimore, Maryland, 1925.

BOYER, JOHN Q.; STROHM, RUFUS T.; and PRYOR, GEORGE H. *Real Puzzles*. The Norman, Remington Company, Baltimore, Maryland, 1925.

BREWER, E. COBHAM. *Dictionary of Phrase and Fable*, New Edition. J. B. Lippincott Company, Philadelphia and London, circa 1895.

BREWER, E. COBHAM. *The Reader's Handbook*, New Edition, Revised. J. B. Lippincott Company, Philadelphia, circa 1897.

Brewer's Dictionary of Phrase and Fable, Eighth Revised Edition. Harper & Row, New York and Evanston, 1963.

BROWN, A. F. *Normal and Reverse English Word List*, Eight Volumes. University of Pennsylvania (under contract with the Air Force Office of Scientific Research), Philadelphia, 1963.

BROWNLOW, C. V. *Gould's Medical Dictionary*, Fifth Revised Edition. The Blakiston Company, Philadelphia and Toronto, 1941.

BURGESS, GELETT. *The Purple Cow and Other Nonsense*. Dover Publications, Inc., New York, 1961.

CALDWELL, WILLIAM. *Parts of Two or More Word Phrases*. Contest Books, Los Angeles, 1951.

CARROLL, LEWIS. *The Annotated Alice,* with an Introduction and Notes by Martin Gardner; a Forum Book. The World Publishing Company, Cleveland and New York, 1963.

CLARK, G. R. *Palindromes.* Bryce and Simpkin, Glasgow, Scotland, 1886–1887.

COLLE, E. N. *The Animal Kingdom Index.* Specialty Publications, Cleveland, 1951.

Complete 2 to 23 Letter Word Book from Merriam-Webster Pocket Dictionary. Research Book Company, New York, 1955.

COOK, JR., NORMAN W. *Cook's Revised and Improved Puzzle Dictionary.* National Crossword Puzzlers, Brooklyn, New York, 1950.

COOPER, WILLIAM R. *An Archaic Dictionary.* Bagster and Son, London, 1876.

COX, CHARLES ROY. *ABC's Apralist: 9-Letter Words.* American Book Concern, Columbus, Ohio, 1953. (NOTE: Similar lists have been published for words of 4, 5, 6, 7, 8, and 10 letters.)

Crossword Puzzles from The London Times. Hawthorn Books, Inc., New York, 1964.

DAVENPORT, DORIS K. *Delving A to Z for Variants and Reformed Spellings.* Doris K. Davenport, St. Petersburg, Florida, 1951 (distributed by Robert Spence Publications, Inc., also of St. Petersburg).

DUDENEY, HENRY E. *The World's Best Word Puzzles.* The "Daily News" Publications Department, London, 1925.

DUTCH, ROBERT A. *The Original Roget's Thesaurus of English Words and Phrases,* New Edition, Completely revised and modernized. St. Martin's Press, New York, 1965.

EARL, MARLIN. *Cash for Untangling Titles.* Robert Spence, St. Petersburg, Florida, 1957.

EASTERN PUZZLERS' LEAGUE, THE. *A Key to Puzzledom, or Complete Handbook of the Enigmatic Art.* William W. Delaney, New York, 1906.

EBY, ANSON D. *Curiosities of Language* (Little Blue Book No. 1750). Haldeman-Julius Company, Girard, Kansas, undated.

ESAR, EVAN. *The Dictionary of Humorous Quotations.* Bramhall House, New York, 1949.

ESAR, EVAN. *Humorous English.* Horizon Press, New York, 1961.

Everything's A Puzzle, 149 Pages. (No author, publisher, or date shown, but published after 1950).

FANSHAWE, L. A. *The Crossword Puzzle Solver,* Second Edition. Sir Isaac Pitman & Sons, Ltd., London, 1933.

FARRAR, MARGARET. *The Crossword Book of Puns & Anagrams.* Simon and Schuster, New York, 1963.

FOSTER, FRANK PIERCE. *An Illustrated Encyclopaedic Medical Dictionary,* Six Volumes. D. Appleton and Company, New York, 1888–1894.

FRIEND, J. NEWTON. *Words: Tricks and Traditions.* Charles Scribner's Sons, New York and London, 1957.

FULLER, JOHN G. *Games for Insomniacs.* Doubleday & Company, Inc., New York, 1966.

GAINES, HELEN FOUCHÉ. *Cryptanalysis.* Dover Publications, Inc., New York, 1956.

GOSSE, HELEN & PHILIP. *Gathered Together.* The Swan Press, Chelsea, England, 1927.

GRIESHABER, HANS. *Forty Years Travelling Round the World,* pp. 141–147. Robert Hale, London, 1965.

HAERTZEN, CHARLES A. *Follett Vest Pocket Anagram Dictionary.* Follett Publishing Company, Chicago, 1964.

HARE, C. E. *The Language of Field Sports*, Revised Edition. Country Life Ltd., London, 1949.

HARE, C. E. *The Language of Sport*. Country Life Ltd., London, 1939.

HILL, H. W. *The Quickway Crossword Dictionary*. Frederick Warne and Company Ltd., London and New York, 1953.

HODGE, FREDERICK WEBB. *Handbook of American Indians North of Mexico*, Two Volumes. Rowman and Littlefield, Inc., New York, 1965.

HODGKIN, JOHN. "Proper Terms". *Transactions of the London Philological Society*, 1909, pp. 1–187, published for the Society by Kegan Paul, Trench, Trübner, & Company, Ltd., London.

HUGHES, RUPERT. *Music Lovers' Encyclopedia*, Completely revised and newly edited by Deems Taylor and Russell Kerr. Garden City Books, Garden City, New York, 1954.

HUGON, PAUL D. *The Modern Word Finder*, New Revised Edition. Grosset & Dunlap, New York, 1934.

Irregular and Unusual Plurals. American Newspaper Syndicate, 1950. (33 Pages).

JACKSON, HOLBROOK. *The Complete Nonsense of Edward Lear*. Dover Publications, Inc., New York, 1951.

"JAX". *Story of "The Jax Square" and 100 Jax Square Puzzles*. J. Wilson (printed by Hugh Evans & Sons, Ltd.), Liverpool, England, undated.

JOYCE, JAMES. *Finnegans Wake*, embodying all author's corrections. The Viking Press, New York, 1945.

KANE, JOSEPH NATHAN. *Facts About the Presidents*, New, Revised and Enlarged Edition; a Pocket Book Edition. Pocket Books, Inc., New York, 1960.

KAUFMAN, GERALD LYNTON. *The Book of Modern Puzzles*, Second Revised Edition. Dover Publications, Inc., New York, 1954.

KAUFMAN, GERALD LYNTON. *New Word Puzzles*. Dover Publications, Inc., New York, 1957.

KEITH, LEE. *Complete 8 Letter Words*. Lee Keith, Pocahontas, Arkansas, 1950. (NOTE: Similar lists have been published for words of 3, 4, 5, 6, and 7 letters.)

KEITH, LEE. *Keith's 2 thru 8-Letter Words*. Lee Keith, Pocahontas, Arkansas, 1952.

KEITH, LEE. *Out-of-Place Words from M-W Dictionary*. Lee Keith, Pocahontas, Arkansas, 1951.

KINNAIRD, CLARK. *Encyclopedia of Puzzles and Pastimes*. Grosset & Dunlap, New York, 1946.

LEE, EDWARD L. *Dictionary of Plants*. Robert Spence Publications, Inc., St. Petersburg, Florida, 1959.

LEE, EDWARD L. *Merriam-Webster Third New International Dictionary Six Letter Words*. Robert Spence Publications, Inc., St. Petersburg, Florida, circa 1963. (NOTE: Similar lists have been published for words of 2, 3, 4, 5, 7, 8, 9, and 10 letters.)

Le Livre des Extremes. Guinness Hachette, Paris, circa 1962. (Text is in French.)

LEVINE, JACK. *A List of Words Containing No Repeated Letters*. Jack Levine, Raleigh, North Carolina, 1957.

LEVINSON, LEONARD LOUIS. *The Left Handed Dictionary*. Collier Books, New York, 1963.

LEWIS, NORMAN. *The Comprehensive Word Guide.* Doubleday & Company, Inc., Garden City, New York, 1958.

LEWIS, NORMAN. *The New Roget's Thesaurus of the English Language in Dictionary Form,* Revised, Greatly Enlarged Edition. Garden City Books, Garden City, New York, 1961.

Long Words (From 15 to 27 Letters). Complete Contest Service, Phoenix, Arizona, 1956.

MARCH, FRANCIS ANDREW and MARCH, JR., FRANCIS A. *March's Thesaurus-Dictionary,* with a new Supplement by R. A. Goodwin. Hanover House, Garden City, New York, 1958.

MARCUSE, SIBYL. *Musical Instruments: A Comprehensive Dictionary.* Doubleday & Company, Inc., Garden City, New York, 1964.

MARSHALL, STEPHEN. *Complete Fourteen Letter Word Book.* Stephen Marshall, Brooklyn, New York, 1951. (NOTE: Similar lists have been published for words of 9, 10, 11, 12, and 13 letters.)

MARSHALL, STEPHEN. *Experts List of High Score 4 to 8 Letter Words.* Stephen Marshall, Brooklyn, New York, 1951.

MARSHALL, STEPHEN. *High Score 3 to 18 Letter Words.* Stephen Marshall, Brooklyn, New York, 1952.

MARSHALL, STEPHEN. *The Puzzle Experts Contest Course.* Contest Service, Brooklyn, New York, 1951.

MARSHALL, STEPHEN. *Signs & Symbols for Contest Fans.* Contest Service, Brooklyn, New York, 1956.

MARSHALL, STEPHEN. *Tricky Crossword Clues and Explanations,* Four Volumes. Stephen Marshall, Brooklyn, New York, 1956–1959.

MARSHALL, STEPHEN. *20,000 Unusual Definitions and Synonyms.* Stephen Marshall, Brooklyn, New York, 1952.

MAWSON, C. O. SYLVESTER. *Roget's Thesaurus of the English Language in Dictionary Form,* Reprint Edition. Garden City Books, Garden City, New York, 1940.

MC WHIRTER, NORRIS D. and A. ROSS. *The Guinness Book of Records,* Tenth Edition. Guinness Superlatives Limited, London, 1962.

MC WHIRTER, NORRIS D. and A. ROSS. *Guinness Book of World Records,* Revised and Enlarged Edition. Sterling Publishing Company, Inc., New York, 1965.

MENCKEN, HENRY L. *The American Language—Supplement II,* pp. 596–642. Alfred A. Knopf, New York, 1960.

MEYER, JEROME S. *Puzzle Quiz and Stunt Fun.* Dover Publications, Inc., New York, 1956.

MILBURN, GEORGE. *A Book of Interesting and Amusing Puns* (Little Blue Book No. 1093). Haldeman-Julius Company, Girard, Kansas, undated.

MILBURN, GEORGE. *Book of Puzzles and Brainteasers* (Little Blue Book No. 1103). Haldeman-Julius Company, Girard, Kansas, undated.

MOORE, JOHN. *You English Words.* J. B. Lippincott Company, Philadelphia and New York, 1962.

"M.R.W." *The Crossword Companion.* Herbert Jenkins, London, 1952.

NEWTON, FRANK EATON. *New Practical Dictionary for Cross Word Puzzles,* Revised, Enlarged Edition. Doubleday & Company, Inc., Garden City, New York, 1964.

NEW PRIMER OF PUZZLEDOM. The National Puzzlers' League, Inc., Greenfield, Massachusetts, 1958.

NICOL, R. J. *A Collection of Terms, denoting Assemblages of Animals, Birds, Human Beings, etc.* Privately printed, Ballogie, England, 1933.

NORDEN, HEINZ. *A Book of Striking Similes* (Little Blue Book No. 1354). Haldeman-Julius Company, Girard, Kansas, undated.

Nyphonium, A. The National Puzzlers' League, Centre Hall, Pennsylvania, circa 1951.

"OEDIPUS" (Charles Jacobsen). *A Complete Chronological History of the National Puzzlers' League, Inc.* Riddlers Club of New York, 1953.

ORLEANS, JACOB and JACOBSON, EDMUND. *The Scrabble Word Guide.* Grosset & Dunlap, New York, 1953.

PARKER, ELLSWORTH DAILEY. *Words Within Words.* Ellsworth Dailey Parker, St. Louis, Missouri, 1953.

PATTERSON, AUSTIN M. *Words About Words,* A Collection of Nomenclature Columns reprinted from *Chemical and Engineering News.* The American Chemical Society, Washington, D. C., 1957.

PEARSON, A. CYRIL. *Pictured Puzzles and Word Play.* George Routledge & Sons, Ltd., London, undated.

PEARSON, A. CYRIL. *The Twentieth Century Standard Puzzle Book.* George Routledge & Sons, Ltd., London, undated.

PFIEFFER, ORVILLE. *Puzzle Lovers Dictionary,* a Gold Star Book. The New International Library, Inc., Derby, Connecticut, 1964.

POTTER, CHARLES FRANCIS. *Is That in The Bible?,* a Crest Book. Fawcett Publications, Inc., Greenwich, Connecticut, 1962.

Primer of Puzzledom. The National Puzzlers' League, Centre Hall, Pennsylvania, circa 1952.

PROCHNOW, HERBERT V. and PROCHNOW, JR., HERBERT V. *A Dictionary of Wit, Wisdom, & Satire.* Harper & Brothers, New York, 1962.

RAFFERTY, KATHLEEN. *The Dell Crossword Dictionary.* Dell Publishing Company, Inc., New York, 1964. (A Delacorte Press Book distributed by The Dial Press.)

Reversed Dictionary of Classified Categories. Scientific Publishing Company, Brooklyn, New York, 1951.

RIDDLERS, THE. *The A B C of Puzzledom.* Charles Jacobsen, Whitestone, New York, 1942.

RIPLEY, ROBERT L. *Ripley's Believe It Or Not,* Two Volumes in One, Reprint Edition. Garden City Publishing Company, Inc., Garden City, New York, 1946.

Ripley's Believe It Or Not, a Trident Press Book. Simon and Schuster, New York, 1961.

Ripley's Mammoth Believe It Or Not. Simon and Schuster, Inc., New York, 1955.

Ripley's New Believe It Or Not. Simon and Schuster, Inc., New York, 1950.

Ripley's 35th Anniversary Believe It Or Not. Simon and Schuster, Inc., New York, 1954.

RODALE, J. I. *The Phrase Finder.* Rodale Press, Emmaus, Pennsylvania, 1953.

RODALE, J. I. *The Synonym Finder.* Rodale Books, Inc., Emmaus, Pennsylvania, 1961.

RODALE, J. I. *The Word Finder.* Rodale Press, Emmaus, Pennsylvania, 1947.

ROGET, PETER MARK. *Thesaurus of Words and Phrases,* enlarged by John Lewis Roget, new edition revised and enlarged by Samuel Romilly Roget. Grosset & Dunlap, New York, 1947.

Roget's International Thesaurus, Third Edition. Thomas Y. Crowell Company, New York, 1962.

ROSELLE, AUBREY C. *Famous $12,000 Prize-Winning Tongue-Twisters* (Little Blue Book No. 1261). Haldeman-Julius Company, Girard, Kansas, undated.

SCHMIDT, JACOB EDWARD. *Reversicon: A Medical Word Finder.* Charles C. Thomas, Springfield, Illinois, 1958.

SHIPLEY, JOSEPH T. *Playing With Words.* Prentice-Hall, Inc., Englewood Cliffs, New Jersey, 1960.

SISSON, A. F. *The Unabridged Crossword Puzzle Word Finder.* Doubleday & Company, Inc., Garden City, New York, 1963.

SLADEN, N. ST. BARBE. *The Complete Crossword Reference Book,* New and Entirely Revised Edition. The Syndicate Publishing Company, Ltd., London, 1949.

SMITH, LLOYD E. *Curiosities of the English Language* (Little Blue Book No. 1350). Haldeman-Julius Company, Girard, Kansas, undated.

SMITH, LLOYD E. *Fascinating Pastimes With Words* (Little Blue Book No. 1433). Haldeman-Julius Company, Girard, Kansas, undated.

SPENCE, ROBERT E. L. *6-Letter Word Book of the Master Series.* Robert E. L. Spence, St. Petersburg, Florida, 1950. (NOTE: Similar lists have been published for words of 3, 4, 5, 7, and 8 letters.)

STARR, MARION M. *Marion Starr's Synonyms.* Marion M. Starr, Kensington, Maryland, 1955.

STRUTT, JOSEPH. *The Sports and Pastimes of the People of England.* T. Tegg, London, 1838.

SUNNERS, WILLIAM. *Categories of Famous People and Places.* William Sunners, Brooklyn, New York, 1952.

SUNNERS, WILLIAM. *How to Construct the Perfect Puzzle.* National Library Publications, Inc., Brooklyn, New York, 1954.

SUNNERS, WILLIAM. *How to Win Prize Contests.* Arco Publishing Company, New York, 1950.

SWANFELDT, ANDREW. *Crossword Puzzle Dictionary,* Revised and Enlarged. Thomas Y. Crowell Company, New York, 1944.

TURLOT, A. *A. Turlot's Book of Personalities.* A. Turlot, Chicago, 1952.

WALKER, JOHN. *The Rhyming Dictionary of the English Language,* Revised and Enlarged by Lawrence H. Dawson. E. P. Dutton and Company, New York, 1936.

WALSH, WILLIAM S. *A Handy Book of Curious Information.* J. B. Lippincott Company, Philadelphia & London, 1913.

WALSH, WILLIAM S. *Handy-Book of Literary Curiosities.* J. B. Lippincott Company, Philadelphia, 1893.

WEAVER, WARREN. *Words.* The New York Public Library, New York, 1960.

WEIDEMAN, HUGH. *The Rapid Fact Finder.* Thomas Y. Crowell Company, New York, 1958.

WEIS, HANS. *Bella Bulla: Lateinische Sprachspielereien.* Ferd. Dümmlers Verlag, Bonn, West Germany, 1960. (Text is in German.)

WELLS, CAROLYN. *A Whimsey Anthology*. Dover Publications, Inc., New York, 1963.

WELLS, EVELYN. *What to Name the Baby*, Reprint Edition. Garden City Books, Garden City, New York, 1953.

WENTWORTH, HAROLD and FLEXNER, STUART BERG. *Dictionary of American Slang*. Thomas Y. Crowell Company, New York, 1960.

WHEATLEY, HENRY B. *Of Anagrams*. Williams and Norgate, London, 1862.

WHEELER, WILLIAM A. *Dictionary of the Noted Names of Fiction*, Twenty-Third Edition, with Appendix by Charles G. Wheeler. Houghton, Mifflin and Company, Boston and New York, 1894.

Winning Words. Original Contest Service, Elmont, New York, undated.

WOOD, CLEMENT. *The Romance of Words (An Introduction to Philology)*—Little Blue Book No. 708. Haldeman-Julius Company, Girard, Kansas, undated.

We have made the circuit from the magic and mystery of words to their romance, in 150 steps, without mentioning any of the periodicals, past or present, devoted partly or wholly to recreational linguistics. Fourteen of the most important ones are listed below. Those publications now out of print are indicated by an asterisk.

°ARDMORE PUZZLER, THE. Published by Edwin Smith ("Remardo") in Ardmore, Pennsylvania, from 1899 to circa 1915, at varying frequencies (weekly, daily, semi-monthly, and monthly).

CONTEST MAGAZINE. Published monthly by A. D. Freese & Sons, Inc., Upland, Indiana.

CRYPTOGRAM, THE. Published bimonthly by The American Cryptogram Association (Editor: Robert A. Hammell, West Collingswood, New Jersey).

°EASTERN ENIGMA, THE. Published monthly by the Eastern Puzzlers' League, in Pittsburgh, Pennsylvania and in other Pennsylvania towns, from 1883 to January, 1920.

ENIGMA, THE. Published monthly by the National Puzzlers' League, primarily in Scranton, Pennsylvania, in Centre Hall, Pennsylvania, and in Greenfield, Massachusetts, from February, 1920 onward.

°INSIDE THE ACD. Published monthly by Harper & Brothers, New York, in the 1950's, in connection with *The American College Dictionary*.

NAMES. Published quarterly by the American Name Society (Editor: Professor Kelsie B. Harder, State University College, Potsdam, New York).

NEWS OF CONTESTS. Published at irregular intervals (several times annually) by Contest Research Company of Brooklyn, New York.

NOTES AND QUERIES. A publication issued weekly by various English publishers, since 1849. Currently published by the Oxford University Press in London; full current title, *Notes and Queries for Readers and Writers, Collectors and Librarians*.

ONOMASTIC. Published at irregular intervals (once or twice a year) in the form of a series of pamphlets (Editor: Professor J. B. Rudnyckyj of Winnipeg, Manitoba, Canada).

PRIZEWINNER (formerly, *What's Cooking in Contests*). Published monthly by Robert Spence Publications, Inc., St. Petersburg, Florida.

°RECREATIONAL MATHEMATICS MAGAZINE. Published bimonthly at first, later irregularly, by Joseph S. Madachy, first at Idaho Falls, Idaho, later at Kent, Ohio, from February, 1961 to February, 1964.

°WORDS. Issued weekly by Temple G. Porter of Washington, D.C., through the facilities of English Language Services, Inc., from December, 1964 to December, 1965.

WORD STUDY. Published monthly by the G. & C. Merriam Company of Springfield, Massachusetts, in connection with its dictionaries.

The author will welcome contributions to the foregoing bibliography from knowledgeable readers.

INDEX

Most books consisting of collections of problems—mathematical puzzles, for instance—list the individual problem titles in the Table of Contents. This practice makes for a long Table of Contents but for a short temper on the part of its user. Since the problem titles are not in alphabetical order, it is impossible to find the title of a problem one wants to look up—or so it almost invariably seems to the reader.

We're different. The problem titles have been sorted alphabetically and are presented in this Index. There is only one deviation from true alphabetical order: in the case of titles starting with THE, A, or AN, the title has been alphabetized on the basis of its second word. Thus, our title, "The Great Pretender", is shown here as "Great Pretender, The" and is found among the G's.

In all other respects, true alphabetical order is observed, considering the entire letter sequence involved uniformly and disregarding word breaks, punctuation and diacritical marks, and other irrelevancies. In such an order, MC ARTHUR occurs between MAZE and ME, and ST. REGINA falls between STREET and STRENGTH.

For each problem, three page references are given:

P (or B) —the page on which the problem (or baffler) begins.

H —the page on which hints helpful in its resolution are presented (none in the case of a baffler).

R —the page on which the resolution begins (none in the case of a baffler).

CORRELATOR

Do not use this Correlator—at least, not until you have absorbed the content of the book.

The Correlator is an alphabetical index to those aspects of wordplay that appear in the book. Consulting the Correlator before resolving the problems we have offered you would, in many an instance, make it too easy for you to dispose of the problem, by tipping you off to an important feature built into it.

The basic function of the Correlator is to provide the serious-minded student of wordplay with a convenient means of comparing or correlating the information about wordplay included here with the usually more extensive exploration of the same subject in *Language on Vacation*, published in 1965.

Additional uses to which the Correlator can be turned will probably occur to you as you go along.

The principle of true alphabetical order adhered to in the Index applies equally in the Correlator.

The numbers following entries in the Correlator are those of the Problem or Baffler within the scope of which the subject is treated. Depending on circumstances, the reference may be in the original Problem, or in the Hints applicable to it, or in the Resolution. The letter "A" indicates a subject treated in the Afterword, the letter "I" one covered in the Introduction.